SCIENCE
and
ECONOMIC
DEVELOPMENT

Richard L. Meier

SCIENCE
and
ECONOMIC
DEVELOPMENT:

New Patterns of Living

SECOND EDITION

THE M.I.T. PRESS
Massachusetts Institute of Technology
Cambridge, Massachusetts, and London, England

PREFACE

INVESTIGATORS are deeply concerned with the rightness of their own vision of what is true and important. How good is the selection of items to which attention is being paid? What factors are being overlooked that will later turn out to be meaningful? What has been overemphasized? Why? When the task is that of formulating proposals and plans for the future, questions such as these become central.

In science and its technological applications, it is especially difficult to achieve a viewpoint that will hold up for decades. The focal theories and preferred modes of explanation shift with remarkable fluidity at the frontier of research. The backlog is redigested into forms best suited for ready reference and teaching, but it rarely keeps pace with the accelerating accumulation of new findings. The recorded body of scientific knowledge appearing since this book was forwarded to the publisher about a dozen years ago is roughly equal to the total that had been accumulated from the beginning of civilization to that date. It is important to know what impact this knowledge has had upon the directions in which world development could advance.

Concepts of world development have also been in flux. When this book was first written and rewritten, it was impossible to agree upon any indexes of social, political, and cultural development. Relativism was dominant, and comparative studies of sociopolitical units were only be-

JUN 25 '75

HUNT LIBRARY
CARNEGIE-MELLON UNIVERSITY

ginning. Scholars therefore retreated to a description incorporated in the title of a journal established in that era: "economic development and cultural change." Recommendations for dealing with the most difficult problems of development, lacking any theoretical distillation from past experience, were guided by common-sense views about the nature of the growth of societies. Will such proposals stand up well in the face of newer and more organized considerations of the development process?

The new edition of *Science and Economic Development* does not attempt to modernize the arguments in the customary manner. Instead it treats the content as the best that could be said at that time, reports briefly at the ends of chapters, sections, or tables where the outlook has now changed, and in conclusion redefines the highest priority research problems that should interest scientists. This edition is treated as *an experiment in judging the effects of progress in science upon the developmental prospects for the world.* It identifies the miscalculations and misplaced emphases of an earlier period when assessed in terms of our own. Thus, it is possible to pinpoint what has been learned in the interval.

The most striking readjustment that emerges is the new view of world population. Although the population growth rates envisaged in the early 1950's were extraordinarily threatening when projected forward to the twenty-first century, the reasonable expectations of that time have turned out to be serious underestimates. Actual increases have been significantly greater than the upper limits held then to be likely. Moreover, population growth now forecast is much more out of control worldwide than ever before. Yet the effectiveness and practicality of the new techniques of fertility limitation have similarly exceeded expectations by far. Therefore, the conclusion arrived at then—that every channel of communications likely to change family values so that adults would feel impelled to avail themselves of contraceptive services—was not misdirected but is more than ever before a prerequisite for development. Scientists have been delinquent in not taking up these problems earlier and reducing them to researchable tasks.

Curiously, as I and my colleagues profit from hindsight, it is possible to find a substantial number of citations in the prior literature that heralded both of these breakaways from expectations. Indeed, I had found this evidence myself when carrying out the researches for this book. Why then did I publish erroneous projections? The answer is simple; orthodox views on population growth were held very strongly by economists and demographers, and medical researchers were no less resistant to the best opportunities for improving birth control. Two earlier drafts of the book had been rejected for their unorthodoxy and indiscipline. Experience had taught me, too, that experts were often right in detecting mistaken claims appearing in the literature, even when a satisfying rationale for their judgment could not be provided. I had vivid recollections of their uncanny ability to detect well-concealed fakery in the oral contraceptive field as well as others. I had no personally assembled data which contradicted the established viewpoint; therefore, it was not my responsibility to undertake a polemic in an effort to change the doctrine. I conformed and so I erred.

Later chapters contained arguments too diverse in their research origins and methodology and too new to have produced any established consensus among experts. In this case the deviant articles in the literature were again identified, but lacking a veto from the academy, they were given consideration equal to that of mainstream reports. Now that the body of knowledge has expanded, and confirmation of the separate proposals can be sought, it is apparent that remarkably few of these speculative attempts to link science with development have subsequently been found to be mistaken. Perhaps more time is needed to discover the errors committed in less organized areas for knowledge accumulation. Nevertheless, it is already quite safe to conclude that scientific knowledge has very significant utility for clarifying choices in the range of possible futures. Systematic and exhaustive methods for using scientific literature for gauging the future have been sketched out in a subsequent book *Modern Science and the Human Fertility Problem* (1959).

The interval of elapsed time, during which I have engaged in many explorations relevant to the theme of world development, leaves me even more profoundly convinced that the search for principles of organization—whether they be of organic substance, mind, machine, language, or of institutional arrangements—is the most fundamental, and the most liberating, task of our generation. The fundamental research in world development lies in that direction.

RICHARD L. MEIER

January 1966

PREFACE TO THE FIRST EDITION

THIS BOOK traces out a new path for economic development which is suggested and shaped by postwar discoveries in science and technology. It shows a way to adequate levels of living, available to everyone, which is still incomplete but can nevertheless be rapidly extended and improved by specific kinds of research. In many of its features the direction recommended is contrary to the most commonly held views and also contrary to the advice now being proffered elsewhere. This is a position that stems not from a willingness to be different, but from a long struggle trying to formulate technically sound procedures for achieving adequate production levels. For this reason the direction recommended here promises first to be a surer, and at the same time a more economical, program than anything that has been brought forward to date. The strategy for development that logically follows from this employment of current innovations is mainly drawn from recorded experience with social and economic institutions.

Many of the specific suggestions introduced are no longer startlingly new. Almost from their scientific infancy, for instance, atomic power and the mass culture of algae have been groomed for a leading role in the improvement of human welfare. However, the provision of a framework for the transition that starts from where the world is now and leads to a reasonable level of welfare accessible to all permits the implications of even these well-advertised new technologies to be traced one or two stages farther than has been possible before. Several lines of scientific advance, hitherto little used and discussed, were needed to fill gaps in the developmental framework. Although they introduce some novelty into the discussion, the roles they play are usually rather subsidiary.

Because scientific and technological data are applicable everywhere on the surface of the earth one can speak with some generality about the possibilities for production. The requirements set by human needs can, in large part, also be described in equivalent terms. Therefore it quickly becomes convenient to argue out the problems of economic development in a way that is not particularistic but fits the world as a whole. Thus wherever appraisals of technical suitability are involved they can be made in terms of world economic development, but whenever specific programs requiring human organization are considered they must be reduced to the scale of whatever political system can effectively deal with them. Sometimes, of course, no organizational means yet exist for achieving desirable ends so that one may ask whether science cannot be stimulated so as to be of assistance in the creation of such means. The interaction between science and economic development is not completely one-sided.

It is curious that, with all the energy and breadth of intellect available to it, the scientific fraternity has not in recent times sought to create tentative models for world development. It is strange because science has had an important influence in changing the world view held by informed persons. Many theoreticians have devoted their careers to reformulations based upon new data and more refined analysis. As a result we have a view of the universe, and man's place in it, that is about as accurate as existing knowledge can make it. Extensions and changes in this view occur constantly, because of new findings, but the modifications are quickly fitted into some consistent over-all system. This is not the case however for world development, which appears— on the surface at least—to be an equally engaging subject for scientific attention. Fitting together the implications of new data in order to establish their various possible effects upon society has not been a popular activity among contemporary scientists and engineers. At best they have been content to carry it out in a fragmentary and disorganized fashion that would be scorned in cosmological or philosophical circles.

Perhaps this is because the concepts of the working natural scientist do not mix well with those from the social scientist. The same term will have different meanings, and using the same methods will introduce different hazards. What is taken for granted in one discipline has dubious validity in another and is a matter of continuing controversy elsewhere. This is a frontier where arguments cannot be promptly settled by referring the issue to the experimenters.

In such circumstances the first task to be undertaken must be one of describing the present world situation in a systematic way that appears to be useful for both the natural and social sciences. This superstructure should be put into as quantitative terms as possible, so as to permit the more precise characteristics of natural science—particularly of the physical sciences—to have their full effect. Fortunately, as a result of the efforts of the secretariat of the United Nations and its associated agencies, the data describing the present state of world development are becoming more detailed and more complete. Eventually it should be possible to judge most of the major effects of a potential new development by making quick calculations on a slide rule, with more careful studies to follow when the results appear promising. The analysis of the present world predicament in this book is followed by critical reviews of the kinds of solutions postwar science and technology may have to offer for the imminent food and fuel crises. It will thus be seen that many of the discourses on development one finds today are beside the point; they anticipate outcomes that are as probable as the development of perpetual-motion machines. Some work out elaborate schemes for increasing food production with new cropping techniques, disease-resistant strains, and synthetic fertilizer but do nothing about the simultaneous increases in population and have very unclear and unquantitative ideas about the transition to an industrial system equipped to supply the mass need. Others pin their hopes upon resource bases that are clearly inadequate for the long pull, but go blithely ahead suggesting the commitment of these resources according to traditional patterns, leaving none for the hard pull that lies somewhat farther ahead.

And then there are some who face the unpleasant truth. They realize that we do not yet, for large parts of the world, have knowledge that permits the attainment of a reasonable level of living. True, if what we now know in the abstract, as confirmed by world-wide measurements and laboratory operations, were translated into commodity flows and divided among numbers much larger than the present world population, there would be more than enough to go around. (Adequacy for all seems to be the desired state of affairs.) However, the basic problem is how to get from where we are to that more desirable state. The problem is a matter of relative rates; the needs in the larger resource-poor underdeveloped societies tend to expand much more rapidly than the goods can be brought forward, even by applying the best local efforts. As will be shown, not even the most optimistic interpretation of our present knowledge—scientific, technical, social, and economic—suggests a clear-cut transition path to adequate levels of living for all people. Faith in the feasibility of such an objective must go beyond the facts as they stand at the moment. But one can come much closer than ever before—so close that the gaps can be judged, and specific problems in applied science, areas for concentrated investigation in fundamental science, and special techniques which require elaboration by social scientists can be outlined.

In the last chapter, entitled "New Patterns of Living," the first- and second-order effects of the new technologies upon the course of development are considered. This takes one quite a long way from the substantial foundation of laboratory investigation and ends up well within the study of society. Not all of society is involved directly but only those institutions and issues that are most bound up in the effort of economic development. The remainder are expected to make gradual adaptations to the change in social climate or to be modified over time in a random fashion.

Thus the invasion of the social studies was carefully considered; it was intended to establish a continuity of analysis that overlaps the experience of social scientists. Only by such means (i.e., the penetration of each other's domain) can the various specialists communicate with each other in order to solve problems of society. The problems, of course, hardly ever respect academic boundaries; they have an economic aspect, a technical aspect, a cultural aspect, and many others, but the solutions require an interleaving and fusion so that the procedures, as employed, quickly lose their identity. The specialist (after all, the majority of the readers will fall into one or another species of this genus) may analyze the product of this invasion as a contribution to his own field, although it was not intended as such, or he may discover important inconsistencies—which would be useful to know about as soon as possible—or he may (this is much more daring!) make counter-invasions and suggest what seem to him to be better alternatives.

Finally, at the end of this work, there are presented a selection of unsolved, but apparently soluble, problems that compose the principal outcome of the work. It is hoped that such problems will develop into recognized challenges for the respective professions. These problems must be given some such special meaning because none of them is central to the development of a specialism, and they are otherwise likely to be neglected by the most competent investigators. Later it will, no doubt, be found that some of the list do not really get to the heart of the matter and new formulations must be devised. This is not unusual in the history of science.

This has been an attempt to grapple with the full implications of world development—or at least their first approximation. Where there are gaps, such as in discussions of world politics or international trade, they occur because no important new light could be thrown upon such affairs, nor did the subjects themselves suggest any novel tools to be employed in world development. In some subjects the implications are believed to be highly significant—the area of human communication is one of these—but the possibilities are still so open-ended and inexplicit that the discussion could not be carried very far.

A final note needs to be added concerning the references. They include, as would be expected, all the sources mentioned for the significant and unusual facts that have been employed in the text. However there have been added to these items many of the most recent contributions that appraise in an illuminating fashion the current state of knowledge regarding the technical features of economic development. Because of the great diversity of materials which may at some stage be relevant, no attempt has been made to assure comprehensiveness. The added references are intended to be of assistance to those persons who wish to push ahead and make new contributions in the same general direction.

I have been given aid and encouraged in this effort over the past half-dozen years by scores of friends and colleagues. To mention any in particular would be an injustice to the rest. This is the best I could distil from their collective wisdom.

RICHARD L. MEIER

July 1956

ACKNOWLEDGMENTS

I was set onto this path of investigation by a grant from the Cowles Publications in 1948 where the intended objective was the appraisal of potential new solutions to the world problems of nutrition and comfort. The first set of findings led to new questions, and they in turn to new studies. Portions of the later work were supported by the Pabst Brewing Company, the Conservation Foundation, and by funds obtained from the Ford Foundation for research in the behavioral sciences. More important than all of these was the encouragement by the faculties at the University of Chicago to follow the crucial problems of economic development wherever they seemed to lead. University funds were made available at moments that were critical to continuation and extension of the study.

The new edition was aided by the School of Natural Resources and the Mental Health Research Institute of the University of Michigan.

CONTENTS

TABLES

FIGURES

Chapter *1*

THE PRESENT
WORLD PREDICAMENT

THE CONCEPT OF WORLD DEVELOPMENT has never been set forth in its broadest sense. Some scholars have viewed the prospects from the limited standpoint of the geologist-geographer, soil scientist-agronomist, international economist, etc. But all of these eventually disagree, and a few of their conclusions are quite incompatible. (Mather, 1944; Spengler, 1947–8; Osborn, 1948; Hansen, 1951; Rosin and Eastman, 1953; Brown, 1954.)

Very likely a large share of the disagreement springs from an inherent unwillingness to abandon one's role as an expert and look at the problem squarely, realizing that it will demand a system of its own. No single specialist is in a position to unravel it. Therefore we must explore all the readily apparent possibilities for the organization of many diverse elements, sometimes to the extent of synthesizing quite new patterns that promise to be suitable. Furthermore we must endeavor to understand the ways in which the various special possibilities may interact with each other. One task will be to examine the outlines of the problem itself, the factors inherent in world economic development, so that the preferred ends, or outcome, of the development can be discovered. Some scholars think of this as the dynamic equilibrium, the steady state, or the stability point toward which the global system, however it may be described, is headed. We must also try to establish which of the identifiable factors or elements is measurable, and immediately thereafter attempt to assemble all the regularities, or invariant relations, to be found among these quantifiable factors. Then, as the order in any system of thought concerning world development evolves, expeditions into the miscellany of human knowledge and experience may be planned and executed. In this manner many missing links in the argument and many fruitful suggestions for further measurement may be uncovered.

The concept of world development therefore has a grand design. It starts with the not unusual assumption that men have certain needs and aspirations in common. Then it proceeds to determine what kind of action is required to reach these objectives, beginning where we are at the moment. Many of the requirements can be stated in scientific and technical terms, and so must be put as explicitly as it is possible to quantify them before satisfactory solutions can be proposed. When this is done the corollary social and political measures required for reaching the goals of development can be defined much more clearly. Incommensurables will always remain with us, but the best strategy seems to be that of reducing the influence of the imponderables and thus gaining more control over our collective destiny.

An analysis of the present world predicament must penetrate the tangled interaction of:

> Human needs
> Population
> Resources
> Technics.

Moreover it must be carried out on a macroscale, dealing with aggregates—the sums of many measurements. Thus, most of the refinements of analysis introduced by the specialist disciplines becomes superfluous; only the basic concepts are employed.

What one wants from all of this is a consistent series of targets for world consumption and a summary of the resources available for meeting these demands. The targets are too often stated in purely qualitative terms, such as "a decent standard of living for everyone," so that their implications are not readily explored. We need to have such targets translated into quantities of materials that must be produced. The quality standards, or specifications, of such goods also need to be stated. The inventory of world resources should fall into the same pattern. Such efforts are the foundation for any system of world economic development.

Once the targets and the resources have been assessed in as quantitative a fashion as is possible, the scientists and engineers are qualified to suggest what uses, modifications, and extensions of technics can be made to achieve these targets most readily. (By the term "technics" is meant the complete range of methods for transforming resources into goods and services. At one extreme are the arts and crafts, often limited to a single culture and locale, and at the other are the science-based technologies, but mostly one finds hybrids. The term "technology," which will be more often employed, embraces only those aspects that are systematic and applicable in any part of the world.) Scientists and engineers can consider the various ways in which the nutritional targets, or the shelter targets, might be reached. They can compare the costs of one alternative set of methods against another, or they can look for short cuts. They might also find ways of tying one effort to another so that each would become more efficient. Such work would, in effect, bring into contrast the needs and the resource-use potentials in such a manner that the prospective deficiencies would be high lighted.

This approach to the subject is similar to that of the Woytinskys in thier omnibus *World Population and Resources* (1953). However, in such a multi-purpose and relatively exhaustive survey of statistics those features most relevant to world development are difficult to pick out. More important even than that, the statisticians responsible for the original compilations seldom reveal either the extent of probable error in their tables or the peculiar kinds of bias to which the various entries are subject. Therefore, one must pick and choose his way very carefully through international statistics, often going back to the original operations by which the data were collected. Finally, much of the available statistics are old and obsolete, and the clues to the nature of the changes required to bring them up to date are scattered through the trade journals and reports.

Within this rather uneven state of knowledge one must assess what is the present world situation. The Woytinsky book is a good place to begin, but it still allows great latitude. A position must be taken, a point of view expressed, which is more to the point for the task undertaken here.

A first step must be the establishment of useful categories over which summations can be made. Accuracy to the second significant figure is seldom worth while, since many large components in the needs-resources picture are known hardly more closely than a factor of ten. Within such a set of lumped sums, simple accounts can be set up that will tell us just how far our present technics miss the mark of supplying the needs, and in what broad categories the gaps are the greatest.

1. HUMAN NEEDS

The individual human being may be thought of as having a cluster of limited needs—in order to survive and function—and a virtually unlimited potential of wants. The innate physiological needs that require a significant amount of effort to acquire are

> Food
> Protection from stress.

In most instances the amount of food can be measured in terms of calories per day, and the units of protection may take the form of kilograms of fiber per year and square meters of permanent shelter, but important qualifications will appear.

TABLE 1. FOOD REQUIREMENTS: CALORIC

	Cal/day*
As a function of sex:	
Male, 25 yr, 65 kg body wt., moderate activity, 10° mean temp.	3200
Female, ditto	2700
As a function of temperature of environment:	
Male, 25 yr, 65 kg, moderate activity, 0° C mean temp.	3360
Male, ditto, 15° C	3120
Male, ditto, 30° C	2880
As a function of body weight:	
Male, 50 kg, 25 yr, 10° C, moderate activity	2640
Male, 60 kg, ditto	3000
Male, 70 kg, ditto	3380
Male, 80 kg, ditto	3730
As a function of childbearing:	
Female, 25 yr, 10° C, 55 kg, housekeeping	2300
Female, ditto, pregnant, last months, less active	2750
Female, ditto, lactating, housework	3300
As a function of activity:	
Male, 20–45 yr, 10° C, 60–70 kg, light work	2600–3000
Male, ditto, moderate work	3000–3600
Male, ditto, heavy work	3600–4500

* Caloric requirements for individuals are quite variable, but averages over a total population in average health can be made to an accuracy of perhaps 2%. These figures assume a relatively balanced diet which leads to no change in body weight for any of the categories considered.

Sources: F.A.O. Nutritional Study No. 5, 1950; Lehman et al., *Arbeitsphysiol.*, **14** (1950).

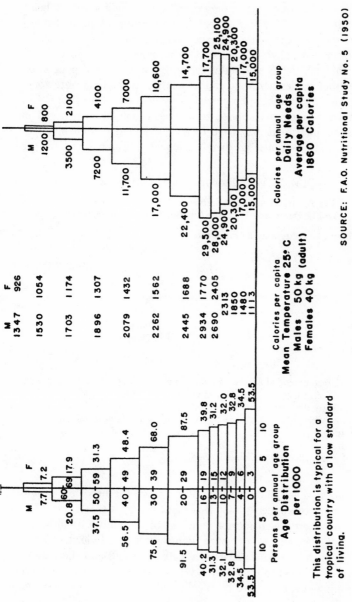

FIG. 1. FOOD REQUIREMENTS FOR A POPULATION

SOURCE: F.A.O. Nutritional Study No. 5 (1950)

The differences in age and activity in a population introduce wide variations in caloric needs. When rationing is required, the caloric requirements for various age classes can be demonstrated in this fashion. If one multiplies the number of persons in an age-sex group by its specific caloric requirement then the total need can be established for nutritional planning.

Whenever a relatively stable, organized mass of individuals is being considered it is possible to deal in averages and norms. Thus in Table 1 the caloric food requirements are expressed in terms of the norms for different classes of individuals, so that it becomes possible to estimate the effects of such trends as the decreasing age of the world population or the apparent tendency toward milder winters in the temperate zones or the increasing numbers employed in sedentary occupations. In Fig. 1 similar averages are applied to a typical population pyramid in order to show how food may have to be distributed to individuals of various ages if the supplies are barely adequate. Table 2 restates the

TABLE 2. FOOD REQUIREMENTS: COMPOSITION

For Adults Whose Caloric Needs Are 2800 Cal/Day
(Food as Purchased Will Need to Be 10 to 15% Greater)

Protein (about half containing animal protein factor)	66 g/day *	300–400 Cal
Fat		2400–2500 Cal
Carbohydrate		
Calcium	0.9 g/day	
Iron	12 mg	
Vitamin A	4700 intl. units	
Riboflavin	2.3 mg	
Thiamine	1.6 mg	
Ascorbic acid	70 mg	
Niacin	16 mg	

* These are recommended allowances which are sufficient—liberal enough—to meet the needs of at least 90% of the individuals. In order to allow for spoilage and waste at least 10% more should be made available in countries with efficient distribution services, and 15% more for those regions lacking dependable services. The animal protein factor can now be accommodated by adding vitamin B_{12} to the diet.

Source: National Research Council, 1945.

requirements so that the emphasis is placed upon the needs for various essential dietary components. Clothing and energy use, as reviewed in Tables 3 and 4, are much more a function of the culture than of the physiology of man and so are more highly variable. Indeed it is not possible yet to distinguish satisfactorily between needs and the requirements for being in conformity with style in most of the social environments within which data have been collected.

Human groups (as in families, villages, factories, parishes, etc.) have need of additional facilities for:

Education
Work
Health
Government
Ritual
Recreation.

There must be a series of points where such activities can take place effectively. These points are usually households, schools, workplaces, clinics, town halls, and churches in the developing social system, although their functions have been intertwined and inseparable in older

TABLE 3. FIBER USE

	Fiber use (kg/yr)	
Cold or Temperate Climates	1947	1965 (est.)
United States	13.1	16.3
Canada	9.5	11.1
Western Europe (OEEC)	7	10.4
Western Europe (others)	4.5	6.0
U.S.S.R.	3	10.2
Balkans	3.7	9.2
Japan	6.6	10.2
China	1.8	2.9
Mild or Tropical Climates		
Oceania	7.6	10.6
Latin America	4	4.8
India	2.0	2.3
Pakistan	1.9	2.1
Africa	1.8	1.7

Sources: World Fiber Survey, F.A.O., 1947; World Fiber Review, *American Fabrics*, **60**, 1963, p. 51.

and more primitive cultures. Perhaps group needs are best measured in terms of energy, of square meters of permanent shelter for community services, and of the proportions of the population needed to maintain the services.

For human societies, "need" is a much more relative term. It designates what is required not only for linking together its constituent groups but also for survival in a world containing other powerful societies that threaten to overwhelm the latecomer in development. In many cases, absorption or integration may be the simplest choice, and even a preferable one, but this only transfers the responsibility to the dominant social organization. A society's needs may be expressed in such terms as:

> Communications
> Commerce
> Internal order
> Justice
> Planning
> Defense.

The equipping of each of these functions takes a great accumulation of savings from prior income and requires a large continuing effort for administration and maintenance. In a modern society the communications, the transport element in commerce, and the defense categories must be backed up with a huge complement of energy-using industry which produces replacements and extensions to their equipment. The allocation of effort is generally carried out within the framework of a

TABLE 4. ENERGY USE IN SOME REPRESENTATIVE AREAS

Area	Energy Consumed,* Cal/yr per capita	
	1951	1962
United States	5.8×10^7	6.0×10^7
Canada	5.2	4.3
United Kingdom	3.4	3.6
Belgium-Luxembourg	3.0	3.2
Sweden	2.6	2.7
France	1.7	1.9
U.S.S.R.	....	2.2
Japan	0.63	1.0
Brazil	0.20	0.27
Turkey	0.20	0.16
Greece	0.19	0.42
Pakistan	0.029	0.054
Nigeria	0.022	0.033

* Includes coal, oil, natural gas, shale, peat, and a credit for hydroelectric power that shifted somewhat due to changes in efficiency of competing technology, but no allowance for fuelwood.

Source: *United Nations World Energy Supplies*, Statistical Papers, Series J, No. 2 and No. 7, 1957 and 1964.

Comment: Growth in per capita energy use is expected to taper off in developed countries over the next few decades. During this period most household services and industries will have become about as electrified as is technically feasible. Developing countries with less heavy industry are expected to level off below 10^7 Cal/yr per capita.

budget whose units of measurement are in terms of either money or manpower. The size of the labor pool in any society, as well as the proportion that can be assigned to any particular task, is ascertainable in concrete enough terms for the technologist. However, money, since its equivalence with energy and materials is constantly shifting, is rather inappropriate. In the technologist's view the availability and use of energy will be the decisive factor; the large-scale saving and investing functions are made possible only when the energy sources have been tapped.

Whenever it is possible to discuss transactions within a system as having energy components, the scientists and engineers feel at home. A very large share of their training is devoted to the measurements of energy changes, and to tracing through the ramifications of interrelated energy systems. Therefore if one introduces the physiological needs for food energy and warmth, family and group needs for carrying on group activities, such as cooking, and the societal needs for industry, transport and defense, a whole series of operations and principles come to mind. Most of them are applicable to energy systems in general. Scientists and engineers realize that energy resources are scarce and ought to be conserved. Tracing the flow of energy, from its origins in the interior of the sun, through various cycles on Earth, to its dissipation in outer space, provides many clues for explaining contemporary human activities. A scrutiny of energy flows also enables the investigator to establish a connection between various activities that seem otherwise unrelated. This is a line of systematization which has been sensed in the past few years (Ayres, 1952; Putnam, 1954; Furnas, 1954) but has still not been adequately exploited.

The consumption patterns of the more advanced economies reflect a large outlay of energy and materials, especially for the items of defense and commerce. In such items it is really impossible to distinguish between what is need and what is surplus, or luxury. Therefore, in this effort at establishing over-all needs, a broad range is the best approximation that can be obtained for the moment. In the less organized economies the needs of the society for energy and materials are small, while those of the individual, the family, and the immediate community are very nearly what they are elsewhere. Thus a feeling of adequacy—where all felt needs are met—may be achieved somewhere not far removed from the consumption levels of a primitive society. On the other hand, when a society has a tradition, a culture, and an extensive investment to maintain and defend, its actual felt needs may be only slightly less than the present levels of consumption.

Human needs, as broken down into convenient categories, are summed up on an energy scale in Table 5. The most modest levels

TABLE 5. OVER-ALL HUMAN NEEDS

Population Averages, per Capita Basis

	Quantities	Energy Spent,* Cal/yr
Water	50–500 liters/day	——
Food	2000–3100 Cal/day	$8.0–10.7 \times 10^5$
Fiber	3–10 kg/yr	$1.2–5 \times 10^4$
Fuel	100–5000 kg coal equiv./yr	$7.2–36 \times 10^6$
Power	200–2000 kw-hr/yr	$1.7–17 \times 10^5$
Materials (construction)	200–2000 kg/yr (3–30 sq meters standing shelter)	Small
Iron	20–200 kg/yr	$3.4–34 \times 10^4$
Nonferrous metals	5–50 kg/yr	$3.7–37 \times 10^4$
Paper & cardboard	10–50 kg/yr	$4–20 \times 10^4$
Total energy requirements		$1–4 \times 10^7$

* Care was taken to prevent double counting.

in the ranges presented are set at what is felt to be adequate by people in less developed societies (but is obviously much higher than the per capita consumption in those areas, which is shown in Table 4). The upper limit of the range approximates what is needed for decentralized living in North America, where the dispersed character of dwellings and services make the family automobile a virtual necessity. These are definitions of "need" according to the standards of the local culture, applying current technics.

Incorporated in this over-all requirement for energy are many losses due to the interchanging of one source of energy, which most often is fuel or impounded water, into another more convenient form, such as high pressure steam or electric power. Perhaps only about 20% of this 10^7 Cal per capita per year minimum is energy applied directly to the purposes of man. The remaining 80% are losses incurred in the interconversion of one form of energy into another. The losses are dissipated into the surroundings as low grade heat before they serve the specific intentions of man. A realization of this inefficiency alerts the scientist, suggesting that more efficient systems for fitting energy to the needs of man may still be worked out. A more thorough analysis, starting from fundamental physiological concepts and the best foreseeable technics, is developed in Chapter 3. It is a completely independent treatment which shows that the energy need of 10^7 Cal per yr per capita may be reduced, perhaps by as much as half, in a well-organized society living in a tropical climate. However, the estimate arrived at here seems to be quite a satisfactory approximation of energy need for the world as a whole.

The technology for many of these convenient and energy-saving interchanges has already been developed, some of it to a stage where engineers see very little hope for improvement, but in some conversions one still finds extreme inefficiency (converting electricity into liquid fuels, for example, is a particularly poor transformation). Therefore it may be expected that there are energy sources especially suited to a certain set of uses, indifferent to some others, and unacceptable for the rest. Under these circumstances the more urgent human needs will tend to get prior claim to the choicest and scarcest energy sources. Also, in order to achieve greater economic efficiency, a large number of transformations, substitutions and redistributions of energy and materials will always be required. Thus, one cannot draw too many conclusions from lumped-together energy needs. The over-all totals will tell us mainly whether currently employed transformations will be adequate if they were to be extended to cover the needs of the whole world.

There are other ways of measuring and classifying human needs than by the energy component involved in the technologies that strive to satisfy them. A system that relates to food will be taken up separately. Those which are dependent upon minerals will also be given special treatment. The remaining major item is that of water. It is possible to construct a table, like that of Table 5, which would express water requirements in the manufacturing process, but the ranges would be much broader, so broad in fact that the effort does not seem worth while. There is a good reason for this. Minerals and energy sources move into the manufacturing stage valued at something ordinarily in the range of $10 to $1000 per ton, whereas water costs fall in the range of 1¢ to 10¢ per ton. With transport costs normally quoted in terms of cents per ton-mile it is easy to see that the more valuable transportable materials are likely to establish an equilibrium so that costs are roughly comparable on sites that have access to world trade, but water cannot be moved very far before its cost becomes exorbitant. Therefore water supply and water-use standards have remained a local affair. The consumption will depend upon local soils, topography, and climate. As long as water is valued in pennies per ton, water needs, like water resources, must be appraised at the watershed level. Water costs may have a ceiling on sites adjacent to the ocean, however, since a variety of techniques are being perfected for separating potable water from the sea water; therefore, in the long run a stabilization of industrial water-use patterns seems likely. Some previews of this era of manufactured water will be found in the subsequent discussion of urbanization.

2. POPULATION

When human needs are multiplied by human members, the totals (world needs) must be matched against resources in order to assess the present position. Therefore the next step requires counting the people.

The establishment of the census as a part of government has made possible a fairly accurate rendering of the current numbers in the population. It also provides very satisfactory information about sex and age distribution, geographical location, and the makeup of families. It is much less satisfactory when dealing with economic status, education (literacy), and religious ties. All enumerations commonly attempted however are still likely to be a great deal more precise than the foregoing survey of over-all human needs.

In order to establish the size of the development problem as a whole these things must be known about the world's population:

> Present numbers
> Rate of change
> Growth potential.

Each represents an extrapolation; they are taken up in the order of decreasing confidence.

A large gap has existed in the world's census tabulations, a very large share of which lies within the territory of China. Previously, estimates for China were based upon small partial samples that disagreed not only with the official estimate but also with others. The discrepancies were as high as 200,000,000 persons. Recently a registration has been completed for continental China whose preliminary reports suggest that the higher estimates of Chinese population were more nearly correct. This will mean that for some years to come there will be some confusion about authoritative figures for world population. There may be quick revisions amounting to 3 to 4% of the total world population, even though the normal accuracy of a census is better than 1%. At the moment it appears safe to use 2.7 billions as a working figure for the 1955 population of the world. (See Fig. 2.)

Establishing the rate of change is fraught with much greater uncertainty. To do this requires accurate knowledge of birth and death rates (migration is ruled out when dealing with global figures) so that

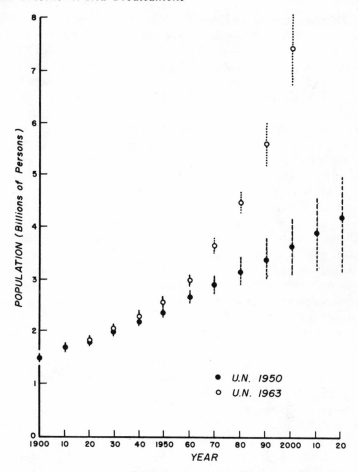

Source: *Provisional Report on World Population*, U.N., 1963 (for data 1920–1960).

Fig. 2. World Population Trends

An extrapolation of the present rate of growth suggests that the world's population might double in the next 80 to 90 years.   There is a fair possibility of *less* growth than this because the onset of either a series of world catastrophes or of extensive family planning would lead to such an outcome.   However, growth may *accelerate* if the present international aid programs, which emphasize public health improvement and food production but are unable to give equivalent attention to birth control, turn out to be successful.   Since each of these outcomes is not unlikely, the number for which we must plan becomes rapidly more uncertain the farther into the future the projection is made.   *Acceleration occurred even more rapidly than the most pessimistic anticipations, for the reasons mentioned.*

the difference can be established. Now that major epidemics and large-scale famines seem to have come under control, the prognostication of a slow downward drift of the death rate is not too difficult. However, the spread of contraceptive practice has led to a greater dependency of the birth rate upon the prevailing attitudes toward children. Attitudes regarding family size are rapidly changing at the moment, with North America, for example, looking forward again to larger families while the Middle East is seriously considering the bearing of fewer children. At present, the net annual rate of increase for the world is close to 1%. Because of the social inertia found in rural and largely illiterate peoples it must be expected that this rate of increase will continue for some decades to come. Even in the event of war or catastrophe it seems extremely likely that the rate of change will remain strongly positive for at least the remainder of the century.

Changes in attitudes toward family size are also affecting the concept of growth potential. Only a few years ago it was thought that birth and death rates would come into approximate balance as soon as the normal span of life in a population approached seventy years. In fact, this ultimate stage was characterized as one of "incipient decline." However, the experience of North America in the past decade, as well as its expectations in the next, suggests that "mature, aging populations" still have amazing capacity for growth. A continuing rate of growth of more than 1% per annum is not at all unlikely in North America; whereas for poorer, more crowded areas, such as Western Europe, rates of $\frac{1}{2}$ to 1% seem more probable.

The growth potential is much greater for those populations which have high birth and death rates (35 to 45 per thousand) and a short life expectancy (less than 35 years). They tend to grow intermittently when retaining high mortality conditions. As soon as life expectancy improves, however, these populations enter into a transition phase that is characterized by a very rapid growth, as high as $2\frac{1}{2}$% per annum. All populations which now exhibit maturity and have a low growth potential spent two or more generations in this explosive transition status. During transition their size multiplied many fold (4 to 10 times). Table 6 presents a brief summary of the populations in the respective stages of growth potential.

Because of the extensive changes in social outlook that are involved, it seems to be necessary for a population to spend at least a generation in the transition stage before it can enter a mature phase. Therefore, doubling or trebling present population in the course of economic

TABLE 6. GROWTH POTENTIAL IN HUMAN POPULATIONS

Type	Areas	1952 Total Pop. Est., millions	Average Growth Rate
I Maturing	Western Europe, Australia, U.S., Canada, New Zealand, U.S.S.R., Japan	430	½–1½%
II Transition	Mediterranean areas, Balkans, Latin America, Caribbean Islands, Philippines	730	2–2½%
III High growth potential	Moslem areas, India, Africa (remaining), Indonesia, China, Persia	1250	1–2%

Up till 1965 the Type I areas fulfilled expectations with an average annual growth rate of 0.9%. Some Type II areas now have natural growth rates in excess of 3% per year. However, the advance of large countries in Type III category up to rates of 2 to 3% has been the source of most of the misjudgment of population growth. This mode of analysis is no longer useful.

development seems inevitable. However, nations which manage to attain transition status do not automatically graduate to the mature level since there is a fair chance that they may slip back and resume equilibrium characterized by high birth and death rates. In human terms this would signify a catastrophe—loss of life on a tremendous scale would be accompanied by a morale-shattering defeat of aspirations. Nevertheless those regions which enter into economic development programs with swollen populations and scanty resources are taking very real risks of this sort.

3. RESOURCES

The levels of resources can never be constant. They increase with progressing technology and diminish because of exhaustion and waste. If demand for any resource should increase, so that greater effort can be allocated to its exploitation, then supply also tends to increase because what were formerly submarginal reserves have been brought into a profitable position. Therefore any quantitative appraisal of resources must, from its start, assume:

> A given state of technics.
> A given set of needs and wants.

It has been customary to measure resources in terms of technology and skills that have already been used and tested on a large scale. Any system of exploitation that appeared feasible but had not proceeded beyond experiment has been ruled out. Such agreement is helpful because the sets of wants to be fulfilled, or the standards of value for consumption, are highly variable. It has been recently estimated, for instance, that only 30% of the coal in the underground "reserves" of the United States is worth the effort required to extract it. However, if that coal were valued at what it is in Europe, then a much larger proportion would be economic.

The most important resources are those which are most common and are noted only upon their loss or absence. Among these are

> Air
> Light
> Water
> Soil.

From these, man obtains various kinds of food, fibers, wood, medicinals, and other minor products, but by far the most important of these, as signified by the effort devoted to its acquisition, is food. One way of attaching meaning to such resources is to measure the quantity of harvest per year that these resources could regularly produce, assuming reasonably intelligent management of the holding. It is feasible to convert all feed, forage, and wood crops into *original* calories suitable for consumption.

The first appraisal of the worldwide resources available for food production was made by Salter (1947). Table 7 describes the extent of

TABLE 7. Soil Resources: Soil Classes and Soil Uses

Class	10⁹ Acres	Principal Uses
Chernozems, chernozem soil of prairies, tropical black soils	2.0	Cereals, tubers, vegetables, pulses, sugar
Chestnut & brown soils	2.5	Cereals, grass
Gray-brown podzolic, brown forest soils	2.5	Cereals, tubers, vegetables, sugar, pulses, wood
Alluvial soils, marshes, swamps in tropical regions	1.5	Cereals, sugar, wood
Podzols (including bogs)	3.0	Tubers, cereals, wood
Red loams, terra rossa, tropical red & yellow soils, laterites	7.0	Grass, fruits, roots, nuts, oils, wood
Sierozems, desert soils	6.0	Fruits, nuts, grass
Soils of mountains & valleys	6.0	Wood, fruits, grass
Tundra	1.5	Moss

Source: Salter (1947).

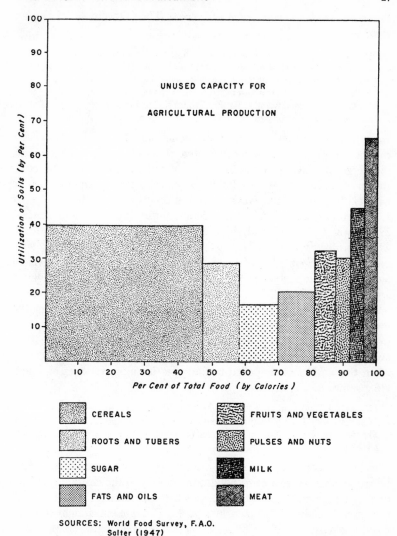

SOURCES: World Food Survey, F.A.O.
Salter (1947)

FIG. 3.   SOIL RESOURCES: FOOD, 1934–1938 AVERAGE

The world's food potentialities have been used quite unevenly.   The possibilities are greatest in categories that are especially rich in carbohydrates—sugar, fats, roots— where the unexploited soil resources lie mainly in tropical regions.   The capacity for distinguishing between these categories is much poorer than might be judged from the diagram; the uncertainty for any single item is perhaps 20 to 30%, but becomes less for group comparisons.

the resources when expressed as soil types. The following set of assumptions were made:

> Better farm practice could be extended to all presently cultivated land.
> 1,000,000,000 acres of new tropical lands could be brought into cultivation.
> This land would produce at levels already attained by the Philippines.
> 300,000,000 acres of new northern lands can be brought into cultivation.
> This land would produce at levels already attained in Finland.
> Fertilizer use would not greatly exceed present levels in France.

By this means Salter arrived at the conclusion that soils suitable for the various crops were being exploited at widely differing efficiencies. (See Fig. 3.) Among the predominantly carbohydrate foods the cultivation of cereals had achieved 40% of the estimated maximum possible with existing techniques, while roots and tubers reached 29% and sugar 17%. Among the proteinaceous foods, pulses and nuts had reached 29%, meat 67%, and milk 46% of what seems possible. The foods which protect against dietary deficiencies, fruits and vegetables, were produced at about 33% of what seems possible. Put on an over-all basis, prewar production of food amounted to 2.0×10^{15} Cal as against a potential of 5.7×10^{15}.

To Salter's figures however should be added the product from the rough, less productive soils which are best devoted to the culture of wood. Glesinger (1949) has assembled rough estimates for the land available for managed forests and the yields to be anticipated, especially when the world feels impelled to find uses for more varieties of wood. He assumes:

> The present 3000 million acres could be brought to yield a ton per acre.
> Afforestation of 1000 million acres could result in equal annual yields.
> The development of 5000 million acres of virgin, mainly tropical forest to yield 2 tons per acre.

This last assumption is more of a distant hope than a present day possibility, but the first two correspond quite closely to the customary definition of resources. The extent to which these resources are converted into useful products is shown in Fig. 4. The present annual yield of wood is almost 5×10^{15} Cal against a conservative realizable potential of 16×10^{15} Cal. Thus soil resources suitable for wood production are being utilized to about the same extent as those employed for food.

The dimensions of the world's soil resources can be made to expand by improving technology. Increasing the productivity per unit area with better adapted strains of plants and animals will have such a result. So will finding intensive uses of straw, bagasse, lignin, and other

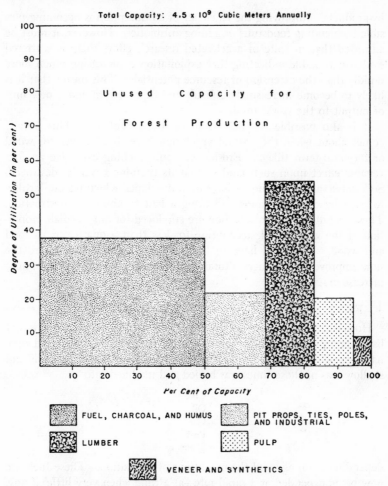

Fig. 4. Soil Resources: Wood

The growing of trees and the optimum utilization of forests is a resource use not so far advanced as agriculture. This is indicated in part by the low proportion reaching the most high-valued uses. The uncertainty for any given item may be 30 to 50%, but for group comparisons it is less.

Growth in wood use to 1960 was only 25%. Fuelwood remained constant. Greatest increases in resource use were in pulpwood and industrial wood. Conclusion: Efficiency of resource use is steadily improving.

by-products. Improving the efficiency of consumption is becoming possible by blending foodstuffs or adding antibiotics. However, it must be
admitted that in spite of accelerated research effort there is scattered
evidence available indicating that exploitation is increasing much more
rapidly than the extension of resource potentials. This means that it is
likely to become increasingly difficult and expensive to add a new unit
of output to the world total.

It is also possible for soil resources to be depleted. This usually
comes about when the natural vegetation is removed either for wood
or for short-term tillage. Erosion and sun-parching can have an irre-
versible effect upon such land so that its usefulness can be destroyed.
Soil conservation techniques have been developed which restore fertility
to partially damaged lands and bring a halt to abnormal destruction.
These techniques of conservation are employed for only a small proportion of the world's soil, accounting for less than a quarter of its food
and wood. They will have to become virtually universal before the
slow improvement in agricultural technique is paralleled by a similar
increase in resources.

4. F u e l

However, most of the energy employed in the world today is not
based upon current production but is derived from the fossilized rem-
nants of plant life of prehistoric periods. The product of the soils and
shallow seas of those times was buried and modified into

> Coal
> Oil
> Gas
> Peat
> Shale

depending upon age and the conditions of deposition. These fuels are
now being expended at a rapid rate—at a time when very little, if any,
are being laid down by natural processes. Thus, resources, in this instance, must be depleted to be used. There is some energy, such as that
derived from falling water, that is not subject to depletion-by-use, but
much of this potential is to be found in inconvenient mountainous
locations. Even when water power is fully used it can provide only a
minor portion of the world's total energy needs.

One of the most notable features about the fossil fuels is their un-
equal distribution over the Earth's surface. North America seems to
have accumulated preponderant quantities of all the energy-rich fuels

and at the same time it is one of the most thinly populated areas. Therefore, its per capita reserves are enormous, extending beyond a thousand years even at the present extravagant rate of consumption. At the beginning of the Industrial Revolution, the western side of Europe was almost as well off, but a five- to six-fold increase in population coupled with considerable depletion of reserves has reduced the supply to something less than two centuries at the present rate of extraction. Europe has, in the past decade, become highly dependent upon liquid fuels brought in from the Near East to supplement its own inadequate supply. On the other hand, South America and the northern stretches of Africa are virtually barren, a factor that has greatly hindered industrialization. Asia has rather significant amounts of fuel, but when this is allocated on a per capita basis, the quantity available is insufficient to support an industrial development of the pattern set by Europe, or even the more economical style set by Japan.

A question often raised is whether the explorations for fossil fuels are sufficiently complete to make valid assessments of the future. The "proved reserves" for oil in the '20's and '30's were misinterpreted to the point that gloomy predictions were commonly made picturing a petroleum-starved world of the '40's and '50's. We know by now that the predictions were fallacious and unwarranted. The reason is to be found in the definition of the term "proved reserve," which is based upon field by field measurements of oil residing in known strata that can be brought to the surface economically. The world total is now about 80 billion barrels (10^{10} metric tons); however, actual or "probable reserves" are several times this figure. Probable reserves include all the oil likely to be found by exploratory drilling which can be raised by the use of presently known techniques and recovery methods; probable reserves therefore conform to the standard that has been accepted for measuring resources in general. The supplies of natural gas should be estimated in the same manner as for oil. The deposits of shale require a different procedure because they are not yet well defined as to what will be economic (shale utilization is relatively expensive so the shales have been exploited only to a small degree up till now). Altogether the petroliferous reserve that can be depended on is still large and is likely to last at least a century or so, even with accelerated demand. Nevertheless, the gaseous and liquid fuel reserves are small as compared to the total for coal.

Improvements of method in exploring for coal and estimating the available reserves have led to a deflation of early estimates made in less

TABLE 8. Probable World Resources of Fossil Fuels

Type	Quantity*	Thermal Value, Cal
Coal	4×10^{12} tons	2.5×10^{19}
Oil	3×10^{11} bbls	4.5×10^{17}
Gas	3×10^{13} cu meters	3×10^{17}
Shale	10^{12} tons	10^{18}
Peat	10^{11} tons (dry)	3×10^{17}

* Palmer Putnam in 1953 published an assessment which was undertaken simultaneously and independently. He deflated the present "official" estimates somewhat more and did not try to compute any totals until he had subtracted normal processing losses. His total is a "net" figure which comes to about one fourth of the estimates given above. Considering the grossness of some of the assumptions that must be made, this is reasonably good correspondence for a category as vague as "probable resources."

developed portions of the world. Since 1944, China, India, and Canada have found it necessary to revise their estimates of coal resources downward quite drastically. Experience shows, therefore, that further exploration is unlikely to increase the present global figure for coal deposits to any important extent.

The world can look forward only to a decline in these energy resources that is due almost entirely to depletion. The only imaginable increase in resource levels might arise from the perfection of a new and cheap technique for mining deep seams of coal of less than 50-cm thickness. The current developments in underground gasification still do not promise anything close to the efficiency required to justify increasing the coal reserves.

5. Rocks and Minerals

The other minerals, including the metallic ores, exhibit wide differences in characteristics. Some, such as salt or lime, are to be found in almost every part of the world, while others, such as nickel, are scattered much more unevenly than the fossil fuels. These other minerals were also concentrated and deposited by some accident of nature over geological time; they also need to be discovered, assayed, sounded, surveyed, dug out, and refined, just as is done with the fossil fuels. The exploitation of most of the high-grade deposits has already begun—in many places it has also been completed—so that measurements of resources would require the definition of the volume of ordinary deposits and an indication of the extent of low-grade deposits.

There are still other factors that must be taken into account. Depletion is a real phenomenon for most of these minerals, but the prod-

TABLE 9. Availability of Minerals in the Earth's Crust

Elemental Material	Relative Abundance	Useful Forms	Current Critical Uses
Water	1,000,000	Fluid, fresh	——
Silicon	165,000	Sand, silicate	Construction
Aluminum	53,000	Bauxite, clay	Light metal
Iron	31,000	Magnetite, hematite	Primary metal
Calcium	22,000	Lime, gypsum	Construction
Sodium	17,000	Salt	Food and chemicals
Potassium	15,000	Soluble salts	Fertilizers and chemicals
Magnesium	13,000	Dolomite, chloride	Construction and metal
Titanium	3,800	Oxide	Paint pigment
Manganese	560	Oxide	Steelmaking
Phosphorus	470	Rock phosphate	Fertilizer
Carbon	300	Fossil fuels	Energy source
Sulfur	300	Native, sulfide ores	Chemicals
Chlorine	290	Salt	Food and chemicals
Strontium	250	——	——
Barium	230	——	——
Rubidium	190	——	
Fluorine	160	Fluorspar	Steel and chemicals
Chromium	120	Chromite ore	Plating, alloying
Zirconium	120	Oxide, metal	Atomic pile construction
Copper	60	Sulfide ores	Electrical goods
Nickel	60	Sulfide ores	Plating, alloying
Vanadium	60	Complex ores	Alloying
Tungsten	41	Complex ores	Filaments, alloys
Lithium	39	——	——
Cerium	26	——	——
Cobalt	24	Sulfide ores	Alloys
Tin	24	Oxide ores	Plating, alloys
Zinc	24	Sulfide, oxide ores	Plating, alloys
Yttrium	19	——	
Lanthanum	11	——	——
Lead	10	Sulfide ores	Batteries, paint
Molybdenum	9	Complex ores	Alloying
Thorium	6	Oxide	——
Cesium	4	——	——
Arsenic	3	Complex sulfides	Chemicals
Bromine	3	Soluble salts	Chemicals
Uranium	2	Complex ores	Weapons

ucts do not disappear in smoke. They tend to reappear in the form of scrap, and the greater the value of the material the greater the proportion salvaged. Scrap generally moves into lower-grade end-uses where specifications are less stringent. Each cycle of use and reprocessing results in loss so that eventually the mined product is distributed in low concentrations over the surface of the earth and precipitated at the bottom of the seas. Theoretically there are virtually unlimited quantities of any of the desirable minerals, but the question remains as to whether society can afford to pay the cost in energy and effort which is required to obtain them from the low-grade deposits.

For each desired mineral material the current technology for separation and concentration sets a "cut-off point"—a minimum occurrence below which the methods now in use do not permit extraction of the mineral. This level is somewhat below the concentration in the tailings of contemporary flotation units, smelters, and refineries. For copper mining this cut-off point ranges between ½ and 1 part per thousand of original ore, which is about a tenth of the concentration of the lowest-grade copper ore now mined. For zinc the cut-off point appears to be in the range of 3 to 5 parts per thousand. As this limit is approached, the energy expended and the over-all cost must be distributed over a smaller and smaller yield of metal. Thus the costs per ton of marginal output begin to leap upwards; a very high price for the material would bring forward no significant increase in supply. After most of the ore with concentrations greater than the cut-off point has been consumed, the total world production would be forced into a slow decline.

How far in the future are these supply crises for critical minerals? One can infer, by analyzing the report of the President's Materials Policy Commission (1952), that some of the current methods of extracting useful minerals from low-grade ores will have to be abandoned over a period 25 to 100 years hence. The scarcest metals in prospect are lead, nickel, tin, chromium, copper, and cobalt. If the reserves, as estimated in the most generous sense possible, are to last even that long, then a very low rate of consumption must be postulated for the rest of the world. The United States, with 6 to 7% of the world population, is expecting to consume more than 50% of the total supply of these scarce industrial raw materials.

Once a metal becomes too scarce or too expensive to use, the world economy is forced to resort to substitutes. It seems quite probable that altogether new methods for extraction from the ore can be devised. That would constitute a substitution of one process for another. However the product itself can also be displaced by competition with other metals, whose ores are available in virtually unlimited supply. Iron, aluminum, magnesium, and titanium can go into uses which now require copper, lead, zinc, and tin. However the metals now used mainly in special ferrous alloys—nickel, chromium, and cobalt—require a much more complicated chain of substitutions. Stainless steels constitute a major group of these alloys. If they are ruled out as being excessively expensive, the design engineer may either accept a more rapid rate of corrosion using variations of mild steel, he may try aluminum, titanium, or ceramics, or he may abandon the application altogether in favor of a reasonable alternative. It is thus impossible to predict the net effects of the adjustments required to meet a shortage of nickel, chromium, and cobalt.

It is rather unfortunate that the ores that are the most abundant, and therefore require the least effort for obtaining a high-grade concentrate, are so stable chemically that large amounts of energy must be spent in order to accomplish their reduction to metal. Iron, aluminum, magnesium, and titanium belong to this category. At present about 3% of all the energy released for useful purposes in the world is applied to the production of ingots and castings of virgin metal. Approximately three times that energy is committed to fashioning and shaping the metal. Thus for every ton of metal fabricated into machinery and equipment almost ten tons of coal and oil are required. As long as this quantity of energy is available it appears that the increased cost incurred in utilizing low-grade mineral deposits is not significant, whereas if energy becomes scarce it appears that certain metals requiring a great deal of energy (such as aluminum and titanium) will diminish in importance. Iron seems to cost the least energywise.

Other common materials of construction, such as concrete, ceramics, and wood, cost less energy but cannot be shaped precisely enough to displace much metal. The greatest metal-saving technique known is that of alloying or plating with traces of scarcer elements (especially beryllium, boron, chromium, cobalt, manganese, molybdenum, nickel, silver, tin, tungsten, and vanadium) to improve specific properties, such as tensile strength, hardness, or resistance to corrosion. It is impossible to establish either the long-run requirements or the resources of the auxiliary metal. Their energy requirements are large per unit weight, but the total is trivial as compared to what is required for the major metals. (See Table 10.)

Uranium and, to some extent, thorium fall in quite a different cate-

TABLE 10. ENERGY REQUIREMENTS FOR PRINCIPAL METALS

Refined Products	Density	Weight-Energy * Cost, 10^4 Cal/kg	Volume-Energy Cost, 10^8 Cal/ cu meter	Annual World Production, metric tons
Iron and steel (ingot and cast)	7.0–7.8	1.1	0.85	2.3×10^8
Aluminum (primary)	2.7	10	2.7	1.5×10^6
Copper (primary)	8.9	3.5	3.1	2.4×10^6
Zinc (recoverable)	7.1	2	1.4	1.7×10^6
Lead	11.3	1	1.1	1.0×10^6
Magnesium	1.75	12	2.1	2.0×10^4
Silver	10.5	20	21	6.0×10^3
Titanium	4.5	13	5.8	10^4

* Not in the form of electricity but only in the form of combustible fuels from which it may be generated.

Source: *U.S. Census of Manufactures*, 1947; *Minerals Yearbook*, 1950; U.S. President's Materials Policy Commission, and assorted technical publications.

gory. The energy requirements for reduction and refining, including isotope separation, can be quite large. The established technologies, however, lead only to weapons, which provide a disturbing facet to the present world predicament. The weapons may aid in preserving the present state of affairs but they offer no solutions to problems of world development. When these metals are introduced into a nuclear reactor they will release vast quantities of energy, and so are likely to become fuels in the not too distant future, but the technology is not yet stabilized. Their utilization must be discussed in a more speculative vein, and is taken up in the chapter covering fuels.

The nonmetallic minerals are generally in good supply. The sulfur shortage of the 1950's has brought the world to the point of using its inexhaustible supplies of gypsum and anhydrite. Thus the availability of sulfur depends upon the availability of the energy needed to release it from sulfate deposits. The most critical of these nonmetallic minerals is rock phosphate, which is essential to any program of expanded food production. Salter has calculated that raising agriculture up to its practical limits would result in about an eight-fold increase in fertilizer phosphate use. The probable reserves would then last about 2000 years. Thus the world phosphate extraction picture is at least as good as that of the fossil fuels. Long before then it is likely that techniques of phosphate salvage will have been perfected.

6. HUMAN NEEDS UNFULFILLED

The hardship that much of the world feels today can be attributed to a large extent to the inability to use resources to build production to meet the growing needs. The foregoing scrutiny of human needs, population, and resources enables one to gage, almost quantitatively, the size of the world development effort which must be planned:

$$\text{Human needs} \times \text{world population} = \text{world needs}$$
$$\text{World needs} - \text{world production} = \text{gap (or surplus)}.$$

For food production, the existence of this gap (there has never really been a surplus from the consumer's point of view) is enough to define the present predicament, because soil resources need not be exhausted, even though, through neglect or over-utilization, destruction of fertility often occurs. For energy resources, which were shown to be a key feature of all minerals exploitation and use, another operation is necessary in order to take depletion into account:

$$\text{World reserves} \div \text{annual world needs} = \text{outlook}.$$

The outlook gives a crude indication as to how long the present technics, which were assumed in the measuring of the reserves, will be able to persist—if world development is given the greatest possible encouragement.

World needs for food, as measured in calories, have always led production by a 10 to 15% margin. During the '30's the margin narrowed, but the disorganization of agriculture by the war in the decade increased the deficiency to a point that is probably as large as it ever has been in history. The slowness of the rate of diffusion of the improved techniques for handling soils and crops seems to prevent any rapid improvement of food supply.

According to Salter's estimate of soil resources the lack of calories should be the simplest hurdle to overcome because the capacity for cereals, sugar, roots, tubers, fats, and oils could easily be doubled, or, with effort, even trebled, merely by applying known technics in somewhat more difficult terrain. The proteins and protective foods however are more critical. Before 1970, soils ordinarily allocated to pulses and nuts, milk, and meat (and also bodies of water devoted to fishing) will have been pushed to foreseeable capacity and beyond. It appears that there will be even greater pressure on the balance of diet, or its

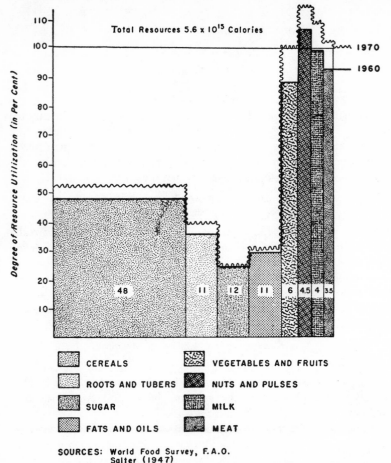

SOURCES: World Food Survey, F.A.O.
Salter (1947)

FIG. 5. WORLD FOOD NEEDS, 1960–1970

When will world food needs exceed the capacity of soils to provide for them? To estimate this requires first an estimate of what the various soils can be expected to produce, which Salter has done, and also an estimate of what the world needs of each food type, which the Food and Agricultural Organization has done for 1960. If such a program were to be extended to 1970, and was to deal with an estimated 7 to 9% increase in population, the requirements should resemble closely the uppermost line. The goals of the F.A.O., as laid down in the World Food Survey, still did not everywhere in the world reach the levels set by their experts for adequate diet. Therefore the crisis indicated by contrasting future needs with available resources is actually understated.

The concept of soil resource capacity is now being abandoned as we acquire increased knowledge of fertilizer applications and improvement of crop varieties. Substitutibility of crop types is particularly enhanced. However, the unexpected population increase in Asia has already resulted in a hundred million Asians becoming dependent upon North American surpluses.

nutritional quality, than upon the calories available. It is possible to convert the grain, tubers, and sugar into acceptable protein and fat; they reappear either as milk, meat, or food yeast, but there is an important 60 to 85% caloric loss involved, so that unused resources for carbohydrate production would disappear quite rapidly when making up a comparatively small protein deficiency.

The inaccuracies and inadequacies of the world food totals, and the even greater guesswork involved in estimating soil resources, together mean that the time of the world food crisis is not to be predicted with very great confidence. Much depends, too, on the degree of co-operation between nations and the efficiency of international administration achieved over the next few years. Nevertheless, the evidence is very strong that it will occur during the '60's or the '70's. That is the time that present food-producing technics, diffused over the whole world, are likely to approach their practical limits. By then either some major development must come on to the scene which permits more food to be produced or the population must look forward to continuous deprivation. The nature of the crisis is illustrated in Fig. 5.

The estimate of the lifetime of world fuel reserves must be based upon the achievement of some average consumption level which is necessary to acquire the scarcer mineral resources, fabricate them into capital equipment, and operate that equipment, incidentally providing shelter and living conditions sufficiently comfortable and healthful to permit efficient industrial labor. If the world average is assumed to reach the level now achieved by the Netherlands and Scandinavia, then about one and one-half tons of coal or its equivalent per capita per year (10^7 Cal) would be required. Actually world fuel use is not too far now from that level, but a predominant proportion is concentrated in North America. Because the major American coal and oil resources are located in mid-continent, and because the American economy can no longer function without high-level energy expenditure, it appears wise to separate the fuel-using capacity of North America from the rest of the world. By this reckoning, the world fuel crisis, i.e., the time of enforced retrenchment, is about a century off. The existing reserves will support a slowly increasing consumption of fuel to improve standards of living and to make up for the need to exploit thinner soil and scarcer mineral resources until about the year 2050. (See Fig. 6.) For North America, even if it increases its present prodigious energy use, the crisis is due some centuries later. At that time, digging for fuel would become so expensive there could be no alternative but to reduce its use.

A crisis does not imply immediate catastrophe, but is more like a challenge. It means that governments, industries, families, and other human institutions must make major adjustments which lead to efficient use of new sources of food and fuel, or they must find some way of reducing the total number of claimants for products derived from scarce resources. Some customary practices will have to be abandoned, or drastically revamped, or else man's scale of operations must be greatly reduced.

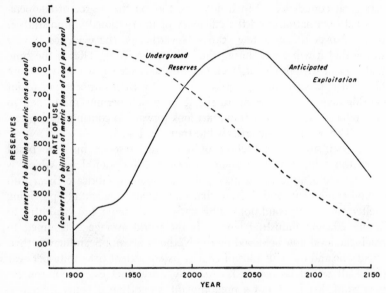

Fig. 6. Fossil Fuels outside North America, Outlook for Future Utilization

If world development should proceed fairly smoothly, then the ordinary exploitation curve—which occurs where demand is virtually unlimited—can be anticipated. Such a pattern suggests that fossil fuel reserves outside North America will permit a maximum depletion rate 2 to 3 times the present level. It is not likely ever to exceed present per capita levels in those areas by more than 100%. Because of large reserves and low population density, the equivalent diagram for North America would show a peak perhaps twice as high and a century or two later.

Most resources are expansible. At one time expansion occurred largely by discovery and exploration. But by now all of the accessible portion of the earth has at least been surface prospected and estimates are available which set the limits to what will very likely ever be found

or developed by contemporary methods of exploitation. Methods however can be improved by research, and there remain many points where
research is still likely to be fruitful. To meet the food shortage, for
instance, new methods for irrigation agriculture, for laying down fertilizer, for evolving better crop plants or controlling crop pests, for
harvesting and processing altogether offer considerable potentialities.
Estimates of the total increase in food capacity likely to come out of
this research range from 30 to 100%. To meet other shortages, such as

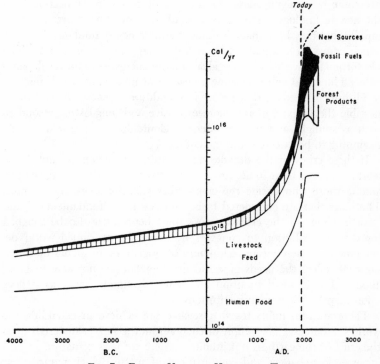

FIG. 7. ENERGY USE OVER HISTORICAL TIME

This graph gives a sweeping view of the intensity of human activity on the surface
of the planet. As far as it is possible to extrapolate present resources a peak should
be reached around the turn of the millennium. The rate of capture of solar energy
by land and ocean plants under natural conditions is roughly 4×10^{16} cal/yr. It is
estimated that about 6×10^{20} cal/yr are received at the earth's surface, which means
that 10^{20} cal/yr is the extreme limit of what is available for man's use. Related
extrapolations employing lesser time spans, and limited to non-food energy uses, are
to be found in Furnas (1954).

paper or fodder, the poorer soils may exhibit an even greater increase in potential productivity; their yields of forage and wood may be stepped up several fold.

Critical problems of supply, which threatened to limit world development in the recent past, have often been solved by the introduction of new technology arising from scientific research. A review of the outcome of these crises—electric power and light, fixed nitrogen, mechanized agriculture, synthetic rubber, light metals for air transport, and telecommunications are good examples—shows that practically all were overcome by applying massive quantities of power in connection with the new technology. Thus the demands for power have pyramided so rapidly that they have made imminent a more nearly fundamental crisis which comes to a climax when present energy sources give out. The old formula of wedding a new idea to more energy is no longer dependable. The world will need now a new set of inventions which manage to fill human needs with a reduced expenditure of energy or will make possible the tapping of the more expensive and long-lasting resources, such as sunlight and nuclear energy. Contemporary research is only beginning to be directed to these ends.

If these crises of the decades and centuries to come are not to be world debacles, then some new conceptions will need to be developed among those who decide the course that scientific work should take. The ideas that are considered to be "interesting," "fundamental," and "worth while" in the classical sense must henceforth also be weighed for their contribution to concepts necessary for continued world development. The delicate reshufflings of priorities and modes of thinking that reflect the needs of world development are not easy to bring about. The hand of tradition lies as heavily upon science as it does upon many other human institutions.

There are also limits to what science can achieve in extending the world's resources. The supply of energy from the sun, or materials from the crust of the earth, is not infinite. There are laws of nature governing energy exchanges and combinations of matter which reduce their utility much further. A careful investigation of the practical limits of world development would be valuable since this would make it possible to define some of the alternatives open to man for his continued occupation of the earth. Realization of the alternatives might eventually lead to some settled view of man's place which would obviate the staggering from crisis to crisis so evident in current prospects.

SELECTED REFERENCES

H. V. Sverdrup, M. W. Johnson, and R. H. Fleming, *The Oceans*, Prentice-Hall, New York, 1942.

K. F. Mather, *Enough and to Spare*, Harper and Bros., New York, 1944.

F. W. Notestein, "Population—the Long View," in *Food for the World*, T. W. Schultz, ed., pp. 36–57, Univ. of Chicago Press, Chicago, 1945.

World Food Survey, F.A.O., 1946.

World Fiber Survey, F.A.O., 1947.

R. M. Salter, "World Soil Fertilizers in Relation to World Food Needs," *Science*, 105, pp. 533–538 (1947).

J. J. Spengler, "Economics of Population Growth," *Southern Economic Journal*, 14, p. 123 and p. 233 (1947–8).

F. Osborn, *Our Plundered Planet*, Little, Brown & Co., Boston, 1948.

W. Vogt, *The Road to Survival*, Sloane Associates, New York, 1948.

"Recommended Dietary Allowances," Food and Nutrition Board, *National Research Council, Report and Circular Series*, 129 (1948).

E. Glesinger, *The Coming Age of Wood*, Simon and Schuster, New York, 1949.

M. K. Hubbard, "Energy from Fossil Fuels," *Science*, 109, pp. 103–109 (1949).

Demographic Yearbook of Statistics, United Nations Secretariat, 1949–50.

F.A.O. *Nutritional Studies*, No. 1, Rice and Rice Diets, 1948; No. 3, Food Consumption Tables, 1949; No. 4, Dietary Surveys, 1949; No. 5, Caloric Requirements, 1950; No. 6, Teaching Better Nutrition, 1950.

H. J. Barnett, "Energy Uses and Supplies, 1939, 1947, 1965," *Bureau of Mines, Inform. Circular*, 7582 (1950).

G. Lehman, E. A. Muller, and H. Spitzer, "Der Calorienbedarf bei gewerblicher Arbeit," *Arbeitsphysiol.*, 14, pp. 166–246 (1950).

Statistical Yearbook No. 5, World Power Conference, London, 1950.

Yearbook of Forest Product Statistics, F.A.O., 1950.

E. P. Hanson, *New Worlds Emerging*, Duell, Sloan & Pearce, New York, 1951.

E. Ayres and C. A. Scarlott, *Energy Sources—The Wealth of the World*, McGraw-Hill Book Co., New York, 1952.

U.S. President's Materials Policy Commission, *Resources for Freedom*, Government Printing Office, 1952.

P. Putnam, *Energy for the Future*, D. Van Nostrand Co., New York, 1953.

J. Rosin and M. Eastman, *The Road to Abundance*, McGraw-Hill Book Co., New York, 1953.

W. S. and E. S. Woytinsky, *World Population and Production*, Twentieth Century Fund, New York, 1953.

H. Brown, *The Challenge of Man's Future*, Viking, New York, 1954.

U.S. Department of Agriculture, *Water*, Government Printing Office, Washington, 1955.

The foregoing evaluation of the population-resources predicament limited itself to technologies in use at the start of 1954. Since then some food-producing technologies have become more efficient (maize offers perhaps the best example) and nuclear energy has set a relatively low

ceiling to the cost of electrical power generation. However, the un-
expectedly rapid population growth has counterbalanced these gains.
On balance, therefore, one must expect major Malthusian catastrophes
within the next two decades, with loss of life on the scale of a world
war—unless new technology and effective planning stimulate production
everywhere to such an extent that production outpaces growing consumption requirements.

Chapter 2

NEW FOODS

MOST SCIENTISTS coming to the study of nutrition for the first time will tend to think of food as the fuel and reconstruction material required to keep organisms functioning on an even keel. Diet, in their view, has a representative chemical composition, and some compositions, when taken as population averages, are measurably better than others. This reasoning presumes that when the optimum composition of diet is provided then health and welfare, as far as they can be affected by food, are, *ipso facto*, maximized. If this were true, and an adequate approach was as simple as that, then the task of the natural scientists would be reasonably straightforward.

There is however another logical system for improving human diet that starts from altogether different premises and tends to yield quite a different set of conclusions. Social scientists point out that eating is a process that is learned by each member of society in the context of a family or a small community group. The child is given rules at a very early age for discriminating among articles that are "foods," weeds or indifferent substances, and "unclean" or "poisonous" things. A routine or ritual is passed on to him for preparing and consuming the food. By the time he is adult he can make thousands of distinctions as to what is edible and how well it is prepared. Practically all of these distinctions are also based upon tradition since they too were learned from associates, whereas only a very few appear to be personal idiosyncrasies.

New conceptions of food for an individual are usualy acquired from new sets of associates. Therefore, the constant flux observed in dietary patterns is ascribed almost entirely to the intermixing of communities and societies and seems to be closely related to these movements. The maximization of welfare under these circumstances is the increased availability of traditionally prized foods or of staple foods introduced by a stronger culture; any other change would encounter either indifference or disgust.

If one were to compare social theories of nutrition with those deriving from biochemistry and physiology for their capacity to predict consequences in a realistic situation, then the former would most frequently be declared the most effective. The social theories are simple, not being far removed from the common sense of sophisticated persons, readily applicable, and highly consistent even in complex urban societies. In general, these two approaches are not conflicting, but can be superimposed upon each other. It is possible to adduce arguments from one framework, and then the other, in order to arrive at rather specific conclusions about how the world's food supply should be improved.

1. Dietary Needs and Supplies

The appraisal of world resources and world needs is a technique that permits a more precise evaluation of future food requirements than any available up to now. By this means one may deduce what kind of food production has the greatest urgency. The pressure is expected to come either from some human needs that will remain unfulfilled when present programs are completed or from situations where soil of a type now employed quite satisfactorily does not appear to be adequate to meet future needs. Thus when an international program is considered which will meet the food crisis, not only must the scale of the total effort be known, but also a basis for deciding which projects should come first.

What kinds of projects would be most worth while? There are at least three different sets of priorities to be considered in taking a look at the world food future. The first deals with immediate measures, which might be started in the next year or two and have their maximum effect five or ten years later. They are generated primarily from the studies and reports of the various missions of experts in the field. These proposals and projects are judged by what improvements they may bring about in the locales affected and the indirect contributions they may make to the respective regions and countries. It is not at all likely that the world deficits high lighted a few pages back will be significantly diminished by following the advice of these experts because, with very few exceptions, they recommend the standard, established technics used earlier in determining the extent of the resources. They are unable to bring to light substantial new resources that have not already been included by Salter in his estimate of soils resources. The priorities in the short-run studies and projects depend, therefore, upon local surpluses and shortages, only occasionally having an impact upon the world market, so that there can be no consistent world pattern. The missions must go on, and the local projects must be generated in a steady stream, lest the food supplies fall still farther behind the needs, but we must look for additional ways out of these difficulties.

There is a second priority list that emphasizes the applied research and development that are needed to generate new, outstandingly productive projects five to ten years hence. Drawing up priorities for technological investigation, or applied science research, requires extrapolation to a point farther in the future than most administrators and managers are accustomed to think. Such a priority list is based upon the existing stock of unused scientific knowledge. Each potentiality which has not been exploited in practice would be carefully scrutinized. What new resource would be brought into use? In what quantities? At what cost? How much research and development effort seems to be required? Out of such a review would emerge a series of proposals to be developed and perfected. The items could be set down in order, according to the amount of ultimate benefits promised and the probability that they could be obtained. Such estimates can be made by experienced research personnel on the basis of their ability to make deductions from existing knowledge. It may easily turn out that, in one commodity or another, the existing knowledge is inadequate, and that applied research and development programs would have to wait for the scientists to fill the gaps.

A third set of priorities is one for scientific research which may have its very first effects ten to twenty years hence and its major impact a century or so in the future. If it is to be realistic such a scheme of priorities must be very vague, because the role of fundamental science has been that of providing novel and unexpected opportunities for the technologist and establishing more precisely the natural constraints upon his operations. To some extent it will depend upon whatever gaps are revealed in the review of applied research opportunities. Our best strategy is to go back and take a closer look at new technology, before attempting to set the problems for scientists.

The following list of commodity types is proposed, in their order of urgency, for technological development:

> Plant proteins
> Vegetables and fruits
> Vitamins and minerals
> Cereals
> Sugar
> Fats and oils
> Dairy and eggs
> Meat and fish
> Others.

Plant proteins were assigned the highest priority because (1) the prospective supply of proteins is far from sufficient to meet human needs, (2) the soils that might be transferred from other crops to high protein-yielding crops are not readily available, (3) plant proteins are inherently cheaper than animal proteins, but (4) the marginal cost of protein using present agricultural techniques rises steeply as unused resources are brought into production. An important related argument is that there exist no reasonably economic proposals for the rapid expansion of the production of plant proteins since the demise of the Groundnuts Scheme for Tanganyika in 1950 (which was justified economically on the basis of its contribution to the margarine shortage, rather than its yield of proteins).

Protein lack participates in one of the very important vicious circles affecting peoples in poverty-stricken portions of the world. When a society is reduced to less than 50 g of protein per capita per day, it is held captive by a lassitude that prevents it from taking advantage of most other opportunities for self-improvement. Yet, to complete the circle, the incomes of practically all persons in such societies are too low to meet the cost of added edible protein. They can survive and reproduce, but they cannot prosper.

The production of fruits and vegetables, second on the list of needed commodities, is really aimed at alleviating shortages of vitamins and minerals. This may seem to be an uneconomic means for assuring adequacy of these nutritional components, because the latter can now be synthesized at very little cost. However, in the parts of the world suffering from malnutrition there is very little control and inspection of foodstuffs going to most levels of the population, so it is not possible to assure an intake in accordance with day to day needs. In short, it has been found that it is easier to start by incorporating certain fruits and vegetables into a new balanced, dietary pattern than by dealing with the shortage directly by distributing pills or enriching staples. When vitamin and mineral intake is high, the utilization of low levels of proteins in the body is significantly improved. In other words, fruits and vegetables, carefully chosen, may serve indirectly as a limited, small-scale protein substitute.

Cereals and sugar are the most popular sources of calories. Temporarily they are expected to become "surplus commodities" in the food-exporting nations, but only at prices which food-short nations are unable to pay. A decade or so hence, as new soils are brought into production, equally high or even higher costs must be anticipated. Fats and oils, also sources of calories, are part of the standard cookery in most parts of the world. Therefore consumption is expected to increase as quality and quantity of diet rise above bare subsistence. However, the rapidly increasing production of synthetic detergents is freeing large supplies of fats that can be refined for human consumption. Therefore fats have a relatively favorable long-term supply picture.

Animal proteins were put low on the list because the yield of meat and other high quality food is only 10 to 30% of what was fed. Therefore, wherever calories or proteins are scarce, a heavy emphasis upon livestock could only result in a maldistribution of food (this is less true for fish culture). Yet there are extensive soil resources, especially in tropical areas, which can only be utilized by livestock. Therefore animal husbandry, especially dairy and poultry, is given a somewhat higher ranking than roots and tubers. The luxury crops (also subsumed under "others") will of course come last in this mode of weighting, although they are often given a high priority in regional development because of good profit potential (tobacco, wine, apples, nuts, etc.).

2. The Protein Problem

According to Fig. 5 the world's soil resources for producing protein foods are quite limited. What foods are protein foods? How are they produced? What steps are necessary to expand their production? These are questions which come immediately to mind, but an inspection of current information indicates that straightforward answers are not easily obtained. Practically all foods have some protein, but the proportion varies from a few tenths per cent in potatoes to about 40% in soybeans. A generally suitable diet will contain 2 to 3% protein or, using a more stable reference, close to 10% of the dry weight. If there is less energy used up in heavy work and other activity, then an even higher proportion of protein is advisable.

It is a rather common observation that foods that rank high in pro-

tein content cost more than other foods. Determining the absolute
cost of protein has its complications, however, because all these foods
contain carbohydrate and fat as well. The simplest means of determining the cost of protein in various foods is to value all carbohydrate
at the retail price for sugar, and all fat at the retail price for lard, so
that the residual cost can be assessed to the protein content. When
this procedure is carried out for a number of foods, as in Table 11, then
some remarkable differences in cost appear. If this same analysis were
to be undertaken in other parts of the world, with cassava, perhaps, as
the standard for low cost carbohydrate, and peanut oil for the cheap
fat, very similar results are to be expected. The pulses and grains are
the most economical sources of protein; animal products are many times
more expensive.

Proteins are first created in the leaves of plants. There the process
of photosynthesis is responsible for the creation of many reactive intermediates, among which are the keto acids. The plant brings soluble
nitrogen compounds and minerals up to the leaf, where the ammonia
portion is combined directly with the keto acids, to make amino acids.
From them, the plant cells proceed to build up protein aggregates.
The proteins accelerate the synthetic activity of the leaf by providing
the structural supports for enzyme catalysts. They make up the bulk
of the nonaqueous matter of vigorous, newly created cells. Thus a
young, green leaf is richest in protein. In many plants, particularly the
cereals, a reversal takes place when the flower stalk is sprouted. Then
the plant redirects its energies, concentrating all its reserves upon reproduction. The protein in the leaf undergoes a process of solution or
digestion, returning to soluble amino acids. These pass from the leaf
via the stem to the flowers and seeds. Synthesis of protein in the leaf
continues, but the rate of dispatch to the rapidly forming grain accelerates, so that the net protein content of the leaf decreases. Eventually, synthesis in the leaf dwindles toward extinction and the leaf
turns from green to gold or brown quite suddenly. Then the grain is
ripe; the resources of the plant itself have been exhausted. At the
harvest more than half the protein created by the cereal plant has
been concentrated in the seed—if soil and moisture conditions were
not too adverse.

The production of protein in legumes differs only in that the nitrogen
portion may be abstracted from the air and fixed into useful nitrogenous
substances (especially ammonia) by co-operative bacteria in nodules
formed in its root system. More nitrogen is made available to the

legumes so the proportion of protein to be found in the seed is generally much higher.

The means of production employed by Nature suggest that one would get more protein by harvesting the leaves instead of the seeds. A com-

TABLE 11. COST OF PROTEIN TO THE CONSUMER

Item	May 1952 Representative Market Price	Residual Cost of Protein *	April 1965 Representative Market Price	Residual Cost of Protein
Flour, white	$0.10/lb	$0.21/lb	$0.10/lb	$0.21/lb
Oatmeal	0.123	0.33	0.23	1.40
Beans, Navy	0.15	0.39	0.13	0.33
Soya flour	0.26	0.50	0.23	0.42
Milk, dried	0.375	0.87	0.37	0.85
Macaroni	0.195	1.06	0.23	1.40
Bread, white	0.16	1.12	0.172	1.25
Peanut butter	0.41	1.24	0.33	0.90
Rice, polished	0.17	1.34	0.13	0.85
Bread, rye	0.18	1.39	0.20	1.55
Milk, evap.	0.154	1.88	0.154	1.88
Chicken, dressed	0.55	2.65	0.35	1.50
Pork sausage	0.49	2.66	0.39	2.05
Cheese, cheddar	0.76	2.72	0.69	2.40
Fish, fillets	0.53	2.76	0.45	2.30
Hamburger	0.65	2.87	0.47	2.07
Eggs, large	0.37	2.95	0.27	2.05
Milk, fresh	0.113	3.00	0.113	3.00
Frankfurters	0.65	3.18	0.59	2.84
Cabbage	0.06	3.30	0.10	5.00
Beef roast	0.85	3.60	0.49	2.10
Beef steak	1.08	4.70	0.99	4.25
Lamb chops	0.95	4.75	0.85	4.20

* The fuel components in these foods were assessed at 10¢ per lb of carbo-hydrate (the price of sugar and many starches) and 16¢ per lb of fat (the price of refined lard or cooking oil). The compositions were drawn wherever possible from UNFAO *Food Composition Tables*, October 1949, and Lange's *Handbook of Chemistry*. A sample calculation for evaporated milk would be

9.9% carbohydrate @ 10¢ per lb	0.99¢
7.9% fat @ 16¢	1.26
credit for fuel constituents	2.25¢

then the 7.0% protein (0.07 lb) is worth 15.4 − 2.25 or 13.15¢, and a pound of protein costs $1.88. American measures are used here because quite different distributions of prices exist in countries using cgs. units.

parison of the various methods of preparing protein for the market indicates that a large advantage might be achieved.

TABLE 12. TYPICAL PROTEIN YIELDS UNDER GOOD MANAGEMENT

	Yield per Acre, dry wt	Protein
Alfalfa	4.0 tons	1500 lbs
Grass	1.2 tons	600
Soybeans	20 bu	450
Peanuts	1300 lbs	350
Maize	55 bu	280
Wheat	35 bu	220
Hogs (maize and alfalfa meal)	800 lbs	160
Milk (grass, silage, alfalfa)	3000 lbs	120
Beef (grass, maize)	300 lbs	50

Can leaves of plants supplement pulses, cereals, and meat? The subject has interested scientists for many years. A grass food protein concentrate and "grass milk" have been developed in the United States; the former has even been approved for human consumption by the American Medical Association, but the source—cereal grasses grown on very fertile land—does not contribute much to the problem of increasing world supplies at reasonable costs. The most complete summary of early progress was made in the report to the Agricultural Group of the Royal Society by Slade, Branscombe, and McGowan (1945). In it they point out that there is no reason why the protein from leaves should not be extracted by mechanical and chemical processes. The obvious method is to rupture the cells and squeeze out the liquid contents—a sugar cane mill will supply the desired shearing action. They were able to separate out 30% of the protein as a dark green curd, the remainder being closely held by the lignin portion of the plant, adhering more lightly to the cellulose fibers, or being lost in the waste liquors. The curd has a crumbly texture. It can be preserved by canning. It analyzed 57.5% protein, 9.3% chlorophyll, 0.2% carotene pigments, 0.3% xanthophylls, 9.1% waxes and fats and 5.6% ash. When fed to rats, it appeared to be as digestible as other vegetable proteins.

The critical difficulties in obtaining proteins from foliage are those of engineering and economics. Even with alfalfa, only about 50% of the protein may be in the leaves at the time of cutting, and only a third of this can be recovered as protein concentrate. The best use for the remainder would be as cattle food (in the form of silage), where the net recovery of protein at best would be 20%. If a good plot of alfalfa were to be fully processed in this manner, the following results for one acre over a full growing season might be expected:

Initial protein content	1500 lb/acre
Protein content of leaves	750
Protein concentrate from leaves	250
Protein in stems	750
Protein in expressed leaves	400
Waste and fermentation loss	100
Protein in meat and milk @ 20%	210
Total protein in potentially edible form	460
(To convert to kg/hectare multiply by 1.10)	

The labor and machinery requirements for such a process are quite extensive since the foliage has to be expressed before wilting. The ensiling of the stems and fibrous portion of the leaves requires additional power, both for chopping and for transport. The efficient feeding and care of the cattle needed to consume the stems also requires much labor and attention. Thus the cost of the edible protein obtained would be very high, and the net yield would be no greater than that to be anticipated from peanuts or soybeans. Although much ingenuity has been displayed in this research, it still fails to suggest where any practical developments may arise.

The status of soybeans, peanuts, beans, gram, and other pulses is quite different. All are legumes which produce a fruit that is simply harvested. Peanuts and soybeans have a valuable vegetable oil content as well which is generally extracted and hydrogenated for human consumption. (See Fig. 8.) The residual pressed cake is usually fed to cattle, but it can be adapted to human consumption with little waste or inconvenience. (The product called Multi-Purpose Food, developed at the California Institute of Technology primarily for low-cost protein nutrition, is based upon soybean meal as the major raw material.) In traditional Oriental foods, soybeans are usually processed into foods without separating the fat, but a similar treatment of peanuts has not become popular, except as a confection in the United States.

At least one or more of the pulses can be grown wherever grain, cotton, or potatoes can be grown successfully. The difficulty is that the yields cannot always be raised to a profitable level. Some special varieties of soybeans have recently entered the warmer climates, but, in the most common soils, the yield tends to drop—often to averages of only 10 to 12 bushels per acre (600 to 800 kg per hectare), even under good management. This would mean that a soybean crop would do no better than pulses longer adapted to the tropics and grown under primitive conditions.

The problem turns out to be a familiar one for the agricultural re-

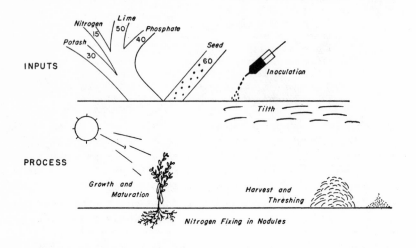

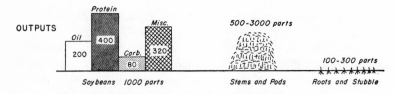

SOURCE: Markley: *Soybeans and Soybean Products*

FIG. 8.   PROTEIN PRODUCTION IN THE PULSES: SOYBEANS

The soybean is presently the most efficient crop in the production of protein. The inputs represented are, as closely as it is possible to estimate, the average requirements over a period of time, using the same soil. The nitrogen requirements are those above the amounts normally fixed from the atmosphere. It is still relatively seldom that present agricultural practice puts back as much as it takes out.

search scientists. Its solution involves selecting from among the hundreds of strains of plants available those that appear to yield well in sunny climates and in heavy soils. It also involves discovering what kind of parasites and diseases become important, and breeding for resistance to that set of hazards. As the plant is moved into alien climates its maturing cycle may become unbalanced so the seeds fall out of the pod during harvest, or sprout on the vine. Therefore, new selections must be made which aim to minimize the losses at harvest time. Choices at this point are mostly based upon the technics of the harvesting. Simultaneously, the soil conditioning must be taken into account so that the essential minerals are accessible and nitrogen fixation is encouraged. In order to get maximum vigor, two pure strains may be crossed, or hybridized, and the seed distributed for planting in the more fertile areas. These procedures are typical for what has been done for hundreds of crop plants. Among the pulses it is furthest along for soybeans, although some progress is being made in peanuts, and scattered efforts are being applied to other representatives of the group.

What kinds of results are to be expected? On this score the agricultural scientists refuse to commit themselves very explicitly. From past performance, it appears that the major gain is dependability. The chances of crop failure have been greatly reduced where agricultural practice has been affected by science. Research has provided means for preserving the original fertility of the soil. It can also adapt crops to mechanized farming. By many devices it makes possible an average yield close to what was once considered a bumper harvest.

But agricultural science can have little effect unless it is embedded in a vast bureaucratic "extension system" which interprets the results of research in terms of explicit changes of behavior and recommends those to the "man in the field." There must be an institution that would persuade the farmer that it was in his own interest to alter his activities. It engages in a form of adult education, and encounters all the difficulties expected of later learning. Wherever most farmers are illiterate, then teaching is arduous, change comes slowly, and crop increases are uncertain. The progress of science does not determine the rate of increase in the production of the pulses, but only shows the way to the responsible civil servant. The rate at which these gains are realized is then principally a measure of the efficiency of the governments in most parts of the world. If one is to judge from present and past performances of these governments, it must be admitted that the prospects of rapid improvements of supply are rather poor.

The conclusions reached here for the future of pulses are the same as for most other edible crops produced by small farmers. When the whole social system on the rural scene must be revamped in order to achieve a doubling or trebling of the yield of protein, then it cannot be expected that such increases will be achieved in less than a generation. (This slow transition is unfortunate because the population tends to expand 1½ to 3% per year over the same period so that the per capita share of the pulse protein remains virtually unchanged.)

It is quite expensive to provide the perquisites that assure decent yields of pulses on soils for which they were not previously adapted. The capital costs for water, fertilizer, drainage, and improved soil structure are expected to fall generally in the range of $500 to $1500 per annual ton of crude protein. Assuming that a billion people need an extra 20 g per day and another half billion or so are added to the world's population at 60 g per day, half of it from pulses, then the direct capital outlay needed between now and the end of the century would come to $7 to $20 billion. This is a range to keep in mind because it sets a kind of target for alternative proposals for producing low-cost proteins.

3. REAPING THE WATERS

The soils do not offer the only resource potential for protein production. The oceans continually synthesize tremendous quantities of organic material, at least half of which is protein. According to Rabinowitch's evaluations (1947, 1951), photosynthesis occurs in the oceans at a greater rate than in forest or grass land. What becomes of this huge reservoir of organic materials?

Marine ecology is still insufficiently understood to establish the full picture, but the qualitative outline is now apparent. The diatoms and algae (phytoplankton) which are responsible for the original photosynthesis are consumed by many families of microscopic fauna which are collectively called zooplankton. The total concentrations of plankton reach as much as 2 g per ton of surface waters—at the time of spring "bloom" in the colder seas. Whales, shellfish, small shrimp, and other marine animals live on them.

The question of human utilization of plankton has often come up for discussion (there was a fascinating series of "letters to the editor" in British publications at the height of the blockade during the last war), but no one has yet made a proposal that offers any hope for harvesting them economically. Most investigators use a very fine nylon net for filtering the microscopic life from sea water, but this is rapidly rendered ineffective by the gelatinous nature of the organisms. Once obtained, the plankton have many of the properties of a thin sardellen paste. The fishy flavor may vary from mild to extra strong. Its composition, taste, texture, and variability put it in a class of fish products that ordinarily find a market as cattle food or fertilizer—a low-valued end-use.

A similar problem is posed by the finding of the "deep scattering layer," a stratum of living organisms in the deep oceans discovered through their property of scattering or reflecting sonar pulses. The layer tends to move upward and downward in a daily cycle. In general it is believed to be composed largely of euphausid shrimp and their natural predators and is usually found several hundred meters deep (Moore, 1950; Hersey et al., 1952). If some way can be found for economically harvesting the population of this layer and transforming it into an edible product, there seems to be a large enough reservoir available to supply all the world's craving for marine foods. Very little progress, if any, seems to have been made in the direction of utilizing the deep scattering layer for food, but one cannot tell for certain because the possibility of submarine warfare has introduced secrecy into these and closely related investigations.

Up to the present, therefore, the only dependable method for collecting edible marine protein is that of catching fish. This is a highly developed profession that tends occasionally to be more successful in harvesting than Nature is in replenishing the supply. The time-tested approach then, given a set of circumstances where the hunter's skill becomes far superior to that of his quarry, is to domesticate that species of wild game and use it as a new variety of livestock. Western culture has not appreciably developed the art of pisciculture which it initiated during medieval times, but, fortunately, several independent developments in the Orient have prospered, and offer some measure of the potentialities of fish-farming.

The Chinese seem to have advanced the farthest in fresh-water environments. The high yield and the efficiency of Chinese fish ponds is due to a technique in which the feeding habits of the various carp varieties are so utilized that no feed goes to waste. That is, varieties are so stocked that the surface feeders, bottom feeders, and scavengers are in proper ratio to each other. There has also developed in China a group of skilled fry sorters who differentiate between the varieties of baby carp on the basis of their oxygen needs. Unfortunately the best varieties of these carp do not breed in captivity. The fry are therefore caught in the wild state and distributed to the commercial ponds for feeding up to market size. The most common food is waste from silkworms, grass, soybean cake, offal, and night soil. These materials are consumed in part directly, but mainly function as fertilizers in the pond and assure a luxuriant growth of plankton for the fish to feed upon. Under good management 1 kg of fish is obtained from about 4 kg of food, and 3000 to 6000 kg per hectare (1 to 2½ tons per acre) is a fair annual yield. There is a considerable amount of labor and capital required so that the final cost of the protein is not cheap; its local value is intermediate between soybean cake and meat. The technique is therefore limited not only by the supply of "fish-food" but also by low consumer incomes.

In the Philippine Islands and Java an unfertilized sea-water technique has been developed. There the plankton cultures will develop in still tidal water when it is enclosed in a shallow pond. The pond is then deepened with fresh sea water and the fry are added. The yield of milk fish and mullet so obtained is only about a fifth of that achieved by the Chinese, but the costs appear to be no greater. The limitations are to be found mainly in the topography of the shore line, so that capacity in the Philippine Islands is believed to amount to about a third of present Filipino fish consumption. Developing techniques of fertilizing the ponds may increase capacity, but the extent to which this is possible is still unknown.

The great advantage of pisciculture is that it uses land and water resources which otherwise cannot be adapted to food production—the swamps, marshes, and eroded areas. It provides an efficient use for many agricultural waste products. In Japan, fish have even been grown in conjunction with paddy rice, achieving yields of fish up to 500 kg per hectare of rice field. All these techniques will not come close to supplying the whole of the world's protein needs at reasonable cost, but they do provide a net increase in places where the shortages are the greatest. They are therefore a highly suitable art to be encouraged by the United Nations' agencies.

Another possibility for protein production is suggested by the differences in the utilization of soil resources in the world. (See Fig. 3.) Sugar resources are expected to be used at only a fifth of capacity, and yet, in terms of the amount of organic matter produced per unit area, they are the most efficient means available today for fixing solar energy in a readily utilizable form. Can this standard of excellence be applied to the production of scarce proteins and the not-too-abundant fats? The most tractable converters turn out to be microorganisms.

A special strain of Torulopsis yeast was developed by Thaysen (1943) which is bland to the taste and larger than the common Torulopsis (also called Torula) so that it can easily be filtered or centrifuged from suspension. This is an organism that would thrive on the cheapest of fuel foods—molasses, starch wastes, or solubilized wood pulp—plus the most economical of the synthetic fixed nitrogen compounds—ammonia and urea—and the simplest, cheapest fertilizer minerals. The product is obtained in dehydrated form, a very light brown dusty powder, containing 44 to 48% protein. The process was put into commercial operation in Jamaica, where the cost was somewhat higher than might be expected because it was required to pay off charges on a plant design rushed to completion with inadequate data at the end of the war in order to alleviate some of the critical food shortages at that time.

Experimental plants have also been erected at Rhinelander, Wisconsin, and in Hato Rey, Puerto Rico. The former utilizes wood sugars in waste sulfite liquors from papermaking, but its product is mainly incorporated into cattle feed as a vitamin-rich high-protein supplement. The Puerto Rican facility uses by-product molasses, but has evolved an improved method of processing. Because there has been such extensive experience with quite large-scale operations it is not very risky to estimate the long-run costs when employing mass-production techniques.

The world's molasses supply, containing about 10^6 tons per year of fermentable sugars, can meet only about 2% of the projected protein needs, even if the molasses were to be used for nothing else. Therefore, many other suitable carbohydrate sources, including cane juice, beet juice, wood molasses, etc., would also need to be adapted to the culture of yeast. For any production unit that has been envisioned, this adaptation of the substrate material would ordinarily constitute the first step in processing. (Many potentially valuable raw substrates, such as beet or cane sugar, contain mysterious organic substances which inhibit the reproduction of yeasts and therefore require preliminary treatment for the removal of inhibitors.) Then the sugar solution is introduced in a large continuous fermenting vat, along with the ammonium sulfate, urea, and superphosphate solutions. This large vat, containing perhaps 10 tons of yeast culture, is the heart of the operation. Extremely fine bubbles of air would be admitted at the bottom while the foam is depressed at the top. The overflow, containing yeast and a largely consumed substrate, would be centrifuged so that it is obtained as a thick cream. The harvested yeast would be dried and bagged.

As industrial operations go, this is quite a simple process requiring relatively uncomplicated machinery and very little labor. The cost of food yeast obtained from an installation based upon sugar cane utilization (Table 13) suggests that the protein component should cost around 35¢ per lb ($0.77 per kg). This is less than a third of the cost of protein in the form of fish, but the product is also further removed from the edible state. Processing into articles of diet and distribution to the consumer may double or treble the cost of yeast. It has an advantage over fish, in that it can be stored for long periods of time at low cost.

TABLE 13. Economic Characteristics of Torulopsis Yeast Production
from Cane Juice

Assumptions as to Yield

Total soluble sugars (11 tons per hectare)	10,000 lb/acre
Dried yeast per unit weight of soluble sugars consumed	0.45
Protein in the dried yeast	48%

Assumptions as to Size

Yeast production, annual capacity (9000 tons, metric)	20,000,000 lbs
Requirements for land in crops (1800 hectares)	4,000 acres

Estimations of Cost *

Food yeast plant	$1,500,000
Cane mill, cane juice treatment, and storage	$500,000
Contract cost of sugar (6.5¢/kg)	$0.03/lb
Labor requirements, semiskilled @ $2000/yr	50 men
Managerial and technical staff @ $5000/yr	8 men

Annual Expenses

Cane juice (molasses might be used out of season)	$1,300,000
Chemicals (1952 prices in Caribbean plus 30%)	500,000
Water and utilities	500,000
Labor and maintenance	200,000
Packaging and sales cost	200,000
Amortization (10 years) and Interest (8%)	300,000
Taxes and miscellaneous	300,000
	————
	$3,300,000
Cost $0.363/kg or	$0.165/lb

* This outline of costs is based upon both Jamaican and Puerto Rican experience, anticipating economies due to larger-scale production. In each case
rather liberal allowances were made so that it seems quite possible that initial
enterprises of this sort could operate at a cost level 20 to 30% below this.

The most important advantage is that the yield of protein per unit area
cultivated is increased by a factor of ten or more. The culture of Torula
can therefore make a substantial contribution to the world's protein
deficits. This can be done without making important inroads into the
supplies of scarce resources.

There is even greater promise in the growing of a red yeast, *Rhodotorula gracilis,* under slightly different conditions. Recent Swedish and
German investigations have shown that yeasts and molds can be induced
to produce fat as well as protein from a sugar substrate. However, these
studies encountered a major difficulty—the organisms must grow old
before they can grow fat! In the present factory-scale production of
yeast, the number of yeasts doubles every four hours, but growth under

such ideal conditions for reproduction leads to a fat content of only 3% (dry weight basis). If nitrogen compounds in the substrate are drastically reduced, the doubling time for yeast can be extended to twenty hours, or even longer. The fat content rises rapidly to 18 to 20% and then more slowly to much higher values. If enough oxygen for efficient respiration is brought to the yeasts, they can achieve a remarkable efficiency in converting sugar into fat and protein—as much as 60% of the energy content of the sugar is retained by the cells. However, providing oxygen (which is brought to the surface of the cell by compressing air, forcing it through very small orifices, and releasing it to form the tiny bubbles pervading the substrate) requires much more power for slow-growing fatty yeasts—probably at least ten times as much per unit of product. *Rhodotorula gracilis* seems to be the species that is most efficient and most economical under mass culture conditions. Its fat is very interesting because it resembles very closely palm oil, which is used widely as a butter fat substitute.

The best strategy for developing *Rhodotorula* would appear to be one of producing a combination of fat, protein, and carbohydrate resembling that of milk. Then it would be possible to draw upon a vast amount of experience in milk-products manufacture, especially ice cream and cheese-making, or the sausage-making arts, especially the fine-grained type, such as liverwurst or bologna. Then, if milk or meat should become truly scarce, a successor will have been groomed that can be adapted to most niches in an adequate diet now filled by milk and meat products.

Although fatty yeasts have not advanced beyond the pre-pilot plant stage of development, it seems very probable that they could compete effectively with milk. Costs per ton would be higher than for the Torulopsis strains, perhaps almost twice as great if liberal allowances are made for power costs, but such costs are still only a third or a quarter of the average cost of milk today. Surprisingly enough, the loss in protein yield expected in order to produce fat simultaneously in a modified continuous-flow process is very small. Until more complete data are obtained such losses can be neglected.

It is only fair to mention at this point that many nutritionists have been highly skeptical about the value of yeast protein in the human diet. Over the last decade or so three controversies have arisen among technical people which brought into question the nutritional value of food yeast. They are (1) the poor showing made by growing rats when yeast is used as the chief source of protein; (2) the high purine nitrogen content which was suspected of increasing blood uric acid to the point where it might put a strain on the elimination system; and (3) the appearance of massive liver necrosis in some high-yeast diets. The first can be dealt with by adding 0.2% methionine, either natural or synthetic, to the yeast, which brings its biological value up to that of milk protein. For human diets based upon cereals, this enrichment is usually not necessary because surplus methionine is provided by the cereal foods. The second objection is not important in a society where the total protein in the diet is otherwise less than sufficient, as is the case in most poor communities. Nor is it important where yeast intake is less than 25 g per person per day . In the third controversy it has been difficult to assess the special conditions under which liver necrosis can occur at all. A recent paper, for instance, places the blame upon a simultaneous deficiency of cystine, methionine, vitamin E, and an unknown material which is inactivated by the presence of fat (McLean and Beveridge, 1952). The presence of a small amount of milk protein in the diet (only 4%) seems to prevent liver necrosis in rats.

Thus there is a broad range of consumption where food yeast is agreed to be perfectly safe. Then there is another area, embracing relatively high rates of ingestion, which is under a cloud because of the physiological effects which occasionally have been attributed, and as often disproved, to food yeast. In order to satisfy the professional doubters, rather large and comprehensive studies would have to be undertaken under the most trustworthy auspices. One can conclude that food yeast is at least as satisfactory nutritionally as any other "new" protein source, such as soybean flour, or new varieties of edible legumes, because the latter have generated even more serious doubts in certain restricted circumstances of use.

Does microbiology offer any other approach to protein synthesis which evades the methionine problem, eliminating the need to create special chemical plants to manufacture methionine? If one is engaged in a search for the most balanced protein (see Fig. 9), where is such a protein likely to be found? Recent data have suggested that the amino acid constitution of the protein of any species of microorganism is fixed generically, only minor variations being permitted in the course of a major change in environment. The constitution of any parasitic bacterium is therefore likely to be quite similar to that found in its natural habitat and environment. Microorganisms with the same protein constitution as man might be suspected of living on the same food as man. Thus bacteria which continue to live and propagate in human intestines are a group worth investigating. Gale (1948) has shown that one of the most common varieties of intestinal flora, *Eschirichia coli,* actually does have an amino acid constitution identical with that of the human being, and very close to that needed in its food. *Eschirichia coli* can be grown on practically the same substrates as yeast; up to the present this species happens to have been studied more inten-

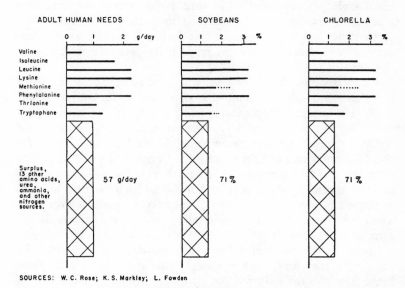

SOURCES: W. C. Rose; K. S. Markley; L. Fowden

FIG. 9. THE KEY TO PROTEIN QUALITY

W. C. Rose and co-workers have found that eight of the amino acids cannot be synthesized sufficiently to meet the needs of the healthy human body. Studies on rats also showed that these eight, plus arginine and histidine, are needed. If any one amino acid were to be reduced to less than half the amount indicated a normally healthy person would start losing weight (nitrogen imbalance). If soybeans or *Chlorella* should be the sole source of protein then deficiencies are to be expected, particularly in methionine. They are, nevertheless, about the best balanced of plant proteins.

sively by scientists than any other bacterium. However, no simple, inexpensive technique has yet been suggested for growing them in mass culture for food. No one seems to have taken the trouble to investigate carefully the possibilities for large-scale economic culture; therefore no conclusions can be drawn regarding its feasibility.

4. OPTIMIZING THE USE OF SUNLIGHT

It is surprising how few scientists question the ultimate usefulness of the basic techniques of agriculture. Practically all techniques employed by primitive man in his struggle for existence have been discarded, but agriculture has stayed on in a greatly modified, but still quite recognizable, form. There has never been any alternative practice for food production which has been seriously considered. Even the microbiological possibilities of yeast, molds, and bacteria imply the growing of familiar crops by standard methods, but switching from ambient livestock to microscopic, free-floating types; the raw products are not much different from the crude home brews developed before the dawn of history.

This perspective changes however when one asks the question: What is it that sets an absolute limit to food production on the Earth's surface? The answer is simple and specific: It is light. All other requirements for the synthesis of food, such as water, carbon dioxide, and fertilizer minerals, are now under the economical control of man, but the dominant source of light is not. The question that follows directly from this is: How does one get the most from the limited quantities of light available? Basic, searching questions such as these have led to the recent exploration of a wholly new alternative which gives promise of being many times more efficient in protein production than any form of agriculture.

Interest in this fundamental approach was deflected for a while because of a false lead. It was thought that if the culture of plants broke free from the soil itself and optimum concentrations of mineral nutrients were continuously brought to the root tips then the plant would be able to make the best possible use of the sunlight. Thus the techniques of hydroponics, or soilless gardening, were developed. Many yields were increased, and the proportions of stunted, blighted, and diseased stocks diminished, but only at a tremendous cost of building concrete troughs to distribute the aqueous culture medium and for hand labor at harvest time. Experience shows now that only the higher-priced vegetables, mainly luxury foods, can be grown economically by hydroponics methods; the staples of life—the pulses, tubers, and grains —are in most locales several times too expensive.

In the meantime, other scientists concentrated their attention on the natural process by which all plants transform sunlight into a form of chemical energy—photosynthesis. Every tool of modern scientific investigation was brought to bear upon the phenomenon, and many new laboratory techniques were created specifically to elucidate some interesting feature. Although much has been learned, scientists are still far from satisfied with their present ability to describe the mechanism of photosynthesis. The process cannot yet be set forth in terms of either the simple, easily treated model that fundamental researchers take delight in achieving, or the elaborate, but comprehensive system expressed in quantitative concepts of all the related sciences, with which they must often be satisfied.

The applied scientist does not need to wait upon the "solution" to the problem of photosynthesis. Once a certain level of information has been accumulated, he can begin to propose many different sequences of practical steps by which plentiful natural resources can be converted into scarce commodities. The limitations of photosynthesis, and the constraints laid upon the organisms that employ it, will determine what shall be the optimum use of light energy.

The principal restrictions upon yield in the case of hydroponic culture of the higher plants were long maturation cycles, low diffusion rates to the points where photosynthesis actually occurred, and the waste of effort involved in building up inedible stems, leaves, and roots. This suggests turning toward microscopic plants which have no stems and roots and therefore have the best possible diffusion potentialities. Microscopic plants can mature and undergo fission in as little as five hours. Sexual differentiation and cross-fertilization needs become unimportant. Simple logic carries one all the way back to the familiar phytoplankton, especially the algae. It happens that photosynthesis itself can be studied with the most convenience and the least ambiguity in some of these same organisms. Therefore, most of the experience with ideal conditions for growth, changes in composition, metabolism, and interspecies differences has been accumulated in the course of preparing for theoretical researches. The present opportunities available to food technologists are an accidental by-product of fundamental studies on the mechanism of photosynthesis. There has not yet been time for the exhaustive empirical investigation of all promising possibilities such as has already occurred in agriculture, or is now occurring in the relatively new field of antibiotics. This means that the systems and data employed for estimating possibilities of obtaining more food will yield understatements of what can ultimately be achieved when the research and development is comprehensive.

The fixing of the radiant energy from the sun occurs in green-colored subcellular foci called chloroplasts. In the neighborhood of these foci there is established one of the cycles of metabolism that completes the slow degradation of cell substance to the waste products common to all organisms—water, carbon dioxide, amide nitrogen. But this cycle is distinctive in that it can be reversed by the chloroplast, if light that can be absorbed by its constituent pigments is received, and if the supplies of water, carbon dioxide, and soluble nitrogen are adequate. Upon continuing to introduce these raw materials, and the energy in the form of light, this cycle will manufacture surplus PGA (phosphoglyceric acid), an energetic intermediate that has the capacity of reversing many cellular processes by which cell substance is digested. The PGA poured into the cell functions by the chloroplast's action becomes both building material and energy source for creating more cell substance. Once the cell has grown to an unwieldy size, fission becomes inevitable, and two cells come into existence where there was one previously. These intracellular processes stimulated by photosynthesis may be high lighted as follows:

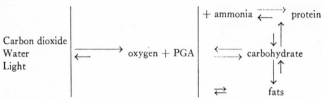

where the length of the arrows indicates the relative tendency for the transformation to go in the direction indicated. Thus if none of the pathways is blocked by poisons or by an insufficiency of raw materials only small amounts of carbohydrate and fat are synthesized; the major product is proteinaceous cell substance. The optimum conditions in the cells containing the chloroplast appear to be:

Carbon dioxide, 10–50 times atmospheric concentrations
Water, 10–20 times the weight of dry matter present
Light, visible, preferably longer wave lengths, 300–30,000 lux intensity
Oxygen, held to a trace
Temperature, in the range of 18–30° C
Magnesium, potassium, iron, and various trace elements
Nitrogen, phosphate, and sulfate, about 50:10:3 parts per thousand.

These are quite stringent conditions. They are difficult and expensive to maintain for any of the crop plants commonly used for food production. On the other hand, the microscopic, unicellular, primitive algae are much more homogeneous when immersed in their environment and so are subject to more thorough control. For them optimum conditions can be maintained rather easily in a culture tank exposed to light. As will be seen, their utilization of light is quite typical of photosynthesis in general, but there are some oddities that arise that can be used to advantage.

Fogg (1953) has assembled very neatly in a monograph the rapidly growing knowledge about algal metabolism—the processes by which these organisms transform the raw materials at their disposal into cell substances and elimination products. Only the high-lights, which appear to affect their eventual usefulness, can be taken up here.

In the absence of light, the unicellular algae behave very much like bacteria and yeasts. Most species will grow and prosper on a sugar and minerals substrate. A few need vitamins and other growth factors in order to reproduce. While in the dark they slowly consume oxygen and produce carbon dioxide. Light does not affect the extraction of fixed nitrogen from the medium and its incorporation in the proteins. They use the same enzymes to carry out the standard transformations of substrate into energy available to cells and into cell substance. They reproduce by fission (only a few species appear to be able to recombine) but more slowly than bacteria or yeasts of equivalent cell size. Most algae are extremely adaptable—upon being transferred from one environment to another the redundant enzymes gradually diminish in concentration while those newly required are quickly synthesized and set to work.

In the presence of light, and in the more favorable growing conditions occasionally found in Nature, algae are roughly as efficient as well nourished green leaves in their conversion of sunlight into stored chemical energy. If, by trial and error experiments, optimum conditions are found and established, efficiency is increased three- to five-fold. Algal cells then accelerate their reproduction and multiply their population until some nutrient becomes scarce (in the work prior to 1950 it was an undetected shortage of dissolved iron which set a limit upon growth) or until the accumulated minor excretions of algae become inhibitory (for some species).

Low intensities of light, equivalent to a deep twilight, can be utilized with utmost efficiency (about 30% net) by healthy cells. As the intensity increases the extra light is less effective until, in sunlight, doubling the incoming radiation adds only 10 to 20% to the net output of the cells. They are then said to be "light-saturated." Strangely enough, however, if the algal cell receives its bright light in bursts of 10 to 40 milliseconds, and is permitted three to ten times that period in the dark to deal with the light so absorbed, the efficiency of light utilization remains high (Myers, 1954).

The algae are best harvested by being allowed to settle from their culture overnight and then being concentrated further by a centrifuge. When they are grown under relatively ideal conditions, an accomplishment of only the last few years, most of the earlier information about their metabolism and ultimate composition becomes misleading. Optimum growth culture conditions lead to a product which, instead of being rather indigestible and strong flavored, is "suggestive of vegetables, and generally palatable and acceptable" (Fisher and Burlew, 1953). The dried material contains about 50% protein, whose amino acid makeup is quite similar to that of food yeast. (See Fig. 9.)

Practically all of the work leading up to the large-scale culture of algae centers around one species of green algae, *Chlorella pyrenoidosa*; because it gave the highest yield, this was selected from among the pure cultures scientists had collected in the course of their researches on photosynthesis. Experience with this organism has been assembled in the Carnegie Institution of Washington monograph *Algal Culture: From Laboratory to Pilot Plant* (Burlew, 1953). From this study some of the central problems of growing algae as foodstuff emerge. There are first a set of problems that have to do with reducing the cost of production, which will be taken up immediately, and others that are concerned with introducing the raw materials so produced into consumption channels, which will follow later.

In the pilot plant studies, the deep green algal culture was cycled through troughs or transparent tubes. On each round it was aerated with air enriched with carbon dioxide. The major cost encountered, when operating experience was scaled to commercial sizes, was that of cooling the medium. (Most of the radiation in sunlight appears as heat, so that on a sunny day the heat retained by the culture, if permitted to build up the temperature, is sufficient to kill off the organisms.) The solution to this problem lay not in devising better heat exchange equipment, as any engineer might imagine, but in finding a strain adapted to hot media, and oblivious to night-time cooling. Myers (1953) prospected hot springs and shallow ponds in Texas in the belief that some hardy strains might be found there. From these cultures he developed a strain of green algae whose optimum temperature is 39° C (as compared to 25° C normally encountered). Surprisingly, the first isolated thermophilic strain exhibited a rate of photosynthesis in strong light markedly superior to anything encountered previously. Such a finding further simplifies the mass culture of algae. Geoghegan (1953) has shown that some strains work efficiently in a warm culture in daylight and also profit from resting in a cooler medium at night. Thus, with the right strain, temperature control becomes a relatively simple and inexpensive problem—one takes away heat at around 40° C and prevents freezing at night.

The major source of operating difficulties was contamination with other organisms. As long as the *Chlorella* were healthy and growing rapidly, the bacteria count stayed low, and in no case did bacteria cause trouble. Infestations of microscopic animals of several types did cause trouble, but in each case methods were quickly found for reducing the threat to tolerable proportions. Just as maize has its corn borer, and cotton its boll weevil, algae have their rotifers and zooflagellates.

An important long-run source of expense is the carbon dioxide. Except in a few places in the world where there are large volumes of pure by-product carbon dioxide from industry, or from drilled wells, collecting and purifying a dilute gas from factory and kiln chimneys and other sources will be expensive. The release of this gas from limestone in a furnace is economical only as long as a market exists for lime, the co-product of the process. There may be various alternative solutions. One would be to find species, such as the *Scenedesmus*, which will use bicarbonate ion as well as dissolved carbon dioxide. Another would be that of pumping much more air, with its normal 0.04% concentration of carbon dioxide, through the culture medium.

Another important item of expense in the culture of *Chlorella* is the nitrogen source. Urea appears to be ideal, but it is costly. Instead of finding some less expensive substitute, it appears that the best hope is to resort to the culture of species that fix their own nitrogen directly from the air. The opportunities in this direction will be taken up in greater detail somewhat later.

The anticipated costs of production for *Chlorella*, if it should be grown by the thousands of tons per year, have already been reduced to a range of 30 to 50¢ per kg. In some special locations it could be less expensive, but these tend to be in food surplus areas where the demand is not expected to be important. Since they have the same protein content as food yeast, this cost range puts algal protein already in a class competitive with food yeast (Table 12). The most highly developed design in 1955 envisages the circulation of a culture 10 to 30-cm deep over flat terrain. (See Fig. 10.) The expected yield in a sunny climate is about 35 tons per acre (75 metric tons per hectare) on a dry weight basis. There are scientific developments underway that might substantially increase these yields, but their meaning is still unclear; therefore, they cannot yet be taken into account.

It is also possible to grow fatty *Chlorella*. As with yeast, however, this becomes a matter of starving the cells on a low nitrogen medium so that reproduction is repressed and the cell functioning has no choice but to turn to fat synthesis. *Chlorella*, too, must grow old in order to grow fat. The fat is highly unsaturated—a type more suitable for use in paints than for human, or even animal, consumption. Providing the carbon-dioxide-enriched air over this longer life cycle becomes expensive, as does the prevention of contamination; therefore, fat synthesis is not viewed as becoming economic unless some special industrial application is found for algal fats. These fats can be hydrogenated to edible forms, as are some of the soft vegetable oils at present, so that if a severe shortage should develop, up to 10 to 20 tons per hectare could eventually be produced with much the same kind of equipment as is suggested for protein production. However, the chances of using the natural protein and fat mixture obtained with fatty *Chlorella* (making it analogous to the fatty yeasts mentioned earlier) are dim; so the efficiencies inherent in an integration of operations cannot be depended upon.

Some of the blue-green species of algae normally living in soils and fresh water ponds are able to fix their own nitrogen—a highly advantageous property in less industrialized areas. These features are thus far consciously used only in rare instances, such as the fertilization of some rice fields in India and Japan. In the laboratory, surprisingly enough, the nitrogen fixation process appears to be sufficiently divorced from photosynthesis so that there is no noteworthy reduction of dry matter per unit area if the organisms are forced to fix all their own nitrogen. (As might be deduced from this observation, such algae will never grow fat in a normal atmosphere.) The blue-green species grow better in more alkaline media (pH 10), which are also more effective in extracting carbon dioxide from the air; therefore, one might surmise that their mass culture would require less engineering equipment than *Chlorella*. Again, such features are suited to less industrialized areas.

Judging from laboratory data in Berkeley, California, Madison, Wisconsin, and London, England, several species of blue-green algae are efficient enough to fix as much as two to three tons of nitrogen per acre per year. (This is a dangerous sort of extrapolation, but parallel estimations have worked out quite well in the case of the development of *Chlorella*.) The eventual cost may easily be competitive with that of the fixed nitrogen in the fertilizer that appears in cereals, if we remember that 50 to 70% of all fertilizer nitrogen is lost by erosion or destroyed by denitrifying bacteria in the soil. Thus the cost of nitrogen actually incorporated in grain comes to $200 to $300 per ton. Such a figure is quoted mainly to establish a practical target for algal culture when competing with present techniques of nitrogen fixation.

There appear to be two routes to the economical culture of algae. One would aim at developing a technique that would require as low an investment as possible per unit of output. It would depend very little upon by-products as a source of income. It would use easily available raw materials, incorporate standard pieces of equipment, and require no advanced operating skills. This mode of culture would aim at getting a quick return on investment if algae prove easy to sell, while at the same time minimizing loss in case difficulties arise and the enterprise at that location is a failure. Thus units of this type would tend

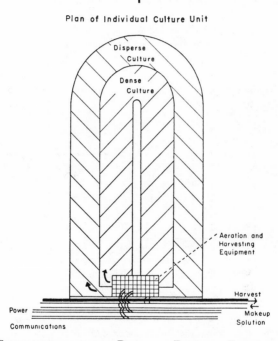

Fig. 10. Speculation upon the Design of Economic Facilities for Mass Culture of Algae

I. All the known characteristics of the free-floating nitrogen-fixing algae were taken into account in this proposal. The ponds may be either plastic tubes or plastic film-lined channels through which the culture is circulated. A level location must be found; it is possible that the culture may be floated upon a protected surface of water. The ideal depth ranges from 10 to 30 cm (4 to 12 in.). The excess heat is removed through the evaporation of water in conjunction with aeration. Harvesting is carried out primarily through pumping most of the cells settling out overnight to the central processing station. A single unit, like that on the right, may be expected to produce 4 to 5 tons algae, of which 22 to 23% is dry solids, per year. Yields may be enhanced somewhat if an extra supply of carbon dioxide is available.

to run 10^2 to 10^3 hectares (250–2500 acres) and the over-all yield would be well below the levels known to be attainable. The prospective costs of production, based upon present knowledge (it is hoped that future findings will have at least as many cost-reducing as cost-increasing implications) are analyzed in Table 14. The other route would lead toward the establishment of a larger and fully integrated system, designed to make use of every by-product, and organized to produce a variety of end-products. Both seem to be most economical when producing nitrogen-fixing algae rather than the presently known *Chlorella*.

II

Plan for a Complete Algae Farm

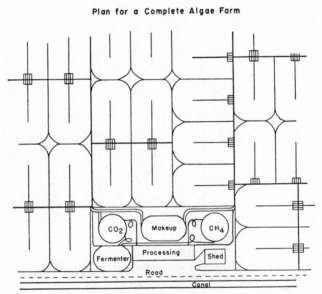

Fig. 10. *(Continued.)*

II. A central processing station must be accessible to transport (indicated here by the proximity to a road) and a dependable supply of water. The methane shown would be manufactured by fermentation of algal cultures which suffered from contamination, or were discarded for other reasons. Methane is therefore a useful product of the waste disposal system. It may be used to drive the pumps, or to desiccate a portion of the algal product, or it may be exported to nearby markets. The anticipated cost of production in favorable locations might be expected to drop to less than $20 per metric ton of algae if the laboratory experience can be translated to mass production without undue complications. Tamiya has proposed a similar design for *Chlorella* based upon his own pilot plant data. At the present pace of development it may be expected that a few such plants will come into operation during the 1960's.

TABLE 14. Prospective Economic Characteristics of Blue-Green
Algae Production

Estimated for a Typical Location in an Underdeveloped Area

Assumptions as to Yield
  50 tons/hectare (45,000 lb/acre) dry wt, 90% of available
    minerals are utilized

Capital Costs
Land leveling (or shore installations)	$ 1,000/hectare
Pump-aeration units (50/hectare)	10,000
Piping and valves (300 m/hectare)	2,000
Frames, channels, repair jigs, etc.	2,000
Central facilities (pro-rated)	1,000
($6,500 per acre)	$16,000/hectare

Operating Costs
Labor (50 workers per 1000 hectares, $1000 annual wage)	$ 50/yr/hectare
Water and minerals	200
Power (at 1–2¢ per kwhr)	300
Plastics replacement and materials for repair	150
	$700/yr/hectare

Total Costs
(10-yr amortization, 8% interest on capital)	$3,500/yr/hectare *
	($1,400/yr/acre)
	or about $70/ton

* The product from such a plant is moist and very perishable, ready for
some nearby food-processing unit. Dried product for storage will cost somewhat more.

Operating such a facility somewhere near its optimum would demand
a high degree of skill. When the ponds are exposed to the weather,
for example, production operations can come to a halt due to storm
or frost, and many forms of local infestations can cause intermittent
trouble. The manager therefore would be continually playing a game
against nature, in much the same manner that farmers do today. It is
extremely unlikely that the operation of the cultures could be made
fully automatic without risking a falling off in yield. On the other
hand, the designs being developed for the central processing station
may well become as automatized as the newest plants manufacturing
antibiotics.

An analysis of the product from nitrogen-fixing organisms shows
that the constituent amino acids exist in proportions suggesting good
nutritional quality (methionine enrichment is again called for), but

there has not yet existed a sufficient quantity of young organisms to carry out feeding tests (Burris, 1952, 1954). The composition is so close to that of *Chlorella* it will be assumed that the products can be used interchangeably in further processing stages. The composition does not change appreciably over wide ranges of operating conditions for the nitrogen-fixing species. Only the yield (rate of reproduction) is affected.

Quite to the surprise of the botanists these unicellular plants, when growing in favorable surroundings, do not produce important quantities of starch or other digestible carbohydrates. However a very interesting possibility has opened up recently for the culture of *Euglena* species, a mobile amoeba-like group containing chloroplasts. The *Euglena* do manufacture and store considerable quantities of a kind of bacterial starch. All the conditions required for such storage remain to be determined, but it is apparent that *Euglena* are slower growing and very likely convert a smaller proportion of sunlight into cell substance than the algae. Because of their motility it is possible that quite different modes of harvesting would have to be devised. Experiments with growing *Euglena* on sewage "oxidation ponds" suggest that it should be possible to set up a continuous-flow process, but that the *Euglena* may thrive best in the presence of bacteria and some algae. No thinking appears to have been done about the isolation and use of such "starch," except that it can be fermented to alcoholic beverages. The principal value of being able to produce carbohydrates via mass culture is that the world has then a means of adding large carbohydrate resources—if it seems desirable to pay several times current prices.

These proposals, which go beyond the experience with *Chlorella*, suffer most from a lack of fundamental information in the biochemical and more strictly biological areas. The gaps in our knowledge are filling in slowly, but progress has thus far not been very rapid. This suggests that the remaining questions be solved by empirical, engineering-oriented investigations. Technology seldom awaits a full, theoretical and experimental elaboration of the underlying phenomena, but usually precedes by several years. The uncertainties in the design are balanced against large "safety factors." As the biological sciences progress they will establish the amount of waste involved in employing such large safety factors, thus suggesting improvements upon existing operating procedures and modifications of the production facilities. This advance should also lead to more efficient new designs.

5. MASTERING FOOD PREJUDICE

A great difficulty that faces the development of food products from microbiology is the existence of man's food habits and prejudices. New foods can be highly digestible and nutritious, but, if the appearance is unwholesome or some feature, such as taste, aroma, or texture, is offensive then the new foods will not be consumed. Thus far, the potentialities for large-scale production of proteins, fats, and carbohydrates have been described. These are not foods, any more than flour or milk curd are foods, but foodstuffs—the materials from which edibles are prepared. It is the assignment of the food processor, the baker, the delicatessen provisioner, the brew master, the confectioner, the chef, and a whole series of such artisans to transform foodstuffs into commodities which are delectable, desirable, and wholesome. These specialists must create products leading to wholly new flavor sensations, duplicate the old standards, improvise or blend; the remainder of humanity chooses from among the offerings what suits each best, frequently indulging in a poor, hasty, home-made imitation of some dish which might otherwise be a luxury. This great gap between a crude bulk product and its final form must be bridged if the contributions of recent science and technology are to be applied.

The various crafts of food processors use concepts and techniques that are replete with prejudice and misunderstanding. Each master learned his skill from a predecessor; his stock in trade is a series of complicated rules of thumb, astute empiricisms, meaningless rituals, and arbitrary standards. Given old-line quality materials, he consistently puts out a good product, one which is acceptable to customers and is not sneered at by the possessors of sensitive palates, but the use of substitute materials is universally scorned except as a last resort. Thus the introduction of a new foodstuff is rendered difficult, its market is developed in a slow and halting manner, and the eventual acceptance remains in doubt a long time. The introduction of oleomargarine, for example, depended not upon its quality or the special features inherent to its makeup, but upon its complete duplication of the flavor and color of butter. Margarine has had rough going in most parts of the world, even when it had been developed to a point where the chemists found it difficult to distinguish from butter, and practically none of the consumers would be able to identify it in a blindfold test. The history of oleomargarine, even though it is a tale of perseverence culminating in success, is not the most desirable example for the introduction of new foods; the creation of new flavors and blends is much to be preferred to slavish imitation.

Nevertheless, tastes do change and diets are modified. The problem is primarily one of assuring that these changes occur sooner rather than later and that they make possible increasing economies in production. If billions of dollars are to be invested in food production facilities by nations endeavoring to cope with endemic food shortages, then some guarantee must be found that the products will not pile up in warehouses, but will be consumed. The distribution of new foodstuffs must be as carefully studied as the technology. Perhaps satisfactory results can be achieved with teams composed of technologists and acknowledged masters of food preparation—a device that has succeeded frequently in the United States when a new product was to be put on the market. They would be able to contrive some recipes which skirt the sensitivities and the prejudices of the bulk of the population. It is possible that, in the long run, a special kind of applied science, dependent upon and closely tied to other sciences, may evolve to deal with these problems. An analysis of the present status of food prejudices and preferences may already suggest certain underlying principles that should be followed, and at the same time provide a realistic appraisal of the chances of obtaining widespread acceptance of the new foodstuffs.

What are the bases of food preferences and prejudices? Examples of these phenomena are abundant in all corners of the globe. Most Chinese, for instance, consider cow's milk and cheese to be an abomination; many central Europeans believe milk to be unfit for adults but are not as consistent as the Chinese in that they will accept many forms of putrified milk curd (ripe cheese). Jews and Mohammedans hold an ancient taboo against pork, the Hindus regard the cow as holy and therefore inedible, fowl are distinctly unpleasant to Mongols and the Guiana Indians, and rabbit has not been acceptable to Chinese and Kaffirs. On the other hand, rotten eggs are a delicacy for the natives of Brunei, maggots and snakes are relished by some Australasian tribes, snails by the Japanese and French, and putrescent meat by North Australians and some north Europeans, the last as a winter delicacy which has been described as "fowl, hung until high." The most consistent worldwide prejudice is that held against cattle which died before slaughter. All kinds of tests have shown that the meat, when cooked, is just as nutritious, and that diseases cannot be conveyed through the cooked flesh. The feeling stems from prehistoric times and would be almost impossible to eliminate. Many studies have been made upon special aspects of this problem but the question always comes up— how much of this apparently irrational and inconsistent behavior stems from physiological and animal drives, and how much of it is an acquisition of culture? If the former is the case, then many attempted modifications of taste and acceptance are sure to fail in the long run, while, if the latter supposition holds, a change becomes merely a matter of astute education or propaganda.

Most of the relevant studies of food preference have been carried out with rats. There is good reason for this choice; it seems that rats consume the same foods and have a digestive apparatus similar to that of humans. In addition, experiments have shown that the taste threshold for rats is nearly identical with that of humans. A cafeteria system was contrived for the rats so that they could select from among as many as a dozen or more foods, eating until satiated. Richter (1943) and associates at Johns Hopkins found that purified proteins, fats, carbohydrates, minerals, and vitamins could be provided cafeteria style and the rats thrived on the menu. Rose's students, in experiments in 1948 upon themselves at the University of Illinois, found the synthetic foods to be adequate. Healthy digestive tracts could even get used to the reduction in bulk and lack of roughage with little difficulty. Thus one answer is obtained. Unadorned, raw foodstuffs are physiologically satisfactory, particularly if the adaptation is made slowly. The phenomena of food preferences must result from psychological and cultural history. Do experiments with rats have anything to say about this?

Somewhat different experiments were carried out by Young (1947), where the rats were permitted to develop a food preference. This was most easily demonstrated with reference to some staple such as refined sugar, wheat flour, or a protein powder, such as casein. The rats with a sweet tooth, which were deprived of both sugar and casein at all stages of protein starvation up to the point where they were nearly dead, still preferred sugar to casein when both were offered to them. They were quite stubborn about their preferences! Subsequent observations indicated the means for getting around these fixations. Some of the factors and mental associations surrounding the presentation of sugar were given to the service of protein at a time of dire need. It was purely a matter of salesmanship! Once they had eaten it, and found it good for what ailed them, they liked it. These studies with rats have barely begun, no firm conclusions can yet be drawn from them, but they are tremendously suggestive. If the claims of advertising men concerning techniques for influencing the choice of the consumer are to be accepted by the tongue-in-cheek scientist, they must be confirmed with rat communities on a small and inexpensive scale or with statistically derived samples of human population on a costly pilot scale.

The situation for a literate population has been best summed up by Orr and Lubbock (1940) when they were discussing the means available to the government for changing the diet of the British people in wartime: "The two factors which effect a change in diet are price and propaganda. Price is more effective among the poorer half of the population; propaganda is more effective among the wealthier half."

A most interesting experiment concerning the use of propaganda in the introduction of new foods was reported by Woodward (1943). Here the assigned task was to determine what method of appeal was likely to increase the consumption of soya foods. The appeals were based upon a pattern of reactions revealed by a preliminary survey, which showed that soybeans were not yet conceptualized as food, but that certain appeals (nutritional value, American rather than Oriental food, good value for your money, variety) might lead to a favorable conceptualization. Many precautions and several varieties of controls were used in the study. A different soya dish was served in an industrial area cafeteria for five consecutive days; all dishes combined soya products with familiar food in a familiar form—in a bread, a meat dish, a meat substitute, a soup, and a dessert. This permitted evaluation of the reactions to the idea of eating soya products. The most significant result was that any mention of nutritive value caused a decline in consumption! The most common reaction was that if a new product was "good for you," it couldn't be really good tasting. This is an interesting commentary upon the effect of American nutritional education. Of course, the negative reaction to a food labeled "good for you" would not occur if the food was generally known and appreciated. A new food would not be objectionable if the propaganda used emphasized variety ("we are introducing here a new and exciting flavor!") and economy ("costs only a third as much as meat for the same food value!"), and if the appearance did not vary significantly from known foods.

The matter of overcoming present food prejudices thus can be reformulated into a more limited task of imitating the appearances, textures, and flavors of existing products. Those that are completely novel must be sorted out by the gastronomes and elevated to the status of a delicacy before general acceptance can be expected.

The over-all approach must combine both empirical "recipe formulation" and the fundamentals of the underlying science. Renner (1944) in concluding his survey upon the origins of food habits, theorizes that there may be certain generalizations regarding the handling, processing, and choosing of foods that hold quite consistently. These generalizations must be considered whenever one is dealing with the elimination of starvation and want. The principles he suggested may be freely restated as follows:

1. Food that has been avoided for one reason or another for a considerable period of time in a social group becomes abhorrent.
2. Food totally unrelated to anything previously experienced may be tried experimentally and be accepted first as a fad, then as a staple.
3. Memories of flavor and texture have many deep emotional ties and contexts, and both are quite precisely recorded in the minds of most people.
4. Acceptability of food also depends upon the amount of work necessary for its mastication and digestion; both too little and too much are rejected.
5. Variety is a spice of food as well as life. Psychological satiety with the commonplace articles of diet provides a constant opportunity for the introduction of novelties.

Further investigations may make it possible to express many of these principles in quantitative terms that take into account the uncertainties in the properties of the product and the differences between people.

6. Creating and Producing New Foods

It is curious that people everywhere in the world have never been satisfied with natural food flavors, but have developed whole philosophies for tampering with them. As a result, a multitude of spices and seasonings have come to be used, even by the very poorest people in a community. Some are local specialties but most are imported—the world trade in spices was one of the earliest and most valuable. Chemists have striven to discover what particular component was responsible for the aroma or taste sensation inherent in the seasoning, and have been quite successful in this respect. Of the sixty most common aromas found in spices listed by Crocker (1945) all but four or five have been analyzed and many have been duplicated.

Half the battle is won if a new food has a pleasant, familiar flavor. It is possible now for the food chemist, using essential oils of spices or the synthetics, to build a flavor, or a series of flavors, into processed foods. They can be designed to fit the tastes of almost any population— thus in Mexico he would use chile and cumin, in Southeast Asia, curry and ginger, in the Balkans pepper and garlic, and for peoples who have adapted their palates to somewhat milder seasoning there is still the range of nutmeg, sage, celery, or even smoke curing. The microbiology and flavor of the aromatic cheeses have recently come under control. Only some of the most complex aromas such as newly baked bread, fresh-ground coffee, and roasting meat have not been successfully captured.

Work on pure taste sensations has proceeded even further. Sourness, for instance, has been found to be a simple function of acidity (hydrogen ion concentration), whereas bitterness has been traced to a few inorganic salts, such as magnesium, and several series of organic components, including the alkaloids. Saltiness is still best represented by salt (sodium chloride), but a strange disconnected group of organic compounds far surpass sugar in their sweetness. The blending of pure taste sensations, however, has turned out to be peculiarly complex. Not only are the blends of tastes temperature dependent, but the thresholds of perception are also disturbed. A bit of salt will make a slightly sweet concoction much sweeter. A dash of glutamic acid greatly reduces sourness, but without measurably changing the hydrogen ion concentration. Since practically all dishes are blends, it seems probable that the technique of arbitrarily breaking down the flavor into components by trained tasters must be followed by the empirical testing of the preferred blends upon a cross section of the consuming public.

The other requirements for new foods are texture and appearance. Texture is particularly important when it becomes a governing factor in the rate of flavor perception. Texture involves such variables as the crunch in a cracker, the chewiness of pumpernickel, the spreadability of butter, the consistency of porridge, the thickness of soup, the tingle of soda bubbles, the body of a beverage, the flakiness of pastries, the many others. Very frequently the sensations of texture are intermingled and associated with those of appearance. Appearance includes such features as the retention of head on a glass of beer, the dimensions and shapes of sausages, the sediment in a cup of coffee, the color and opacity of almost any item, and even the pictures on the packages in which the product came. These factors of texture and appearance are now quite generally controllable, perhaps not to the degree desired by the connoisseur, but at least sufficiently to diminish the qualms of the ordinary peasant and factory worker.

Really substantial and creative work of this sort has yet to be done on microbiological foodstuffs. A little has been started with *Torula* food yeast at the government Industrial Laboratory in Puerto Rico, and on a smaller scale at the Plant Biology Laboratory in Stanford with *Chlorella*, where the wife of a Japanese biologist transformed leftovers from the experiments into dishes suited to the Japanese tastes (Morimura and Tamiya, 1954). What is needed at this point is a rapid accumulation of know-how such as has occurred in the last two decades in the ice cream industry, frozen food production, or the breakfast cereal trade. Only after this phase of development has been successfully hurdled can it be said that a new mass industry serving the specific needs of people has been born, and only then is the way clear for the expansion required to meet the world food deficit.

The best prospects for early success appear to be in the following lines:

> Dehydrated broths and soups
> Ice cream
> Breakfast preparations
> Protein curds (to-fu, miso, etc.)
> Fine grained sausages
> Soft cheeses
> Sauces (sho-yu, curry, etc.)
> Milk substitutes.

The present food-processing industry is fully capable of carrying on a large share of the research, since it is far from being either small or backward. Unfortunately a very large proportion of the effort is devoted to the further refinement of the luxury foods, and to increasing the efficiency of production of the mass-produced items. The amount of research going into the utilization of microbiological foodstuffs is almost less than trivial at the moment, and there is no evidence of interest being shown either in the United States or Western Europe, principally because no large-scale market exists there. Perhaps the other modernized food-processing industry, that of Japan, will develop the processing techniques and equipment suited to the needs of semi-tropical, densely populated areas, since the people it serves experience many of the characteristic problems of food shortage.

7. THE LONG-RUN PROSPECTUS FOR FOOD

The review of recent findings in research suggests that the world food priorities set forth at the beginning of this section are not the same priorities that will be faced a decade or two hence. The need for plant proteins, as well as the vitamins and minerals, can be met rather economically by the culture of microscopic plants, yeasts, and other organisms. These new sources of food render less significant the contribution of vegetables and fruits (vitamin C, roughage, minerals, flavoring, customary patterns for meals, etc.), and they are helped by an understanding of the psychology of food. By modifying the growth of many of these same organisms it is possible to produce fat at a cost no more than three times the present cost of producing vegetable oils. Since the world market price for fats has been known to double within a few months, these possibilities can already act as a damper upon those who might be tempted to embark upon long-term high-cost projects for "banishing the fats shortage."

Lower down on the priority list one encounters the major sources of carbohydrate in the diet—cereals and sugar. The supply in these commodities is not materially changed by recent developments, so that one can envision a slowly increasing scarcity of carbohydrate foods. This is contrasted with an occasional tendency for oversupply of cereals and sugar, which can be found at the present time. At the bottom of the list were the animal proteins, whose production might be increased after basic needs had been satisfied for all people. Surplus plant proteins might easily be channeled into the feeding of animals in preference to any other use.

The conclusion derived from this survey of current science and technology is that the food crisis suggested by a study of needs versus resources should not occur if the world shows reasonable intelligence in developing the newer possibilities. However, there are further deductions which can be made:

> The marginal cost of proteins should decrease.
> The costs of fats and oils should be relatively constant.
> The costs of carbohydrates would increase gradually.
> The role of vitamins would become economically irrelevant.

Such trends are not inevitable or perpetual but merely what might be expected from the mass technology to be created from present scientific knowledge—a judgment that can be expected to hold for no more than 20 to 50 years at the present rate of technological change.

At the very beginning of this chapter on new foods, the physiological theories of nutrition were contrasted with those stemming from social psychology. It was asserted that the latter yielded markedly superior predictions of the effects obtained upon introducing new foods to a community or a society. Perhaps this present superiority is reason enough for the neglect being accorded this area in recent years. There has been a virtual cessation of publication of experimental and theoretical papers of the kind likely to be reported by *Psychological Abstracts* since 1948. It is probable that research on food preferences and food habits, per se, has merely gone out of fashion. It is not altogether neglected, because an important share of the contemporary studies would include such behavior as a special case within a broader province. Whatever is deduced within the broader province would apply as well to choices in foods as it would to choices in, say, friends or destinations. However, there is a great deal to be learned about behavior where an understanding of food preferences may yield more precise results than any other approach. Scientific studies of this sort (it is impossible to be more specific without employing the jargon of psychologists) probably would contribute the most toward reducing world malnutrition in the middle to long run. They appear to rate the highest priority, among the various opportunities to do fundamental scientific work, in any program aimed at long-run (20 to 50 years) problems in provisioning the world. Ordinarily one would give precedence to the biological problems related to photosynthesis, because the ability to produce must exist before the capacity to consume can be realized, but the momentum of the current work in biology is very great, while related work in social psychology must expand from quite small beginnings. Thus it is evident, given the present state of knowledge and the present rates of advance, that top priorities should be accorded large-scale theoretical and experimental studies on behavior toward food. Within this set of givens it is very difficult to formulate any further high-priority subjects for scientific investigation.

TABLE 15. PROSPECTIVE MARGINAL COSTS FOR PROTEIN PRODUCTION

	Anticipated Cost of Protein	Investment Required for New Capacity
Pulses	$0.12–0.20/lb	$ 800–2000/annual ton
Fish farms	0.40–1.00	1000–2500
Cane juice—food yeast	0.35–0.50	600–1200
Cane juice—fatty yeast	0.70–1.00	1200–2000
Chlorella	0.10–0.20	300–600
Blue-green algae	0.05–0.15	300–600

There is one novel implication to these developments. Good quality protein, along with the basic complement of vitamins and minerals, should become more and more available to poorer elements of the population, especially the children. This means that they will tend to be larger boned, heavier muscled, and appreciably taller than their parents. Thus they will require more food. If the world as a whole were to develop the kind of physique now found principally in North America, then per capita food needs would run 20 to 25% greater. The prospective demand for food would eventually be much larger under those circumstances than the numerical increase in population would suggest.

The bogey of world population saturation will always be raised in discussions of these subjects. What is the new limit to global population if some portions of the diet can be produced on a twentieth or less of the Earth's surface presently devoted to it? The centuries-old concept of the "man-land ratio," which has been generally applied in such calculations, is now rendered quite useless. Land itself is not necessary because algal culture could easily be developed to take place on top of protected bodies of water. A level of fat and protein production up to 50 times present levels is not at all unreasonable. Phosphate and other mooted limitations need not apply until much greater production is achieved. This amount of food would permit twenty times as many people (50 billion) to eat well. Such extrapolations make no provision for the other necessities for comfortable and convenient living which would require (according to Table 5) caloric expenditure almost ten times as great as the food itself. Thus it appears that the present achievements of science can make the chronic food shortage an obsolete limitation upon human numbers and welfare, but that the fuel position bears closer study because it may represent the next constraint upon the future of man.

SELECTED REFERENCES

PROTEIN SOURCES

W. F. Gericke, *The Complete Guide to Soilless Gardening*, Prentice-Hall, New York, 1940.

N. Polunin, "Some Proposals for the Wartime Use of Plankton," *Chronica Botanica*. **1**, p. 133 (1942).

K. E. Slade, D. J. Branscombe, and J. C. McGowan, *Report to the Agriculture Group of Royal Society*, 1945.

E. F. Gale, "Synthesis of Protein by Micro-organisms," *Chem. and Ind.*, p. 131 (1948).

K. S. Markley, ed., *Soybeans and Soybean Products*, Interscience Publishers, New York, 1950.

H. B. Moore, "The Relation between the Scattering Layer and the *Euphausiacea*," *Biol. Bull. Woods Hole*, **99**, p. 181 (1950).

R. H. Armstrong, "Amino Acids in the Proteins of Herbage," *J. Sci. Food Agr.*, **2**, p. 166 (1951).

D. M. Greenberg, ed., *Amino Acids and Proteins*, C. C. Thomas, Springfield, Illinois, 1951.

E. Rabinowitch, *Photosynthesis*, Interscience Publishers, New York, v. 1, 1945; v. 2, pt. one, 1951.

E. Schwarz, "Fish Pond Culture for Underdeveloped Areas," *Land Economics*, **27**, p. 172 (May 1951).

J. B. Hersey, H. R. Johnson, and L. C. Davis, "Recent Findings about the Deep Scattering Layer," *J. Marine Res.*, **11**, p. 1 (1952).

T. E. Weier and C. R. Sterling, "The Chloroplast," *Bot. Rev.*, **18**, p. 14 (1952).

J. Verduin, "The Volume-Based Photosynthesic Rates of Aquatic Plants," *Am. J. Botany*, **39**, p. 157 (1952); **40**, p. 675 (1953).

J. W. E. H. Sholto Douglas, "Soil-less Cultivation of Crops in India," *Nature*, 175, p. 884 (1955); "The Possibilities of Soil-less Cultivation," *Impact*, 6, p. 30 (1955)

FOOD YEAST AND BACTERIAL CULTURE

A. C. Thaysen, "The Value of Micro-organisms in Nutrition (Food Yeast)," *Nature*, 151, p. 406 (1943); 152, p. 526 (1943).

L. Encbo, L. G. Andersen and H. Lundin, "Microbiological Fat Synthesis with Rhodotorula Yeast," *Archiv. Biochem.*, 11, p. 383 (1946).

C. Vincenty, "The Present Status of Yeast in Human Nutrition," *El Crisol*, 4, p. 83 (1950).

E. Torqvist and H. Lundin, "The Biotechnical Production of Fat with Cane Molasses as a Raw Material," *Intern. Sugar J.*, 53, p. 123 (1951).

A. J. Wiley, J. M. Holderby, and L. P. Hughes, "Food Yeast from Sulfite Liquor," *Ind. Eng. Chem.*, 43, p. 1702 (1951).

R. B. Johnson, "A Practical Method for Culturing Bacteria," *Science*, 115, p. 362 (1952).

J. R. McLean and J. M. R. Beveridge, "Hepatic Necrosis Induced by Dietary Means," *J. Nutrition*, 47, p. 41 (1952).

ALGAL CULTURE

E. G. Pringsheim, *Pure Cultures of Algae*, Cambridge, 1946.

G. E. Fogg, "The Fixation of Nitrogen by Blue-Green Algae," *Endeavour*, 6, p. 172 (1947).

Jack Myers, "Culture Conditions and the Development of the Photo-Synthetic Mechanism V," *Plant Physiol.*, 22, p. 590 (1947).

R. L. Meier, "The Industrialization of Photosynthesis and Its Social Effects," *Chem. Eng. News*, 27, p. 3112 (1949).

H. A. Spoehr and H. W. Milner, "The Chemical Composition of Chlorella," *Plant Physiol.*, 24, p. 120 (1949).

P. M. Cook, "Chemical Engineering in Large-Scale Culture of Algae," *Ind. Eng. Chem.*, 43, p. 2385 (1951).

R. L. Meier, "Possibilities of Photosynthesis in the Lower Plants," *Proc., Am. Acad. Arts Sci.*, 79, 196 (1951).

W. H. Pearsall and G. E. Fogg, "The Utilization of Algae for Industrial Photosynthesis," *Food Sci. Abstr.*, D.S.I.R., 23, p. 1 (1951).

J. S. Burlew, ed., *Algal Culture: From Laboratory to Pilot Plant*, Carnegie Institution of Washington, 1953. Includes work of L. Fowden, M. J. Geoghegan and A. W. Fisher.

W. Q. Hall, "Feed Cycle," *Ind. Eng. Chem.*, 46, p. 17A (February 1954).

G. E. Fogg, *The Metabolism of Algae*, Methuen, London, 1953.

Vannevar Bush, *Annual Report*, Carnegie Institution of Washington, Washington, 1954.

H. W. Milner, "Some Problems in Large Scale Culture of Algae," *Sci. Monthly*, 80, p. 15 (1955).

R. W. Kraus, "Nutrient Supply for Large Scale Algal Cultures," *Sci. Monthly*, 80, p. 22 (1955).

NUTRITION

K. W. Bash, "Possible Organic Basis for the Hunger Drive," *J. Comp. Psych.*, **28**, p. 109 (1939); "Contribution to a Theory of the Hunger Drive," *ibid.*, **28**, p. 137 (1939).

Sir J. B. Orr and D. Lubbock, *Feeding the People in War Time*, Macmillan, London, 1940.

K. Lewin, "Forces Behind Food Habits and Methods of Change," *Bull. National Res. Council (U.S.)*, **108**, p. 35 (1943); see also "Frontiers in Group Dynamics," *Human Relations*, **1**, p. 143 (1947).

C. P. Richter, "The Self-Selection of Diets," *Essays in Biology*, University of California Press, Berkeley, 1943.

P. Woodward, "Attitudes Toward the Use of Soybeans as Food," Committee on Food Habits, National Reserch Council, Washington, October 1943.

H. D. Renner, *Origin of Food Habits*, Faber and Faber, London, 1944.

E. C. Crocker, *Flavor*, McGraw-Hill Book Co., New York, 1945.

National Research Council, *Manual for the Study of Food Habits*, no. 11, Committee on Food Habits, Washington, January 1945.

P. T. Young, "Appetite, Palatability, and Feeding Habits," *Psych. Bull.*, **45**, p. 289 (1948).

J. A. Goyco and C. F. Asenjo, "Studies on Edible Yeasts," *J. Nutrition*, **38**, p. 517 (1949); see also *Puerto Rico J. Public Health Trop. Med.*, **23**, p. 471 (1948) and *Ann. Rep. School of Trop. Med.* (1945).

W. C. Rose, "Amino Acid Requirements for Man," *Federation Proc.*, **8**, p. 546 (1949).

B. Sure and F. House, "Protein Utilization of Various Food Yeasts," *Arch. Biochem.*, **20**, p. 55 (1949); see also *J. Am. Dietet. Assoc.*, **22**, p. 494 and p. 766 (1946).

Y. Morimura and N. Tamiya, "Preliminary Experiments in the Use of Chlorella as Human Food," *Food Technol.*, **8**, p. 179 (1954).

Reappraisal

1. The principal nutritional lack in the poorest regions of the world is that of protein, and *kwashiorkor* (calories sufficient, protein inadequate) is often the most common cause of death in childhood. It depresses capacity for highly co-ordinated activity later in life even if diet improves. The "multi-purpose foods" designed by UNICEF and others for children's diets combine available protein foodstuffs and fit regional food preference patterns. Infant and child mortality rates show striking improvements in response to the introduction of these foods. Emphasis is now placed upon the *availability* of the protein, and a balanced supply of amino acids. [N. S. Scrimshaw, *American Journal of Public Health*, **53**, p. 1781 (1963); G. R. Jansen and E. E. Howe, *American Journal of Clinical Nutrition*, **15**, p. 262 (1964).]

2. Priorities for foodstuff development set by the FAO, WHO, and UNICEF in order of probable usefulness were: fish flour, soya products,

peanut flour, cottonseed flour, coconut protein, sesame flour, sunflower seed flour. [*Food Technology*, 16, p. 51 (1962).] Due to improved agricultural efficiency and distribution, protein costs have not yet begun to rise as compared to other food costs.

3. No significant progress has been made in the conversion of alfalfa or other high-yield leaf protein into human foodstuffs.

4. Food yeast is experiencing rapidly rising production and refinement in technology (continuous flow processes), but is still used as a minor ingredient, mainly for vitamin enrichment.

5. Fish culture has been spread to many parts of the world through the auspices of the United Nations agencies, but will require decades to reach its full potential. No fully marine fish have yet been successfully domesticated, but the culture of plaice will be undertaken in Scotland, and oysters, clams, and shrimp are being grown in Japan with special cultures of microplankton being maintained as food supply to give superior flavor. [*Food Technol.*, 18, p. 144 (April 1964).] Thus the gourmets have been aided most.

6. The culture of algae has been pursued by Tamiya and associates to the point where commercial potentials appear to exist in Japan. [Hisateru Mitsuda, *Studies from the Tokugawa Institute*, 10, No. 2, Tokyo, Japan, 1963.] In addition to *Chlorella*, a species of nitrogen-fixing thermophilic blue-green alga was found in a Javanese hot spring and developed for mass culture. Pest control and many other practical problems have been investigated.

A thorough review of the state of knowledge concerning the constituents of algae was completed. [R. A. Lewin, *Physiology and Biochemistry of Algae*, Academic Press, New York, 1962.] Later it was shown at the University of London that two varieties of blue-green algae did fix nitrogen in seawater, and *Calothrix scopularum* in particular responded to additions of phosphate and trace elements while at the same time remaining relatively impervious to salinity. [W. D. P. Stewart, *J. Gen. Microbiol.*, 36, p. 415 (1964).] The genetics of algae remain extraordinarily primitive.

Mass culture studies in the United States were shifted in an effort to create a closed ecosystem for long-distance exploration of outer space (about 75 l. will sustain a man), but no interesting sidelights on the world food problem have been forthcoming. Hundreds of acres of algae ponds have been operated by sanitary engineers as a technique for sewage treatment, but algal harvest has remained experimental and has rarely even been used for animal feeding.

7. Acceptance of new foods in developing countries has been enhanced over prior expectations in some areas through the spread of supermarkets, cheaper packaging, television, and accelerated urbanization. A shift to dependence upon new, relatively synthetic foods could probably be accomplished for urban populations in no more than two generations. Traditional foods would be retained, but reserved for ritual occasions.

8. The calculation that the world could feed fifty billion people adequately, after applying the prospective new technologies, still stands. No embarrassing finding has been reported in the interim which would increase the difficulties.

Chapter 3

NEW FUELS

HOW MUCH FUEL does the world actually need? It was shown earlier that energy reserves are insufficient to meet the demands made upon them by world development, therefore, the prospects for new fuels and new sources of energy must be surveyed. A method of argument that can be used for understanding the future of energy is very similar to that just completed for food—new resources and new methods for producing the crucial forms of energy can be scrutinized one at a time. Relative costs and capacities can be estimated for each new source considered. Then the patterns of consumption can be analyzed to see whether there are any hidden disadvantages in the innovations. Still more rewarding in the possibility of hidden economies—neat, direct applications of energy to meet human and social needs with greater effectiveness and less waste than has hitherto been possible.

There is one important difficulty that arises from this procedure. Such a discussion must be carried out at a series of levels, ranging from the macrodimensions of world supplies to the physiology of comfort in typical humans. In order to be consistent and logical we should start with the individual, then carefully work upward and outward, advancing one level at a time—or else start from the outside and work inward. However the data on energy are not adapted to this manner of presentation. Because the middle range (where energy is used by households, communities, and regional groupings) has so few measurements and so little systematization, the standards of performance are still unclear.

The best definition of these needs may be obtained only by starting first from the outside and then from the inside. This will assure that the new methods and resources revealed are more than a string of anecdotes, but contribute to a reasonably rigorous line of argument. The discussion will depend less upon science and more upon the frontiers of technology because considerations of "energy at what cost" are everywhere essential.

Fortunately, energy sources and transformations have, for the last two decades, been studied increasingly on a global basis. The costs are quite well known, and optimal locations are easily recognized. This fact applies to much of the unused potential, as well as that which has been exploited. It means that some fairly sweeping statements can be made, which do not need to be defended in detail, because they have already stood the test of criticism.

A simple and relatively comprehensive survey of the sources of energy was completed recently by Ayres and Scarlott (1952). About a year later an independent analysis by Palmer Putnam (1953) was published. The former covers very simply the current processes and the newest technology, while the latter is somewhat more concerned with assembling a consistent view toward energy resources on a world scale. With material such as this at hand it would be senseless to provide still another investigation of the world picture. However, one must put into perspective what is understood to be true about the energy situation by reviewing just the high-lights, and a responsible analyst ought to add those few interesting developments that have been reported since their books went to press. The summary of world energy potentials that follows is the product of independent study, so that where it differs in details from the preceding works it represents the difference of opinion which can exist in interpreting the same body of facts, or it may take into account more recent researches.

1. SOLAR ENERGY

Energy which emanates originally from the sun is captured and retained on the surface of the earth in many forms. In some localities one or more of the forms is steady enough to warrant exploitation by engineering methods. A catalog of the possibilities includes:

> Vegetation (biological photosynthesis)
> Water power
> Movements of the atmosphere (wind power)
> Movements of water due to wind and temperature
> Temperature difference in the ocean

Direct conversion of sunlight to useful heat
Direct conversion of sunlight to electrical energy
Nonbiological photosynthesis.

Although they no longer make a very important contribution to industry, vegetation (mainly wood, bagasse, and straw), water power, and wind power, the first three of this list of energy forms, were all at one time essential to the transition from the period when the world's work was done by animals to the present era of the power-driven machine. Water power exerted through the water wheel made it possible to operate the first factories in the United Kingdom, France, and the United States. Charcoal was the key ingredient for iron making whereas wood was the fuel of choice for early railroads and river steamers. Windmills pumped the water and ground the meal for much of the seaward fringe of Europe. The technical principles were adapted to farms in the great plains areas of the world, where the lack of surface water was overcome, and large export surpluses of grains were created for the first time, making possible the starting of urban industrial areas. The historic methods for energy generation are quite well known, but most of them are no longer efficient. Only the newest and most efficient means for the conversion into useful energy, some of which are only now moving out of the laboratory and into the field, will be discussed here. Other sources, farther down on the list, have been exploited one way or another in the laboratory, or in pilot-scale operation, but so far only at a high cost or with poor efficiency. They are quite new sources of energy for society, although engineers and inventors have been working with the various possibilities leading in these directions for many decades.

These are all still only potential sources of energy. They must be transformed so as to fit the needs of people and of modern technology. The chain of operations which starts with exploitation and ends with dissipation at the point of use must be kept in mind. Each stage must be demonstrated to be reasonably economic before the resources can be counted upon, with no unfulfilled requirement being left in the consumption pattern.

The greatest need is still for mechanical energy in the form of turning shafts. This rotational energy can be converted quite simply into the kinds of motion required to do useful work. The energy source (fuel) should be homogeneous, intense, and light in weight for mobile equipment, but could be bulky and low grade for stationary equipment. Another major need exists for fuels which will convert ores into metals, e.g., energy sources capable of performing chemical reduction. Then there are a series of other smaller volume needs, such as home heating, cooking, lighting, fibers, plastics materials, etc. Most engineers today think only of converting a potential energy source into electric power, but this quick review of needs suggests that quite a few other possibilities are open, though on a smaller scale.

Before launching into a discussion of the new devices for exploiting all kinds of energy derived directly or indirectly from the sun, it is worth while to state briefly the applications that are now made. In the sources reviewed in the previous chapter (as summarized in Figs. 3 and 4) about half the *vegetation* in the world goes to food and fodder, a quarter is burned for fuel, and small quantities are used as materials of construction, paper, fibers, chemicals, etc. In most cases the combustion of surplus vegetation, such as wood waste or bagasse, is used for raising steam pressure sufficient to energize the on-site processes of exploitation, but at a few isolated points wood also cooks the meals, moves the locomotives, and pumps the water. By improving agricultural and forestry practices up to the limits known to be practical today, and tested in the field, perhaps six times the energy now extracted could eventually be obtained.

This utilization level of 15 to 20% of probable economic capacity for producing vegetation is matched by the degree to which falling water is developed. *Water power*, however, appears almost exclusively as high-voltage electric current. Thus the presently installed world capacity of 10^8 horsepower is more flexible and far more valuable than the use of vegetation for energy purposes. Engineering for the use of wood is up-to-date only in a few forested areas, while other vegetable fuels are being consumed in rather primitive equipment. On the other hand, water power has reached an ultimate stage, in recent instances, where it is being generated by fully automatic hydroelectric stations. None of the other indirect forms of solar energy is currently being exploited in any measurable degree.

The old methods of using *wind power* were too inefficient to survive the advent of the steam engine and the electric motor. Nevertheless, wind power is likely to be the next of the modes of getting energy indirectly from the sun which will be reduced to standard practice, because now it, too, can be used to generate electrical power. However, winds do not blow in order to accommodate the power needs of a community. This fact complicates the design of wind-power equipment, because some means of electric power storage is required and, although there has been extensive research on this problem, no truly economic techniques suited to wind generators have been found. The British

Electrical and Allied Industries Research Association, which has been doing the most advanced work on the subject, feels that an economic design is possible if windmills of several thousand horsepower capacity are linked to an integrated grid which is predominantly supplied by other power sources (Haldane and Golding, 1950). Then the capital cost per installed kilowatt would be only $200 to $300 for supplying up to 10% of the island's needs. If maintenance costs can be held to reasonable levels, the over-all cost of this power would be less than present costs. Experiments and full-scale tests are under way.

It has been suggested that the electric power produced by wind at times of slack demand might be used to pump water uphill in a system of shallow lakes and low-head hydroelectric facilities. A good share of the energy could then be recovered as water power and used whenever it was most convenient. These opportunities will exist in parts of Scotland and North Wales, but are very rarely found in other parts of the world. They are economical only under special circumstances—such as a shortage of coal combined with the existence of large centers of consumption not far from the combined wind power and water power installations.

Thus the limitations of wind power are severe—winds in the range of 15 to 30 miles per hour only are useful—so that even its strongest advocates claim no more than a secondary role for it. At many sites, wind power can be a very useful adjunct to whatever other new sources are developed.

A by-product of wind is the *wave motion* on the oceans and inland seas. Many patents have been taken out upon techniques for generating power from the energy of waves, but none appear to have come close to economic feasibility.

More energy from the sun is absorbed in the water surface of the earth than in the atmospheric envelope but it produces less movement of the water than of the air. To extract useful energy from *warmed water* requires altogether different procedures. The most developed method employs a very low-pressure steam, as produced by the warm water, which is condensed by cold water brought up from the unlit depths of the ocean. Claude demonstrated that three kilowatts of power can be obtained for every kilowatt expended in the pumping of sea water, if a temperature differential of 22° to 24° C existed. A power plant of this type is being designed for the west coast of Africa by the French government (G. Beau and M. Nizery, 1950). If it succeeds, a good share of the tropical coast line which drops off rapidly to 500-meter depths or greater, and at the same time lies close to centers of consumption, might be employed for power production. However, at best these methods could only add a few per cent to the present world capacity, so that, like wind power, they are interesting and significant for certain geographical areas, but do not offer any solution for the world's energy supply problems. (*The project did fail, mainly due to difficulties in the construction of the large turbine needed, but fortunately the uses of this process introduced later in the proposals for photosynthesis technology are not significantly affected.*)

These inabilities encourage the design engineer to turn to methods for the *direct* conversion of solar radiation into useful heat, power, and fuel. The energy is there, in quantities at least a hundred-fold greater than the net requirements, but there is also a long history of failure. The challenge to harness the sun to do work directly has been recognized for more than two hundred years. All of the simpler approaches have been investigated many times; often energy was obtained, but at costs that would remain many times greater than current costs even if all foreseeable refinements were feasible and had been incorporated into the technique.

The principal difficulty is that the energy is not very concentrated and that the expense of collecting it at one point is embarrassingly high. There now appear to be three general approaches open. One would focus the sun's rays on a line or a point and obtain heat of high intensity, but this requires rotation of the reflectors or refractors with a clockwork arrangement so as to follow the sun across the sky and keep the rays in focus. Here, the capital cost would be excessive. Another would trap the sun's radiations uniformly over a surface, and draw away the heat by circulating water or air past the underside of the surface, but then the energy has become very low grade and is hardly worth transporting or converting. A third would transform the light directly into low-voltage energy by using sensitive semi-conductors. All direct schemes for utilizing sunlight suffer from one grave defect—the diurnal cycle, which restricts power production at any point to something less than twelve hours per day average. (See Fig. 11.) This leaves the proponents of solar energy in a quandary. What should be the provision for normal human consumption, which continues into the night?

The most promising innovations are now occurring in household applications. The National Physical Laboratory in India (1953) has led the way in the design of a solar cooker which is simple enough to be operated by uneducated housewives, and cheap enough to be produced by mass manufacture methods for $12 to $16. This device will bring a saucepan of water to a boil in about twenty minutes. It is particularly suitable for use in those parts of the world where the vegetation (or ox dung) is used as cooking fuel and, because of increasing density of population, has been largely cut off. A cooker of this sort (parabolic reflector type) becomes unwieldy if it is expanded to a size accommodating more than one family. However, its possibilities suggest other designs where flat reflectors concentrate the sun's rays into a chemical absorbent in a container at their base causing the chemicals to fuse. When

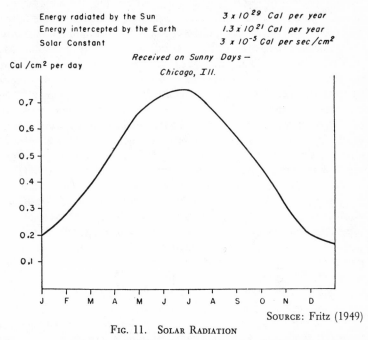

Energy radiated by the Sun — 3×10^{29} Cal per year
Energy intercepted by the Earth — 1.3×10^{21} Cal per year
Solar Constant — 3×10^{-5} Cal per sec/cm²

Received on Sunny Days —
Chicago, Ill.

Cal/cm² per day

SOURCE: Fritz (1949)

FIG. 11. SOLAR RADIATION

Roughly 60% of the radiant energy coming to the earth is absorbed or scattered by the atmosphere. An important share of the remainder is reflected from the surface of any energy trap, such as a leaf or a flat plate collector, before it can be absorbed. Therefore, the total solar energy available for man to work with is about 3×10^{20} Cal per year. At a given location total radiation received is 10 to 50% less than the "sunny day average" shown above.

utensils are placed in such a molten environment their contents are quickly brought to a boil. With this device sun does not need to shine at the time one is cooking. Equipment of this type may be convenient for neighborhood cafes and teashops which cater to an evening trade.

These solutions are most useful in the more isolated rural locations where power and fuel costs are high.

Valuable progress is also being made in home-heating designs. Sharon (1952) has assembled the relevant information for contemporary American solar-heating design in the New York City area, based mainly upon the research of Telkes and Hottel at the Massachusetts Institute of Technology. The key elements are the glass and metal collector plates which are exposed to the sunshine so as to heat water flowing through them. The warm water can be circulated through the flooring in the home, according to standard radiant heating techniques, or the heat can be stored in the form of a molten salt (a sodium sulfate hydrate is most economical at present). When the salt is allowed to crystallize again, it releases the heat as desired. The collector plates can be oriented to the sun so as to be most efficient at the coldest time of the year; they can also be placed on the roof, the south wall, or even separated from the house. (See Figs. 19 and 20.) In the New York conditions, about 65 feet of collector surfaces per hundred of floor space are required to meet the January demands. The economics are currently somewhat dubious, since the system would compete with coal at $30 to $50 per ton, but further engineering development followed by mass production would, it was hoped, reduce costs to about a third of present levels. Jordan and Threlkeld (1953, 1954) have described some fundamental improvements to the Sharon design for dwellings that have access to some electric power. Their work is discussed in greater detail below.

A very new possibility is the operation of an air-conditioning unit by means of solar energy. Perhaps the simplest design for such equipment would involve the use of chemical sprays which extract the water vapor from the air. For the desired cooling effect liquid water can be evaporated into this dried air. This process can be repeated until conditions of comfort are obtained. The solar energy is used to separate the water from the chemical. For small factories, offices, restaurants, and apartment blocks this system is almost ideal. When the sun is most intense, and cooling requirements are at a peak, the source of energy is also at a maximum. Some difficulties will be encountered however in climates with muggy mid-summer weather or with hot, humid nights.

It is quite possible to work out methods for generating electric power from the heat absorbed by these flat plate collectors. By judicious economy it is envisioned that a broad expanse of flat, desert land could be covered at an expense of $5 to $6 per square meter (more than $20,000 per acre). Wherever cooling water was available the methods would not differ greatly from the Claude process now being developed by the French government. The proportion of the heat appearing as power would be less than 10% even under ideal circumstances, and it would also be subject to daily periodicities, which cannot be leveled out cheaply.

The theoretician is quite impatient with this rather low-brow treatment of possibilities. Solar energy comes to us as a broad spectrum of electromagnetic radiations. Therefore if it were possible to propagate an electron gas, these radiations could be used to propel electrons. Since the sun's radiations come from approximately the same point, all electrons could be propelled in the same direction and an electric current generated. (Von Hippel, 1951.) However, broad expanses of glass supporting the high vacuum needed for free electrons are impractical.

Thus, compromises involving plastics and solids have to be considered. Semiconductor materials are known which are sensitive to light, and therefore have the capacity of generating electric current directly. After decades of failures and trivial successes by their predecessors, several Bell Telephone scientists (Pearson, Chapin, and Fuller, 1954) scored a moderate success by obtaining an efficiency of as much as six per cent from sunlight. The semiconductor used is a very thin wafer of highly purified silicon crystal with controlled quantities of impurities. Shortly thereafter others demonstrated that cadmium sulfide was at least as effective for the purpose. If this technique should be employed for very large installations, the cost of materials would render the energy output far too expensive. It does point the way however to a great many special, small-scale uses of solar energy, because it can be used as a permanent installation which should not wear out or decay. Other systems for direct conversion may use thermocouples, or chemicals subject to photochemical reduction, but these appear to be inherently more expensive than semiconductors. In summary, it may be asserted that recent theoretical and experimental investigations have not opened up any promising large scale opportunities that can be grasped by power engineers for energy production.

Even the lowest forms of plants have evolved more efficient systems for the capture of solar energy than any yet designed by the physical scientists. Knowledge of this fact acts as a continuing stimulus for inquiry. However, until very recently, no one has treated biological photosynthesis as if it were a unit process, one of a chain of connected processes, which could convert solar energy into useful work. The properties of photosynthesis for a long time were sensed as a phenomenon to which human society must adapt, much as the plant and animal world must adapt. One did not think to manipulate it the way electric current, or chemical reactions, or beasts of burden are manipulated. But now this is changed. More and more we may consider photosynthesis to be a neat, definable process given us by nature which may be used for energizing other definite processes with an efficient over-all relationship.

Laboratory and pilot-plant investigations of algal culture have shown that from 8 to 20% of the energy in sunlight can be converted to chemical energy under conditions that are practical for large-scale industrial operations (Burlew, 1953). However most of this output of energy-rich substance is in the form of wet protein—of value as food for fish, animals, and humans—but it resembles nothing that has hitherto been used as fuel. The challenge then becomes one of concentrating this new form of low-grade energy, and obtaining it in a more familiar form.

To remove the water entirely by the combustion of fuel would require, for this process alone, almost as much fuel energy as is present. A partial solution would be to resort to multi-effect evaporators, such as are used in the sugar industry to concentrate cane juice, but with modifications required by the plastic granular state of the algal product. Solar energy may aid such a drying process if it is used to heat dry air to a temperature of 80 to 160° C. The hot air can remove the water of hydration which is less firmly bound to the cell-substance, but other more drastic means, such as vacuum-drying, may be needed for the latter stages of dehydration. A pyrolysis, or charcoal-producing step, employing a much higher temperature, would be the obvious unit process to follow, but here one encounters a gap in the scientific and technical literature. No work has been done, utilizing modern concepts, upon the products to be expected from the pyrolysis of proteins, either dry or partially dehydrated. Therefore, one must resort to the use of chemical theory and deduce from it the kinds of products to be expected from the known compositions of algae. The theory does not help very much in establishing over-all yields of the respective products, but it does set the limits of what can be obtained.

The total process blocked out in Fig. 12 comes close to being the most efficient imaginable means for the *direct* conversion of wet protein into combustibles. It should yield a charcoal, a gas that would burn, and several fractions of liquids and tars, most of them combustible. It also has several important limitations. Much of gaseous and liquid output is made up of complex mixtures that are economical to separate only in large volume. Not the least of the difficulties is the penetrating stench of scorched proteins, but perhaps the most significant is the low or nonexistent total energy output. Quite remarkable engineering developments would be necessary to reduce the energy required for processing to a level less than the caloric value of the products. This process, and others related to it, are inherently inefficient, expensive, and unpromising. Such conclusions suggest that *indirect* methods, using biological cycles, be investigated.

Ideally one should try to find a biological process that uses wet algae as a feedstuff and converts it to a mixture of simple anhydrous chemical components. The chemicals should retain most of the free energy accumulated by the algae from the sunlight. A microbiologist will recognize that these requirements fit fermentation processes very well.

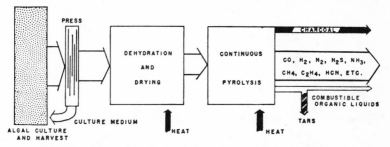

FIG. 12.   DIRECT PROCESS FOR CONVERTING ALGAE INTO FUELS

Until now engineers have thought of algae as a source of low-grade fuel which might be burnt if there were a grave power shortage. The sequence of operations above was selected so as to make the ultimate combustion as efficient as possible while still using present power-producing equipment. The over-all process cannot be very precisely described because of a gap in the scientific literature (pyrolysis of proteins); nevertheless, it is apparent that the thermal efficiency must be quite poor and the cost of the fuels must be very high. Such a process may possibly find small-scale use as a source of crude chemicals.

Commercial products, such as alcohol, butanol, and acetic acid, are already obtained in this manner. However, the high protein content of young algae enables the organisms feeding upon them to cease fermentation and spend their energies upon reproduction. One obtains therefore merely the transfer of algal cell substance into microbial cell substance, with some attendant loss. This means that a special type of fermentation must be sought which will continue under conditions that inhibit growth in the presence of plentiful nutrients. Biologists can devise several devious ways of establishing such an environment, but the raising of the temperature of the medium to a point where only a few special strains of microorganisms can persist seems to be simplest and has already been used for large-scale industrial operations. The organisms are called thermophiles. One well-known fermentation will fill these specifications—it produces methane—but there is another which has been recently discovered and remains imperfectly explored— it produces hydrogen.

Suppose one would ferment the harvested algae with methane bacteria under thermophilic conditions, what would be the products? Carefully controlled experiments of this kind have not yet been published, nor have any others which are closely analogous. Nevertheless, one may deduce from sewage treatment and packing house waste-disposal results which occasionally deal with similar compositions of inputs that the following composition is probable:

Methane	50–70%
Carbon dioxide	20–30%
Hydrogen	2–10%
Hydrogen sulfide	1–3%
Carbon monoxide	Trace
Ammonia	Trace

The mineral salts, including practically all the fixed nitrogen in the form of ammonium salts, would remain dissolved in the liquid medium. The conversion efficiency (caloric value of the inputs divided by the caloric value of the products) for methane fermentation is generally quite high, usually running 80 to 90% or more. However, since the measurements for this particular process have not yet been made we must express this uncertainty in terms of a wider range of probable conversion efficiency, say 65 to 90%.

It is possible now to assemble, on paper at least, an energy-producing cycle. The algae are converted into methane (plus some hydrogen), and these fermenter gases can be burnt in a gas turbine or engine which operates an electric generator. The culture medium left from the fermentation becomes the principal source of algal nutrients. The combusted gas contains carbon dioxide which can accelerate the growth of algae. Thus, there are smaller cycles within larger cycles which make sure that very little is wasted. The hydrogen sulfide in the fermenter gas is a nuisance, but it can be easily extracted and the sulfur in it can be sold as a by-product. Similarly, heat disposal both from thermophilic algal culture and from the fermentation is inconvenient. In this instance, if cooling water is available at less than ambient temperatures, a Claude process temperature-difference plant can be interposed which will convert this low-grade heat into useful quantities of power. The power is produced mainly when the sun is most intense, but it is just at this time that the equipment for an algal culture installation must work at capacity. Thus peak power production coincides with peak demand!

Up to this point bits and pieces of known scientific and technical information, much of it learned from pilot-plant experiments and industrial operations, were brought together to suggest a totally new means of generating steady electrical power. (See Fig. 13.) The over-all efficiency of converting sunlight into electricity by such means is ex-

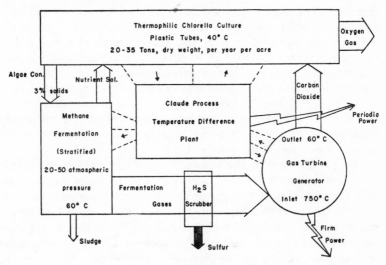

Fig. 13. An Optimum Efficiency Biological Cycle for Power Production Employing the Present State of Knowledge

Each unit process represented here is based upon laboratory data published over the last few years. Each is closely related to pilot plants or commercial operations which have demonstrated that the unit process is workable on a large scale. Implications of linking the processes have been investigated (but thus far only on paper); from this it appears that a stable cycle could be maintained. With the yields indicated a 1000-acre installation could generate 10,000 to 20,000 kw of firm power plus some periodic power—if a fair source of cooling water were available.

pected to be in the range of 1 to 3%—if no further improvements were made in the cycle. This is much better than the direct method of converting algae, but it is still far too expensive. In what direction does an improvement in the economics lie?

The possibility of by-products has not been considered. Careful analysis of probable large-scale markets suggests that the best direction to take is that of culturing a nitrogen-fixing thermophilic algae that grows well in brackish waters or sea water. The cycle would then yield five to eight tons of fixed nitrogen per hectare per year (two to three tons per acre). In addition, the Claude process could deliver distilled water in amounts up to the natural rate of evaporation in that location (several acre-feet per year per acre of culture). There would be no trouble finding markets for such by-products, but it would be difficult to discover uses for the huge quantities of oxygen-rich air and all of the brine that would be major outputs of this form of algal culture; therefore, no contribution to costs should be expected from them. (There is a possibility, which is far from being clearly established, that part of the oxygen could be useful in improving the operation of a fuel cell—a special battery that is charged by admitting oxidizing and reducing gases to the opposing plates. The fuel cell can generate approximately twice the electric current from a given flow of fuel gas that the most efficient gas turbine-generators can achieve today. The optimum characteristics of fuel cells and their special problems of maintenance are still largely industrial secrets, but the prospects seem hopeful enough to stimulate important amounts of industrial research.)

The gas delivered by the fermenter has a composition and caloric value that permits it to be an industrial gas. The fuel value, however, does not allow it to be transported very far. Quite another alternative, however, will meet the demands of more distant consumers. This gas can be smoothly converted into "synthesis gas" and then, by the well-known Fisher-Tropsch synthesis developed in Germany, into liquid hydrocarbons, mainly of the gasoline-kerosene range. For every 100 tons of algae produced (dry weight basis) one could expect 25 to 40 tons of liquid fuels (five to nine tons per acre per year) plus some electric power at many sites.

Fitting together a half dozen or more of the following subprocesses

> Algal culture
> Methane fermentation
> Hydrogen fermentation
> Hydrogen sulfide removal
> "Synthesis gas" production
> Hydrocarbon synthesis
> Gas turbine
> Fuel cell
> Claude process temperature-difference unit

with others that are more peripherally related, either preparing raw materials for use in the above, or utilizing the less-valued by-products generated, such as

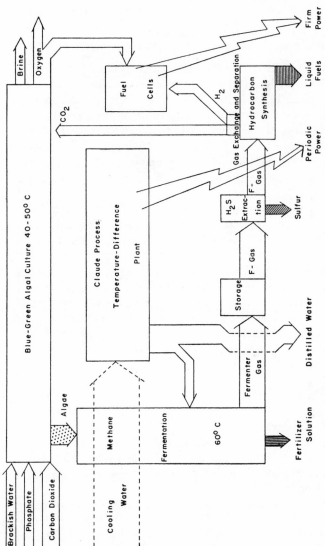

FIG. 14. OPTIMUM BIOLOGICAL CYCLE WITH FULL RANGE OF POSSIBLE BY-PRODUCTS

This is a speculation upon a complement of possibilities for the conversion of photosynthesis products into power and liquid fuels. Material inputs are shown on the left; the outputs are shown on the bottom and at the right. The capital investment implied is large, but it is believed that the cost of fuel and power on favorable sites would be no greater than two to five times present costs. Thus we may think of solar energy as being suitable for many oceanside tropical installations in the very long run when other energy supplies are becoming expensive.

Cement manufacture (uses fuel gas and produces CO_2)
Salt manufacture (uses discarded brine)
Magnesia manufacture (may be either an input or output)
Hydroponic vegetables (uses fermenter liquor)
Antibiotic production (uses distilled H_2O and services)
Phosphate fertilizer manufacture (an important input and uses sulfur)

one obtains the picture of a highly capitalized complex of activities, energized by the employment of photosynthesis, where the efficiency is multiplied several fold. If the photosynthesis step is carried out at 8 to 20% efficiency, the net energy output in the form of fuels and power (but neglecting the fixed nitrogen, distilled water, and the sulfur) could be in the range of 5 to 17% of the solar input. The efficiency achievable in any location depends greatly upon the weather, the temperature of the cooling water, the cost of carbon dioxide, and the interest rate for large-scale investments.

How much would steady solar power cost? It is possible to make rough estimates since the most expensive elements of the cycle have been constructed up to the pilot-plant stage. In the better locations electricity could be produced for $2\frac{1}{2}$ to $5\rlap{/}{c}$ per kwhr and liquid fuels for about \$150 per ton. There is an excellent chance that engineering research can reduce these costs, and make it possible to bring many more sites into this range, but the state of knowledge is presently so poor that the amount of reduction in cost cannot be judged even by indirect means. Solar power production may initially be only a by-product itself of food production but, as world energy costs move upwards, it provides a very large, inexhaustible source, a reserve to be drawn upon if other costs become excessive.

When is it likely that solar power will be available? At the moment there is only sporadic and unsystematic research and development in this field. If this should be replaced by better organized effort, embracing both the science and the engineering, there is a chance that some small-scale uses may be found by 1975. An unexpected breakthrough in research upon photosynthesis or thermophilic fermentations would speed things up.

The foregoing proposals were constructed from fragments found in the technological literature. Later a series of process studies at the University of California demonstrated that the key steps of algal culture and methane fermentation were readily linked and performed better than expectations. The Berkeley investigators projected power costs in favorable locations at 1 to $2\rlap{/}{c}$ per kwhr. Costs would rise with large-scale utilization, however, despite the economies obtained from an industrial complex. [W. J. Oswald and C. G. Golueke, *Mech. Eng.*, 86, p. 40 (1964); *Solar Energy*, 7, p. 86 (1963).]

2. TERRESTRIAL SOURCES

When the earth came into being some billions of years ago, a great deal of energy was incorporated into the planet itself. Some of it existed in the form of rotational energy that has been slowly lost over the eons because of friction at the surface, so that only a small proportion of the original legacy remains. Some of it was in the form of unstable atomic nuclei; these have largely given up their energy in radioactive disintegration and have decayed to the most stable nuclear assemblages. Only the longest-lived nuclei remain now, and radioactivity makes up a tiny portion of the energy dissipated into space by the earth. The effects of gravitation upon the substance of the earth offers still another source; as the earth compresses itself, heat is generated internally. Because of the poor thermal conductivity of the crust much of this energy still remains at subterranean levels, merged with what is left from the radioactive disintegrations.

The rotational energy in the earth's system shows up only where there are some counteracting forces. The lunar tides appear to be the only opportunity offered (the solar tides are discernible at only a few locales) for development. Several tide-power projects have been quite thoroughly surveyed—Passamaquoddy and the Severn Barrage have become stock examples for civil engineers, but there are a half-dozen other parts of the world that offer similar opportunities. The cost ranges from a little less than 1.0¢ per kwhr up to as high as may be found economical. In the long run it is not inconceivable that 10^7 kilowatts of power will be installed. An inconvenient characteristic of the power, which retards its use, is its periodicity. Either a link must exist with a power grid receiving contributions from much larger sources of power, or it requires that the industry, and community dependent upon it, must regulate their affairs according to lunar, rather than solar, time. Thus there are interesting opportunities in tide power but no large-scale contributions.

The internal heat of the earth is most easily tapped through hot springs and fumarellos (steam spouts in volcanic areas). These sources are already employed for power purposes, mainly in Italy, but they are even less significant over the whole earth than tide power.

There are two sources of nuclear energy that remain open. One involves the aggregation of hydrogen nuclei, possibly in conjunction with a light metal such as lithium, so as to produce helium. The hydrogen fusion process is the manner in which the sun produces practically all its energy, but no one has yet been able to imagine how the high temperatures and pressures necessary for the production of continuous energy from hydrogen could be maintained on the surface of the earth. However, since it is now known that nuclear explosions can be exaggerated in intensity by this process, such a method cannot rationally be ruled infeasible. The other nuclear power process involves fission of several very heavy nuclei, such as some kinds of uranium, by procedures that are already quite well explored. The requirement of a high temperature for ignition is not a physical property of the fission process —the greatest technical difficulties to be faced are those of getting pure materials of construction that also have sufficient mechanical strength for continuous operation. These are, in other words, maintenance problems that have no historical parallels.

The prospects for obtaining energy from fission economically are extremely difficult to ascertain. Most scholars have given up in despair because the established methods of fact-finding do not apply. This has been because of the situation wherein an unknown proportion of the data is kept secret. Therefore, in the serious books and articles on atomic power possibilities, one finds only a series of conditioned propositions such as ". . . if atomic power costs 0.6¢ per kwhr then the effects upon the location of XYZ industries will be as follows . . ." Such analysis leads nowhere unless an appraisal exists of the probability of achieving power costs of 0.6¢. Ayres and Scarlott made a careful qualitative appraisal of the prospects for economic atomic power. Several scholars have come to almost identical evaluations, although they started independently with somewhat different backgrounds. However Ayres and Scarlott restricted themselves to qualitative statements on this subject in a book that went to great pains to be quantitative on all other subjects.

The difficulty is a peculiar one. Other analyses in this book are based upon a confidence that an important useful development will be described in the technical journals within a few years after it has been discovered. The motivation behind such disclosure may be either a matter of entrepreneurial gain (in order to take advantage of a new idea a firm must buy equipment, fit it into an urban industrial complex, and sell the product, all of which forces it to disclose enough information to permit any intelligent engineer to deduce what must be the essential characteristics of invention) or a matter of giving credit for highest quality professional accomplishment. The latter tendency is becoming increasingly important. In the atomic energy field, however, it was quite possible until very recently that the most useful developments would be declared to be official secrets, for the very reason that they would be highly useful anywhere in the world. The delayed applications caused by trying to operate under the cover of extreme secrecy could easily be judged preferable to the other alternative, which would make the development available to a mortal enemy of one's own social system. The preparations for the Geneva "Atoms for Peace" Conference indicate that these quandaries should no longer exist after 1955 except in the thermonuclear or fusion region.

At this stage one must be satisfied with the partial and incomplete data that have already reached the journals. The implications of such data are most evident when incorporated into proposals for the design and construction of a variety of new reactors, such as are described in *Nucleonics* (June 1955) and other current journals. Most of the designs themselves are expressly experimental and untested, and are based upon costs for fuel and construction elements which are expected to exist in the near future. There are only a few indications as yet available concerning the specific designs likely to be used in the long-run. Thus a somewhat different mode of argument seems to be appropriate when one is evaluating the possible role of nuclear energy.

A set of propositions follows which have a good probability of being correct. They present a sufficiently complete set of conclusions to permit an appraisal of the role atomic energy may play in over-all world development.

1. At least one design of "breeder reactor" will reach the stage of continuous operation at temperatures of 500° C or higher.

This development may come a decade or so hence. It would mean that the available power from fission can be multiplied as much as 500 times since it makes possible the use of practically all of the U238 isotope, as well as the more abundant thorium. It also means that thermal efficiency in converting heat to electric power should be equivalent to present coal-steam stations (25 to 35%).

2. Power plants must be huge integrated facilities if they are to function efficiently.

Not only does a power plant have the minimum "critical mass" to deal with, but the reprocessing equipment handling strongly radioactive products cannot be reduced in size with any important savings. Land transport of spent uranium may also be rather expensive. These considerations lead to power stations with a capacity of the order of 10^5–10^6 kilowatts, the larger the better.

3. Mobile units will be limited to ship propulsion, but it is still doubtful whether this can be economic for most ocean transport.

The various safety requirements, as well as the weight limitations, work against any important uses in air transport or in locomotives. On large ships the hazards can be minimized, but only a small part of ocean freight can be conveniently carried by large ships. Such units may also be used for special purposes in many isolated landbound sites where diesel generators are inconvenient.

4. The production of hot water and process steam can eventually be competitive with present day fuels.

The design of reactors which operate at 200 to 300° C, and under low pressures, is much less complex than the design of reactors to operate at higher temperatures. This fact is expected to be reflected in lower capital expenditures, and thus lower total costs. The difficulty is that at most points of use (e.g., households, light industry) rates will increase because it costs less to transport energy in the form of coal or fuel oil than to transport it in the form of steam.

5. The cost of electric power generated by nuclear fuels depends very much upon the toleration for radiation permitted.

In recent times, construction costs for facilities that handle radiation have run about three to ten times as much as for equivalent facilities without radiation. The design standards employed lead to a safety record several times better than is obtained in parallel activities. Equalizing safety standards may lead to reductions in the investment required for nuclear facilities by as much as half.

6. The economic feasibility of atomic power is likely to depend upon a fairly low interest rate.

For example, if atomic power costs $500 per installed kilowatt against $200 for a thermoelectric plant, with coal at $20 per ton, then atomic power would appear to be more economical at interest rates up to 5 to 6%, but thermoelectric facilities would be natural choices for areas with higher interest rates (these are mostly underdeveloped areas).

7. The prospective costs of atomic power are likely to be in the range of 1¢ to 2¢ per kwhr twenty years hence when computed without subsidies.

It is assumed that the by-product plutonium is not bought up for bomb production but is consumed on the premises as nuclear fuel, and that the cost of uranium will be somewhat higher than at present. This means that atomic power would find its greatest application in developed areas which are beginning to feel the pinch of reduced fuel supplies. Costs are likely to drop later as larger quantities come into production, and standardization and integration come into effect, perhaps to less than 1¢ per kwhr in the period 30 to 40 years hence.

8. The effect upon the availability of fuels for energizing transport will be selective, but generally small.

Large ships and submarines and perhaps a few heavy locomotives will have their own reactors as a source of motive power. Electrochemicals, such as hydrazine, or products depending mainly upon a power source for operating compressors, such as liquid oxygen, can be produced in large quantities, but these products are suitable only for jet transport. No substitutes for diesel fuel and gasoline have yet been suggested that can conveniently be synthesized with electric or thermal energy.

9. The total supply of energy in the fissile material likely to be available is more than 1000 times as great as the fossil fuel supply.

This estimate presumes that all the rocks above sea level containing more than 12 to 15 parts per million of uranium and thorium could be utilized. It would also imply the leveling of all the world's granitic mountain ranges (the Andes, the Rockies, the Alps, etc.).

Thus the energy available from terrestrial sources is predominantly to be derived from nuclear fission. There is enough energy in the earth to maintain a high level energy-using civilization on a world scale for an age much longer than the recorded history of man. The cost of most of this energy is likely to be expensive as compared to present costs, but if compared to the value of the services to be performed it promises to be reasonable enough.

This optimistic long range outlook for atomic power is quite a different picture from that painted by Putnam (1953) from data available in 1951. At that time one had to depend wholly upon traditional thinking on costs and methods of mining. However, if one starts from the background of geochemistry and process chemistry, new horizons of supply open up. One can imagine removing from shales and special granites all of the readily extractable ores while they were being processed for fissile materials. Most of the ferrous and nonferrous ores could be reduced to ingots at the mine site by use of the atomic power available there. A more detailed description of what the over-all process could be like is presented in the discussion later which speculates upon the long term future for nonferrous metals.

Atomic energy and solar energy appear to be an excellent combination, since the disadvantages of the one are balanced by the advantages of the other. Large quantities of energy emanate from almost a point-source in an atomic power plant, but solar energy is spread extensively and almost uniformly over a large part of the earth. Atomic energy is steady, whereas solar energy has daily and seasonal cycles. Fissile materials have negligible transport costs but the products (heat and electrical power) can be moved only a few hundred miles at most, whereas the source of solar energy fuels must be fixed, but the products of photosynthesis are readily moved about. Nevertheless, the characteristics of this complementary pair of energy sources differ markedly from those of the fuels that have been available in the past, so it may happen that at some critical point in technology neither may be suitable. Therefore, in order to determine with confidnece whether a populous and prosperous world society can be supported, a survey of the specific purposes for which fuels are required must be undertaken.

The information on nuclear power technology is now voluminous. The preceding conclusions were on the conservative side, since some power plants are likely to operate at costs of 0.6¢ per kwhr before the target date of 1975. These are not yet "breeder" reactors, since the latter are confidently expected to be ready only in the 1980's. The delays are due in part to rapidly improving efficiency of new competitive power plants using fossil fuels. By the year 2000 A.D., however, it is projected that fossil fuel consumption will reach its peak, and almost all future plants constructed after that date would use nuclear energy.

Curiously, the present growth rates in power consumption associated with economic development (7 to 15% per year) cannot be met with the scientific knowledge presently available. Economic breeding seems to offer a power production growth rate of only 3 to 4% per year. The properties of the chemical elements have been measured precisely enough so that this situation is not likely to improve with increasing research. In addition, power from nuclear fusion processes using deuterium and light elements seems to be even less likely now than earlier. Thus, a power stringency may be encountered in world development a generation hence which could only be overcome by "wasting" large quantities of fissile elements. Thus there are technological as well as economic reasons for investigating energy-saving patterns of life. [*Development, Growth, and State of the Atomic Energy Industry*, 2 vols., Hearings of the JCAE, 88th Congress, 1963, 1042 pp.]

3. THERMAL COMFORT

Now that it seems possible, even probable, that the world can be assured of a continuing supply of the familiar forms of energy at not unreasonable costs for tens of thousands, or even millions, of years into the future, an embarrassing question must be asked. Energy for what purposes? How much energy is really necessary? In order to find reasonable answers to such questions the basic human needs for comfort and convenience must be surveyed. The ways in which energy is employed in order to maintain an individual in equilibrium with his physical environment ought to be systematized. In addition, the ways in which energy can free humans from routine tasks and enable them to engage in an increasing range of activities should be considered. From such investigations it should be possible to establish how energy might best be used in the future, viewing the application of energy to human needs as a scientific problem rather than one of updating historical precedents, as was done in the first approximation of human energy needs shown in Table 5. This procedure requires a rather abrupt change in the mode of argument. We move from a description of very large-scale science-based technology to the individual human, the family unit, and the technics of everyday living where whatever science has been introduced is haphazard and far from systematic.

When conditions of comfort are barely adequate, the quantity of fuels consumed in the household is undoubtedly greater than that allocated to any other single category of use in the society. Much of this is used for space heating, a large amount for cooking, and only slightly less for heating water. A trifle goes for refrigeration, considerable amounts for lighting, and there are in addition a great number of miscellaneous applications.

Too often it is forgotten that food itself serves as a fuel. The 2000 to 4000 calories which are consumed by a person over a day are in turn emitted by the body. These calories can be conserved so as to keep human beings comfortable, but to do so efficiently requires a great deal of scientific knowledge about human comfort and about the properties of heat. The latter subject was studied exhaustively in the nineteenth century, so that the last fifty years have brought only refinements in equipment and measurements. The research upon human comfort, however, has been quite recent and still affords many surprises as the subject is being advanced. The only comprehensive review of the recent studies upon thermal comfort is that edited by L. H. Newburgh (1949).

The thermal needs of human beings stem principally from properties of their sensory nervous system. If, for instance, the average temperature of the skin should deviate more than 3° C from the standard figure of 33° C the nervous system would mildly, but definitely, protest. Another degree or two beyond that would result in real discomfort or illness. Within this range of surface temperatures a person has a capacity for adjusting his heat production by internal regulatory controls. The control mechanisms have apparently evolved in order to protect the brain and the internal organs from temperature variations, since they are now so elaborate and complex that a 1 to 2° deviation from the normal deep body temperature results in a noticeable loss of mental function.

There are primitive peoples, such as the Fuegian Indians at the tip of South America and the Australian aborigines, who manage to live virtually naked in freezing climates and have always constituted a challenge to this concept of comfort. However the work of Sir Stanton Hicks and colleagues (1934, 1938) suggests that the cold is felt as keenly by them as it is by less well adapted persons but that the natives have developed an additional reflex for reducing the flow of blood in the skin and thereby are able to reduce the loss of body warmth. The skin is thus made to act more like a layer of insulation than a radiator.

In most cultures, sufficient clothing is worn outdoors to permit the release of just enough heat so that the skin temperature stays well within the comfort range. Inside a dwelling the air and walls can be heated so that fewer layers of clothing are required. In this system of thinking, clothing acts as a heat insulator, used for much the same purposes as the wrapping around a steam pipe, and can be measured accordingly. The unit of insulation value for clothing has quite appropriately been called a *clo* in North America. One *clo* is the amount of insulation necessary to maintain comfort in a normally ventilated room, with air movements less than 10 feet per minute, at a temperature of 70° F and a relative humidity less than 50%, while the subject is resting in a sitting position. (A *clo* = 0.648° C sec sq m/Cal; it allows the transfer of 5.55 Cal/sq m/hr at a temperature gradient of 1° C.) The amount of clothing ordinarily worn ranges from about 5 *clo* for bitterly cold weather to about 0.5 *clo* for midsummer.

The quantity of heat generated by the body increases with the degree of activity. Whereas a normal person in a sitting position generates about 100 Cal per hour, a slow walk will double the quantity, and a brisk hike with pack will quadruple it. The surrounding air in the latter instances must be relatively cool in order to permit comfort, even if minimal clothing is worn. The alternative is first, heavy perspiration and later, if cooling is not sufficiently rapid, heat prostration.

The role of perspiration is that of bringing a new cooling process into play—the evaporation of water at the skin surface. Since evaporation is carried out very close to the temperature-sensitive nerve endings in the skin, a large measure of relief may be afforded by perspiration. The rate of cooling however depends ultimately upon the relative humidity and air flow. Control of these two factors generally provides the most economical air-conditioning arrangement. Clothing can also be adapted so as not to hinder, but even slightly increase, the cooling qualities of perspiration.

Once it is seen how clothing can conserve energy it must also be admitted that it costs energy to manufacture. Does it really pay to wear clothing—speaking in purely energetic terms? This is an intriguing problem to which a convincing answer can be given.

In many environments it is possible to achieve thermal comfort by two alternative routes, (1) engaging in more physical activity and consuming enough food to make such effort possible, or (2) utilizing clothing as a means of heat insulation. The fiber in clothing requires soil resources which can otherwise be applied to the production of food, so a basis for comparison exists.

It appears, upon inspection of agricultural yields, that several tons of grain can be grown where one ton of cotton is now produced, making due allowances for cottonseed by-products. Similarly, a ton of wool can be obtained from grazing lands which would otherwise produce several tons of protein in the form of meat. Thus we can set up an equivalent:

1 kg cotton or wool = 2 to 3 kg carbohydrate or protein foodstuffs.

To convert the fiber into garments now requires about 1 kg of coal per kg of fiber. Knowledge of this fact permits establishing the cost of garments in terms of the caloric value of food and fuel (1.4 to 2.0 × 10⁴ Cal/kg of garments).

In order to estimate per capita needs it is necessary to state what climate is assumed. A temperate climate, for instance, might have an annual average temperature around 15° C; it would normally require 5 to 6 kg of fiber. (See Table 3.) Thus the total energy cost of a person's clothing for a year comes to 7 to 12 × 10⁴ Cal.

In the same climate, food requirements can also be estimated by using data available to physiologists. Food needs for a young man, clothed, 65 kg, doing moderate work, are 2880 Cal per day. (See Table 1.) For him unclothed, they can be calculated and come to 4100 Cal per man.

This is an increase in food consumption of 42%, due solely to absence of clothing. For a typical population, which includes both young and old persons, a 42% increase must be added to a basic 2500 to 2700 Cal per day per capita now considered to be barely adequate. Processing costs, transport, and allowance for waste should still be added.

In comparing the minimal annual food cost for thermal comfort (4 × 10⁵ Cal) with the clothing cost (7 to 12 × 10⁴ Cal) it will be seen that every calorie devoted to fibers is returned at least three- to six-fold in the saving of food. For colder climates the margin will be much greater, even if people develop heat-conserving reflexes like those of the Australian Bushmen, whereas for somewhat warmer climates more refined calculations are needed. For the tropics, clothing would need other justifications than energy economy. The newer synthetic fibers, in general, cost no more calories than the natural fibers, but they tend to wear longer, so that the saving in energy is still more marked if they are relied upon.

Clothing has uses and properties beyond those of thermal comfort. The design of suitable clothing for both a specified climate and a pattern of living may require many lifetimes of experience in order to achieve just the right compromise between:

> Thermal comfort
> Convenience (especially pockets)
> Freedom from irritation
> Launderability
> Identification of social status and role
> Cost.

If the world's styles were to be analyzed from the point of view of comfort, convenience, and efficiency (Rudofsky, 1947) no culture would score well on its total array of creations, but each can contribute to an assortment that could appear to be most useful to meet the various combinations of world climate and human activity.

Of what garments would a minimum adequate wardrobe consist? By drawing upon the technical and cultural experience of both the East and the West it is possible to assemble an assortment that seems to be quite suitable.

First layers: ½ to 1½ *clo*
   tee shirts, shorts, blouses, Hindu sari, trousers of cotton or reinforced rayon, broad-rimmed hat, sandals
Second layer: 1½ to 2½ *clo*
   sweaters, trousers or kilts made of moisture-resistant warm fibers, shoes with fabric uppers, socks or stockings reinforced at points of wear, rain slicker
Third layer: 2½ to 3½ *clo*
   lined windbreaker, coveralls, overshoes or lined boots, helmet or hunter's cap, gloves
Fourth layer: 3½ to 4½ *clo*
   roughwoven greatcoat or parka, warm scarf, warmer knee-length boots, better-grade gloves

Because of the unwieldiness of any further layers, it is not convenient to wear more than 4 to 5 *clo*. Besides, Arctic peoples have found that sweaty damp underlayers can be disastrous to the insulation value and also the life of the garments. (Perspiration cannot be avoided whenever, for any reason, the level of activity must be increased.) Therefore, outdoor clothing should be designed so that the heat-retaining capacities can be readily altered. Recently, foamed-plastic garments have been developed which make possible much higher levels of insulation, but they do not yet solve the problem of varying the insulating capacity. Such garments do permit exposure to icy water or sleeping out-of-doors in the Arctic without important discomfort. In the long run, man may be able to improve upon the use of furs and textiles, but developments to date are still scanty.

The upper limit for convenient indoor clothing appears to be about 3 *clo*. Thus it is for meeting the requirements set by the weather immediately outside the shelter, which may be called the urban macroclimate, that the minimum adequate wardrobe must be designed. What this means for various parts of the world is indicated in Table 16.

Consulting the data on comfort collected by the physiologists (see Figures 15 to 18) reveals that it becomes very difficult to maintain thermal comfort at low levels of human activity when the temperature of the environment falls below 10° C (50° F). At the lower temperatures, comfort can be maintained only at considerable inconvenience—

TABLE 16. WORLD REQUIREMENTS FOR THERMAL INSULATION IN CLOTHING

Area	Yearly Average for Comfort per Capita,* clo	Total,† clo
United States and Canada	2.9	4.8×10^8
Latin America and West Indies	1.8	3.5×10^8
Western Europe	3.1	9.5×10^8
Eastern Europe, Russia, Siberia	3.4	9.9×10^8
Near East (including Egypt)	1.9	1.8×10^8
Far East and East Indies	2.1	2.5×10^9
Australia and New Zealand	2.5	2.5×10^7
Africa (less Egypt)	1.9	3.4×10^8
World average	2.35 clo	5.7×10^9 clo

* Population-weighted averages compiled from the monthly maps of world climate zones, Climatology Unit, Research and Development Branch, Office of the Quartermaster General, 1943. They indicate the average amount of clothing to be worn with comfort in a shaded area outdoors, protected from the wind. For a suitable measure of annual needs this figure must be multiplied by a factor representing the rate at which clothing wears out—a difficult variable to ascertain.

† Based on 1950 population estimates, *U.N. Statistical Papers*, **III**, nos. 3–4, 1951.

such as wearing gloves when sewing or reading. Thus, when fuel is very scarce, it seems likely that the most economical arrangement would be that of adding more clothing down to a temperature of $10°$ C, and then finding some suitable mode of space heating which would maintain the $10°$ C level no matter how far the exterior temperatures fell. Such an observation makes it possible to relate climate to thermal needs, taking clothing, climate, and space heating as a complementary ensemble.

4. SHELTER: CONVENIENCE WITH CLIMATE CONTROL

Civilized peoples generally allocate somewhere in the range of 20 to 35% of their incomes to the acquisition and maintenance of shelter. Not all of this expense can be assessed to the need for protection from the elements, because homes, public buildings, and workplaces serve many other needs in addition. The severity of the climate in most parts of the world makes necessary a large proportion of existing structures, but a major share of the space and equipment in them is aimed at improving convenience, privacy, work efficiency, establishing social status, etc.

Estimating fuel and energy requirements for a household, in the long run, will encounter huge variations. If we start by assuming that all but the most private and domestic functions of a household will remain at the communal level—or be thrust there—for reasons of economy, then the principal needs for energy in the home are for purposes

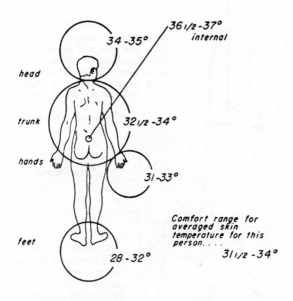

DATA SOURCE: HARDY AND DUBOIS (1938)

FIG. 15. TYPICAL SURFACE TEMPERATURE RANGES FOR COMFORT

Although rather thorough studies of the relation of skin temperature to comfort have been made upon a few healthy, normal young people, very little is known about the requirements of a cross-section of the population. Most design for human comfort starts from this kind of data which is used as a kind of arbitrary standard until further information is available.

of cooking, water heating, lighting, and, in a few places, for some air conditioning and refrigeration. A neat solution for cooking is provided by the solar cookers referred to earlier (Ghai, 1953), but on cloudy days a kerosene burner or an electric hot plate must be brought into use.

Any of these methods is superior to the charcoal, ox dung, or faggots that are now used. Hot water can also be heated in very simple equipment by solar means. Lighting is cheapest and most convenient when it is electric. Adding these up in tropical and subtropical climates gives

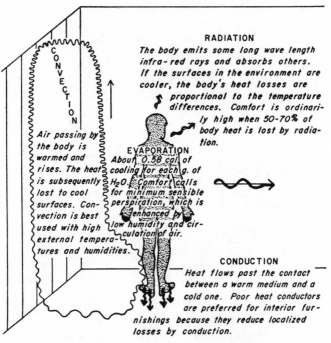

FIG. 16. MODES OF HEAT LOSS FOR COMFORT

Each of these modes of heat loss imposes different requirements upon the environment. The best design for controlling internal environment mediates between the out-of-doors weather and these characteristics of the human body so as to keep the cost as low as possible.

one a range of 5 to 50 kwhr per month per household. This is not very definite but it seems to be the best estimate of the energy requirements for comfort and convenience in households that can be arrived at presently.

Proceeding polewards from the equatorial regions one finds the outdoors temperature dipping below 10° C in the cold season. At first, when the differential is small, it can be met by retaining some of the heat from midday warming well into the evening. The heat escaping from human bodies can also be an important item—if the interior surfaces of the dwelling are excellent reflectors (few houses are constructed in this manner but the snow houses of the Eskimos come closest). Mills (1952) has shown that even a dwelling with no special insulation—buildings have such a long life it is usually more economical to develop techniques that can be installed without much effort in old structures—can be adapted, by covering walls and ceiling with tinted metal foil, so that all radiation, human and artificial, is used very effectively. By such means one can imagine reducing the outdoor temperature on cloudy days to about 5° C (41° F) before the indoor chill need become truly uncomfortable. In climates where the temperature regularly falls below this point some provision for space heating must be incorporated into the dwelling.

The most desirable heat source would be one that is both economical and inexhaustible. Clearly, solar energy is the best prospect. Surveys have already been made of winter weather with solar heating requirements in mind. They usually indicate the upper limit of the zone where solar heating has "engineering feasibility" (assumes an indoor temperature of 77° F (21° C) to be consistently maintained) as varying from latitude 37° with cloudy and damp winters to latitude 46° in dry, sunny regions. However the term "engineering feasibility" has behind it some rather arbitrary assumptions as to what constitutes reasonable cost which would not hold up for long-range thinking.

The use of solar energy in the winter at colder latitudes depends almost entirely upon the costs of storing extra heat to last through the critical midwinter period. For the climate of New York City, according to Sharon's calculations (1952), about 20 tons of sodium sulfate hydrates would be required for a standard 5-room house (100 sq m of enclosed area). This allowed for an 11-day reserve. Further north it would be necessary to have a 30-day or even a 50-day reservoir. One would also need devices for supplying extra heat to it occasionally at a high rate in order to meet the drain of very cold periods. The sodium sulfate hydrate is not scarce—probably unlimited quantities are available at $15 to $25 per ton—but the storage of 50 to 100 tons of a salt with a density of 1.4 to 1.5 in simple heat exchange equipment guaranteed not to corrode for the life of the structure is not cheap. Permitting interior

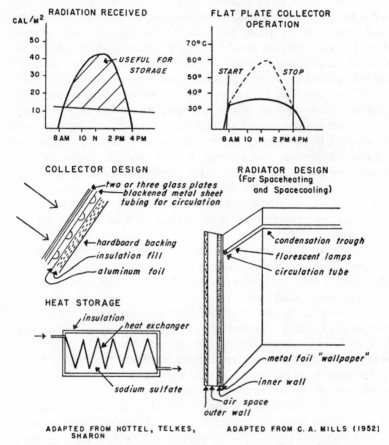

FIG. 17.   ELEMENTS OF SOLAR HEATING ON A SUNNY DAY IN MIDWINTER

By combining the best features of several recent developments, it is possible to visualize how solar energy can be used efficiently for spaceheating.   The energy is absorbed
on a blackened metal sheet and the warmth produced is carried away by circulating
water to either the heat storage unit or a radiator arrangement.   The room surfaces
are designed to conserve and make uniform the radiant heat introduced.   In the past
few years many more ingenious devices have been added to the world's repertory of
techniques in this field.

temperatures to drop to 10° C at the coldest time of the year would reduce storage requirements by half or more. No one seems yet to have suggested it, but hot water under these circumstances, where no by-product heat is available in the household, might most easily be produced by a small heat pump which draws heat from the molten salt reservoir at 32° C and delivers it to the water at 70° to 75° C.

The idea of connecting a heat pump to a solar collector for purposes of space heating has been thoroughly explored (Jordan and Threlkeld, 1954). They conclude that the most efficient system employs two heat reservoirs, one which is sodium sulfate hydrate, and another, as yet unspecified, which stores heat at 15° C. It seems likely that their combination should become advantageous in many locations in the temperate zones when fossil fuel prices move higher.

The molten salt contains a little less than 1% of the energy in an equivalent weight of coal. The energy is so low grade it is hardly worth moving any distance at all. By using this method of storage, however, 30 to 50% of the energy in sunlight can be captured for space heating purposes. It appears that concentrating it into any markedly smaller volume without further loss of efficiency is frustrated by the properties of molecules in this temperature range. If we assume $30 per ton as the cost of salt plus heat exchanger, with 60% of this value being salvageable, and an interest rate of 6% per annum, then the annual cost per ton of the reservoir becomes about $2.10. If a reserve is maintained at 20% of a normal winter's needs (New York City required about 6%) marginal heat storage costs would compete with a delivered cost of coal at $45 per ton, if the energy content were completely used, or perhaps $30 per ton with efficient heating units.

These calculations assume that means would be found for inducing the molten salt to recrystallize readily. If its heat storage efficiency cannot approach the theoretical levels then the optimum storage system is an insulated tank of water. This is a bulkier solution but, in general, no more expensive.

It is not difficult to discover the implications of a 90% dependence upon solar radiation for low-grade heating purposes. The glass and metal radiation collectors would be set perpendicular to the ground, or at a very steep angle. In that position the settling of snow and dust can be prevented and 20 to 35% extra radiation can be collected in midwinter because of reflection from snow and ice. The earth surface which is completely shadowed in midwinter may range from 4 to 10 times the area of the collectors themselves. At 45° latitude the dwelling area served might be equal to that of the collectors (if interiors were heated to 70° F and some hot water was produced) or up to twice that of the collectors (with 50 to 60° F minimum temperatures, etc.). This efficiency permits a reasonable population density, according to

LEFT: **Solar House with South-facing Vertical Collector.**

RIGHT: **Two-level Solar House with South-facing Tilted Collector.**

SOURCE: Threlkeld and Jordan (1954)

FIG. 18.   DWELLINGS WITH SOLAR HEATING

The use of solar energy for the heating of homes imposes severe restrictions upon design.   Certain angles varying with latitude are necessary in order to achieve efficiency, and daylighting is made more difficult.   Nevertheless some interesting alternatives remain, some of which are shown above for 45° Latitude.   The distribution of dwellings over flat terrain becomes severely geometrical.   (Reprinted by permission from *ASHVE Transactions*, Vol. 60, 1954.)

metropolitan standards, but would not accommodate the built-up central portions of the city.   It would also require an altogether novel kind of architecture, and quite different esthetic standards.   The chief objections are psychological—practically all midwinter activities would be conducted in the shade and homes would have very little frontage on the sunny side.   At higher densities the structures would become highly symmetrical and therefore monotonous, according to present judgments. (See Fig. 18.)

If the location swelters in the summer, the solar collector could be used for making hot water, and the heat pump could be reversed and operated for cooling purposes. According to Mills' experiments (1952) near Cincinnati, refrigeration requirements there were only about 20% of the heating needs, and the same radiators in the dwelling can be used for either cooling or heating. Thus a combination heat pump and solar collector seems to be capable of stabilizing internal climates so that they approach closely the zones of optimum human comfort. There may be other innovations in structures and in physical equipment that would reduce the cost of using solar energy for climate control, since the engineering development in this field has hardly begun. On the other hand the technology will always be working against the diffuseness of the energy that is available in sunlight, and the low-grade character of the energy that is captured. Nevertheless, even as far poleward as the arctic circle, comfort could be achieved at a cost of less than $100 per year per capita for persons willing to wear 2 to 2½ *clo* indoors and to be restricted to 10 sq meters of living space throughout the winter. This is obviously not an exorbitant price to pay.

The proposed dependency upon solar heating does not mean that the disappearance of fossil fuels will automatically bring about the decentralization of cities. For a long time to come atomic power is likely to be the cheapest source of low-grade heat for the densely populated areas. The greatest economy would be effected by combining the demand for low-pressure steam for heating purposes with the demand for electric power. Since atomic plants are not convenient facilities to place in the middle of populous centers, it may be necessary to pipe in superheated steam, decompress it through a few small turbines located at the load centers for electric power, and distribute the low-pressure steam within a 2- to 3-mile radius. Commercial activities are large consumers of steam in metropolitan centers, and fortunately for costs, they are not especially seasonal. Residential uses of hot water are also not seasonal. Therefore, the loss of the space heating load in the summer should not cause so large an unbalance as to negate the value of the electric generator-district heating amalgamation as it has in so many such proposals in the past. At the same time, electric current distributed in the lightly settled peripheral areas of the city can in most climates be used to drive heat pumps for space heating. The assembly and installation of dwelling-size heat pumps is about to become a mass-production industry in the United States. It is felt that this would be a somewhat expensive mode of heating in other parts of the Temperate Zone but otherwise quite feasible. One may conclude, after engaging in extensive calculations, that the cost of services provided by cities will be affected only in a minor way by the transition from fossil fuels to atomic fuels as a source of energy. Nor would any striking alterations in appearance, or in patterns of human activity, be brought about solely because of the change.

5. OTHER ASPECTS OF COMFORT AND CONVENIENCE

Because of the close connection with energy consumption, thermal comfort was evaluated in some detail. Comfort has, however, many more features that merit examination, all of them requiring varying quantities of energy. They range from atmospheric requirements, which are usually taken for granted, or food and water, which are treated independently, to light, noise, annoyance by insects, irritation by dust, etc. Looked at in another manner, public health and medicinals might also be considered essential to comfort. A final aspect is that of fatigue and its antidote—relaxation.

But why was the condition of comfort seized upon when discussing and measuring human needs? Why not happiness, euphoria, or the Oriental state of nirvana? These are philosophical questions which cannot be dealt with adequately here but a short justification can be made and another example given, illustrating the general usefulness of the concept.

Comfort is, for the scientists, a property or state of the nervous system. Physiologists and psychologists are now coming to view a human being as a nerve network with a body wrapped around it so as to stabilize the system, giving it opportunity to develop its organization of impressions. A nervous system is built to receive and interpret messages. Occasionally (from its own point of view) it directs the sending of messages. The messages concern mainly the variations in light and sound that reach the nerve receptors, but touch, taste, smell, and temperature are important, as is the condition of the internal organs and tissues of the body.

Starting from these premises it is easy to see that some kinds of messages will be essential to the continued operation and survival of the nervous system. Food and oxygen, for instance, are continuously required and are therefore given a high priority by the network. Their lack is known to result in disturbance; the environment is scanned eagerly for some clue to a known system of relief. Thereafter all messages coming in from various parts of the network are interpreted or analyzed for information that may lead to removing the existing deficiency. The kinds of messages that in the past have had little to do with the deficiency would, of necessity, be ignored. Virtually all attention is paid to removing the distress signals. That is a state of discomfort.

The lack of signal may also be considered a message. The heat receptor nerves, for instance, may create a minor agitation in the network if the surroundings turn too warm, but give a more desirable neutral, or slightly pleasant feeling, in what has been called "the comfort range." Comfort is a composite of messages that together declare that "all is well for the moment." It is a condition that assures that the demands of the body itself do not destructively interfere with the apparatus of consciousness and the selectivity for response it desires. The nervous system can then occupy itself with messages that are likely to give it immediate gratification or improve its long-run welfare. Assuming that a nerve receptor either fires or does not fire—symbolized by 1 or 0—comfort is a state where almost all of the "pain" messages are 0. But when the 1's reach a certain threshold frequency they become noticeable, and, if they increase further, intrude upon the normal patterns of consciousness. Thus the ultimate unit for measuring comfort may be a unit of information, now called the "bit," but science is not yet at the stage where this unit can be used in a practical fashion. Tactile, heat, light, and pain messages are initially all different, each having unique properties in terms of sensation, and each endowed with different thresholds. Nevertheless, people integrate these messages, so that what is consciously judged is an over-all state of well-being.

Discomfort, in this rather mechanistic view, is a kind of noise or "static" in nerve networks, obscuring to some noticeable degree the capacity to communicate with the outside world and participate in society. We know, from both theory and measurement, that thresholds vary from person to person and from context to context, so that standards of bodily comfort are most accurately stated as being satisfactory for a prescribed proportion of the population, such as 90% or 99% of the total, but whether it is one or the other, or some point in between, demands greater precision than the present methods of measurement allow.

The part that light plays in bodily comfort is best understood in terms of this communication-of-messages theory of comfort. There are perhaps a million light receptors in an eye and 250,000 channels to the brain. If all of these should transmit a sensation of light at the same time one would receive the impression of an explosive blinding pain. This pain would diminish as the intensity of light diminished and would probably disappear when no part of the field of vision exceeded a few thousand foot candles (10^4 to 10^5 lumens/sq m). Below this level, comfort appears to be a matter of adjusting the threshold so that glare is eliminated and the contrasts in lighting are not so great that the discrimination of pattern and detail is lost. At some point of decreasing light intensity, usually at the level of a few foot-candles, discrimination starts failing. Relatively little pattern can be discriminated in semidarkness as compared to the capacity of the eye; therefore darkness is an inconvenience. It is, however, not uncomfortable unless one is forced to work steadily at tasks that require the maximum discrimination possible (where fatigue is permitted to build up).

This relationship suggests a differentiation between comfort and convenience. Comfort is a composite of messages from inside the body which permit full rationality, while convenience would assure that the external world was so organized as to permit the flow of relevant information to continue. Thus comfort might dictate that light must be less than 10^3 foot-candles, whereas convenience would ask that it exceed 50 foot-candles during working moments, even at night. Manufactured light extends the period of near capacity information gathering, and is therefore designated a convenience. Comfort is a condition limited to the confines of the human body, but the various kinds of conveniences that can be invented are virtually infinite, because any time-saving contrivance would be, by definition, a convenience. (See Fig. 19.)

Providing comfort permits the human organism to seek individual and social ends at full efficiency. Therefore, asking for adequate comfort is equivalent to asking for equal opportunity, as far as physiological deterrents go. As has already been described, comfort is bought with the expenditure of energy and time, both of which are in limited supply for a mortal organism. Improvements in technology tend to reduce the cost required to achieve the composite set of messages denoted as comfort. Looked at in this way, a strikingly new and more economical approach to comfort may occasionally involve the use of drugs or illusions rather than important quantities of energy carefully applied to the immediate environment. The medical profession already plays an important role in the provision of comfort, but its capacities seem likely to increase beyond present levels.

Whenever man is exposed to extremes in pressure, cold, acceleration, fatigue, or similar stresses in other than routine tours of duty, the techniques of preventive medicine offer remarkable economies. The use of drugs to control motion sickness, for example, appears to be a much

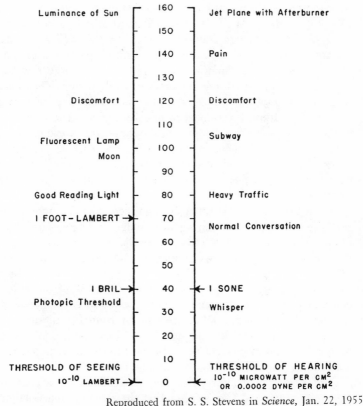

Reproduced from S. S. Stevens in *Science*, Jan. 22, 1955

FIG. 19. COMFORT AND DISCOMFORT IN SENSING LIGHT AND SOUND

It might be expected that human sensory capacities have evolved in a balanced fashion, but it is somewhat unexpected that the effects of increasing intensities should parallel each other to the degree that is observed. The threshold of comfort would, for a preponderance of persons, be experienced in the 105- to 125-decibel range. The preferred environment would no doubt allow for variations within the 30- to 100-decibel range.

simpler and more adequate solution than incorporating gyrostabilizers into all transport equipment.

This view of man as a unitized communications system can be extended into the area of convenience as well, but many more factors must be introduced. The communications viewpoint is handy for describing over-all relationships since it provides bases for comparison, balance, and stability. With it one can quickly deduce substitutes for contemporary practice that promise to economize upon time and effort. For example, in the recent symposium on *Human Factors in Equipment Design* (Floyd and Welford, 1954) the most attention was paid—after the problems of human comfort were resolved as well as possible—to the information-giving aspects of the "display" presented to the operator. Given such an outlook it was apparent that quite new kinds of experiments with promising outcomes can be set up. They may deal with the organization of households, the movement of persons to places of work, education, government or of classes of social institutions, such as the factory, the office, the school, the shop, etc. Some of the experiments may be of a more fundamental nature, such as are being pioneered by Quastler and Wulff (unpublished work, 1955), where the characteristics of skilled human subjects as communication systems are measured.

Developed societies are often distinguished from the underdeveloped by the possession of labor-saving and drudgery-reducing facilities. Too often, attention is concentrated upon the gadgets themselves rather than upon their convenience function. Each of them, in the context in which they were adopted, tended to economize on time or to increase opportunities for personal contacts for most of the individuals concerned. The facilities and artifacts created as conveniences during the development of the West are still far from the ultimate. They may easily be replaced by equipment that does a better job, as judged by this criterion of convenience. In the future, for example, we may not depend so much upon books, automobiles, and face-to-face contacts. A greater transfer of information may be achieved by magnetic tapes, electric railways, and television, so that the more familiar methods are not altogether excluded, but definitely reduced in importance.

For the rationalization of convenience the existence of certain fundamental needs may be presumed:

> Situations that generate emotional satisfactions
> Occasions for acquiring a high order of skill
> Variety of experience and stimuli
> Security from disaster (freedom to plan)
> Others.

With the communication-of-messages system it should be possible to deal with each of these social needs in a fashion that permits comparisons between societies on a semiquantitative basis and to determine, irrespective of the bulk of the facilities, or their economic value, whether the level of convenience is roughly the same in the societies being compared.

Before this has been brought about, the wisdom and common sense accumulated to date in studies on education and human development must be translated into the language and mathematics of the new communications theory—a process that has barely started and would certainly require decades of investigation before it could achieve the purposes set for it here. At present the new communications theory, as initiated by Wiener, Shannon, and successors, stands as one of those areas of science that promise to link up with what has been learned in the study of the individual and the study of society. If this book were to be written twenty years hence very likely there would need to be in it a chapter called New Systems of Communications, including data having roughly the same dependability as those that have been developed here for energy systems. Arguments could then be presented in as great detail upon the subject of economizing on the time-for-communication as are presented here on the subject of economizing on energy use. Many questions about the use of energy for conveniences can only be settled by bringing in such considerations. Therefore, lacking a communication-of-messages framework, the discussion of transitions and economies in convenience-yielding facilities must be largely technological. We know that energy is required for servicing the human group and the society, for transport, community functions, and utilities, but often it will be impossible to prove that the prospective developments in technology are really relevant and desirable.

Convenience is best studied through the analysis of human time allocation. Some interesting researches in this direction have been undertaken, but the systematic work has not yet appeared in print.

A monograph containing material that could be included in a "New Systems of Communication" chapter has appeared. [R. L. Meier, *A Communications Theory of Urban Growth*, The M.I.T. Press, Cambridge, 1962.]

6. MATERIALS OF CONSTRUCTION

Some very special requirements for fuels are set by the materials from which buildings, machines, and other equipment are made. The critical materials, upon which most of the world is dependent, include:

> Cement
> Glass and ceramics
> Metals
> Fabrics
> Plastics
> Paper
> Rubber.

There are two important questions that may be asked. The first asks whether there exists a practical technology for producing the material with either solar or atomic energy, while the second enquires into the possibility of effecting major savings in energy requirements for their manufacture. If, for any commodity, the answers are negative for both questions, then the possibility of substitutes needs to be investigated. If none were available, severe constraints and dislocations would be imposed upon world society, general risks would markedly increase, and the future would be much less predictable. The disappearance of one of these commodities without replacement might actually lead to the decline of our civilization. The technological discussion is thus forced to range widely, and yet be brief, and so it will presume that descriptions of present technology and the terms applied to the various pieces of equipment to be found in a good encyclopedia are available to the reader, and proceed from there.

An important example is that of cement, where the inputs for the current process are coal, clay, lime, and some power for grinding. In some factories natural gas has been substituted for coal, so that methane produced via photosynthesis would permit the present cement-making process to be used indefinitely. The cost of fuel per unit of cement, however, would multiply 2 to 5 times. This would have a chain of repercussions. Cement prices before shipment would increase 15 to 50%, while concrete costs might be expected to rise 2 to 10%, and roads and buildings employing concrete would often show a slight cost increase due to this single factor.

Thus far no one has been able to envision any means of transferring energy *directly* from an atomic reactor to a kiln—without creating radioactive cement. The cheapest *indirect* means appears to be that of generating electricity and preparing the cement in an electric furnace. Such a process would not yield cheaper cement and the energy expended would, if anything, be greater than with methane.

The principal economies to be realized in concrete do not appear in manufacture but in use. The increasing cost of cement would put greater emphasis upon more economical forms, pre-stressing, and more carefully prepared aggregates. The consumer could thus get better service out of less cement with no real increase in cost.

An even more critical instance is that of steel, the material from which most machines are constructed. Iron and steel depend almost completely upon the availability of coking coal. But coking coal is the scarcest of the fossil fuels, and, outside of America, will hardly last a century at the present rate of exploitation. Will some other process of steel making be evolved, or will there need to be some ersatz material found, either for machine building or for coke?

Much research aimed at finding substitutes for metallurgical coke is already underway. The Scandinavians have developed methods for introducing electric power so that 300 kg of coke per metric ton of steel is displaced by 2500 kwhr—a rather inefficient interchange from an energy-using point of view. Many European and Asiatic metallurgical trusts are currently exploring means for preparing coke-like substances from lower-grade coals. None of these substitutes promises to be thermally as efficient as the present open-hearth and blast furnaces when using good coke. However, by enriching the air blast with oxygen, and carefully choosing from among low-grade coals those that contain convenient impurities, the new "low-shaft" blast furnaces now being developed in Western Europe may make by-products such as cement and alumina. Thus part of the costs ordinarily born by pig-iron making may be defrayed by these other outputs. Also the smaller-scale deposits of ore and coal, not hitherto worth while, may be exploited by other new small-scale furnaces at reasonable cost (Economic Commission for Europe, 1954). Actually these recent proposals only postpone the crisis to a day when fossil fuels as a group can no longer supply the steel industry, a situation which must be faced certainly in less than two centuries.

It is possible that the long-term iron and steel picture might revert to an historical pattern and ore reduction will again depend upon charcoal. However the annual yield, even from greatly expanded forest areas (see Fig. 4), would require that the world supply of ferrous metals be reduced to somewhere in the range of 10^7 to 10^8 tons per year as compared to the present rather inadequate level of 2×10^8 tons per year. This would be a real limitation for machine building, because ferrous alloys are the most adaptable of all metal compositions and have behind them millions of man-years of accumulated experience and experimentation. A world in which steel was as scarce as copper would be hard to visualize, and quite impossible to plan for at present. Since the cost of accomplishing many essential tasks would be quite extravagant, it would also very likely be a poor or a depopulated world.

The best hope for sufficient iron and steel is a speculative one since the processes are still in an early stage of development. (See Fig. 20.) In this process hydrogen and small quantities of electricity would serve as a substitute for coke. The physical chemistry governing the process suggests that at the same time some substantial energy savings, as compared to present methods, are possible. It appears also that a fully instrumented continuous-flow process could be designed which, if feasible, should reduce capital costs. Ingots or powder with low carbon content, suitable for many kinds of alloying, would be the normal products. Both now command a considerable premium on the open market.

The principal raw materials, hydrogen and magnetite iron ore, have not been manufactured on this large a scale before, but both are well-known in the chemical and metallurgical industries. The most economical synthesis of hydrogen in prospect employs low-grade coal (it could also be methane) and pure oxygen with steam. At a later stage the hydrogen may be obtained indirectly from solar energy by a hydrogen fermentation process or it may come from atomic power via electrolysis. Because of its abnormally low weight-to-volume ratio, hydrogen is not cheaply transported, even by pipe line. Therefore, the magnetite will tend to move to the hydrogen source, even if this necessitates the transformation of lower-grade iron ores into magnetite by roasting. Much of the relevant technology is now being worked out as a by-product of the large-scale studies on the beneficiation of iron ore.

When this new steel-making process, or some equivalent one that is able to exploit the same potential thermal economies, will come into large-scale use is problematical. Developments come along slowly in this area of technology, so it is likely to take at least several decades— if it comes at all.

The Iron Age could come to an end by having some other metal, such as aluminum or titanium, or another material, such as fiberglass-plastic laminates, displace iron from its pre-eminent position. Each of these materials anticipates much larger markets than at present because each of them has special properties that have not been fully exploited yet. To become dominant, however, the new material must be cheap enough

INPUTS:

    HYDROGEN - *700 - 800 m²*

    POWER - *550 - 650 k w h*

    IRON ORE - *2 1/2 - 3 1/2 tons*

    HEAT - *5 - 10 x 10⁵ calories at 1560°C*

    CAPITAL - *$250 - 350*

PROCESS:

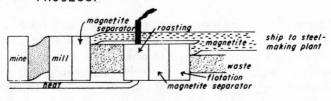

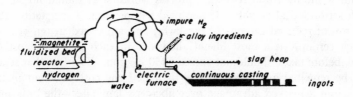

OUTPUTS:

    LOW CARBON STEEL INGOTS - *1.0 metric ton*

    IMPURE HYDROGEN - *100 - 200 m²*

    WASTE MILLED ROCK - *1 - 2 tons*

    HEAVY SLAG - *0.1 - 0.2 tons*

FIG. 20. STEEL BY HYDROGEN REDUCTION, CHARACTERISTICS OF A
CONTINUOUS-FLOW PROCESS

A view of what present technological experiments and scientific knowledge suggest
can be the future means for manufacturing steel without coking coal. The hydrogen
can be obtained either 1) as a by-product of other industrial processes, 2) combining
steam, oxygen and low-grade coal, or 3) combining oxygen with wet vegetation. The
net cost of steel by this route should not be exorbitant as compared to prices during
periods of steel scarcity today.

to fill most of the "general purpose" requirements for a medium of construction. Can these candidates become as cheap, on a volume basis, as iron?

Aluminum aspires, but is held back by the large quantities of power (20 kwhr per kg) that are needed to reduce the ore. (See Table 10.) With the 1 to 2¢ per kwhr projected earlier for atomic power, it will be seen that the cost of aluminum would rise from $400 per metric ton to $500 or $600. Since aluminum has a density only half that of iron, it might displace iron only if the latter's cost rose above $250 per metric ton.

Titanium technology is still more of a promise than a fulfillment. If titanium is eventually extracted from the ore as efficiently as aluminum (its chemistry is complex enough to make this a highly optimistic assumption), about 15 kwhr per kg would be required, leading to an ultimate cost ranging between $400 and $600 per ton. Titanium has a density which would make it competitive with steel at upwards of $250 per ton. Titanium has a reputation for being tougher and less easily worked than steel.

But if the hydrogen reduction process works, steel should not reach such astronomical heights. If one paid $40 per ton of magnetite, $80 per ton of reduced carbon, 2¢ per kwhr, and amortized in ten years— which certainly is a most liberal allowance in each case—the cost of steel, before taxes, should not exceed $150 per ton. The fact that scrap can be remelted and recast at less than half the cost of virgin metal gives iron a marked advantage over fiberglass laminates—the only material that might eventually meet it on a volume-to-volume cost comparison. In fiberglass laminates, as with titanium, the technology has hardly begun to develop so one can make only very qualitative judgments at this time.

One might conclude then, with the qualifications stated earlier, that the Iron Age is here to stay. It is a geochemically efficient feature of human technics that deserves to live on into an era of fuel stringency.

For all the common *nonferrous metals*, except aluminum, magnesium, and titanium, the problem of the future is that of the depletion of ore reserves. These nonferrous metals provide many special properties of matter that would be exceedingly inconvenient for an industrial society to forego. Yet the world faces the prospect of going to lower- and lower-grade deposits so that each successive ton requires a larger input of capital and energy. It is hard to tell when the cost would become exorbitant, but a straightforward extrapolation of trends indicates that such a time should come eventually, and for some metals, such as lead and nickel, at a time in the not-too-distant future.

The work of the geochemists offers a possible way out of the difficulty. They have found that many of the very common rocks and shales have small quantities of a large variety of elements, not far different from the average composition of the earth's crust. (See Table 9.) The proposed solution is therefore a large multiproduct metallurgical facility aimed at utilizing all the desirable constituents in the rock. The uranium and thorium in such rock are sufficient to energize the whole operation and probably would leave a considerable surplus of power for transmission to nearby cities. The unused portion (70 to 95% of the whole) would be dumped in the form of slurry into the nearest convenient hole. Thus the best location for such a metallurgical facility would be at the seaside where marine salt would serve as a convenient source of chemicals used in extracting the useful elements from the rock, and the bottom of the sea would be a suitable resting place for the waste. Until recently the commercial separation of the various metals would have been considered to be fantastically expensive, but the development of ion-exchange and hydrogen-reduction techniques in the last few years has changed the economic picture. It is impossible to establish the cost of any single product when such an integrated process is used, but it does appear that no essential nonferrous metal will become unreasonably expensive.

These huge multiproduct metallurgical plants would very likely be settled first upon the larger expanses of mineralized sediments and the shale deposits. As such sources become depleted, granite would gradually become the predominant raw material. The limestones, sandstones, and basalts usually have too low a proportion of uranium and thorium to establish self-energized extraction. If such processing were to proceed to its ultimate conclusion, perhaps a third or so of the land mass would be consumed and levelled. The essential metals and chemical raw materials could be assured for 10^6 to 10^7 years—assuming around 10^7 Cal per capita per year were to be expended for approximately the present population of the earth. By that time man should have contrived methods for depending completely upon solar energy.

Very few difficulties can be foreseen for the other essential materials of construction. *Glass and ceramics* can be adjusted quite easily to the use of methane as a fuel, or the adaptation of an electric furnace. Costs would increase markedly, but so would precision; therefore, it is quite possible that glass and ceramics will serve a still larger market in the future than at present. Brick and tile will exhibit still greater cost increases and therefore may easily give ground to cheaper materials, such as stabilized earth building blocks, or to superior products, such as laminated sewerage piping. *Fabrics* are already rapidly becoming synthetic. The raw materials, now largely coal tar and petroleum, must change, but this is not a difficult problem to solve. Chemical technology in this area is highly flexible, so that substitutes are possible at every stage in the process, and are usually introduced with no marked increases in cost. This flexibility is now taken for granted by chemical technologists and they point to their successes with synthetic *rubber* as an example of what might be done within a few years. In 1940 the world's rubber was almost entirely natural in origin, the synthetic being very expensive and inferior in quality for most purposes. By 1950 almost half the rubber capacity was synthetic, the quality was approximately equivalent, and the price was less. Rubber may now be synthesized from coal, oil, wood, molasses, or natural latex with barely noticeable changes in the cost or quality of rubber products as a result of a change in raw materials source.

For *paper* the picture is somewhat different because its price is still based in part upon the exhaustion of a resource that later will need to be conserved. However if paper ever reached a price level twice that of the present (now $150 to $180 per ton) many substitutes with potentially unlimited supply would appear. Bagasse and straw would certainly be used extensively, as would many more of the hardwoods.

Thus a quick survey of the essential materials of construction suggests that the world may manage quite well without the fossil fuels. Adequate technical solutions do not yet exist for steel production, or the various nonmetals, but the underlying fundamental science indicates that satisfactory solutions are quite feasible. Except for electrometallurgical materials, the costs should not change markedly. Although twentieth-century technology is based upon coal, oil, and gas it appears flexible enough to shift to solar and atomic sources without real strain.

Now it appears that even electrometallurgical materials will profit enough from economies of scale that their prices should not rise significantly over the long run. The improved ferrous technology is settling upon variants of the process that was illustrated in places like Mexico and Venezuela. Paper is not likely to become too scarce because fertilized forest plantations have been shown to be almost economic.

In the future the feasibility of precise quality control will often determine the choice of material of construction. Thus plastics may eventually displace much of the cement, plaster, brick, and lumber in housing because color, acoustic properties, reflectivity, density, and other properties can be controlled.

7. Moving People and Goods

Perhaps the greatest change brought about by this shift in major energy sources must occur in the conceptions of the engineer. Removing the coal mine and the oil-and-gas field as a locational factor for energy use and industrial operations permits a more systematic approach to the integration of facilities. At the same time it deprives the contemporary engineer of many rules of thumb which have been the mainstay of the profession when forced to make decisions upon complex matters. Very likely the most drastic reconsideration must be given to transport, since it is precisely this area of technology that has been most gluttonous in its demands for energy and for capital equipment.

In a contemporary society which manages to provide a relatively adequate standard of living, somewhere between 10 and 20% of all energy is expended for transport purposes. An equal amount, roughly, is used for manufacturing the equipment designed to meet transport needs. Altogether somewhere between 25 and 40% of all energy is committed one way or another to transport. A reasonable allocation in the future will depend greatly upon the distribution of population over space and upon how long the user of transport can afford to wait before he arrives at his destination.

There are two contrasting services in transport that permit separate treatment—the heavy duty, main-line movement and the local feeder or distribution services. The characteristics of the main-line facilities—double track railroads, cross-country pipe lines, overland trucking, intercity bus lines, scheduled deep water shipping, and major air routes—are already fairly well elaborated and in them have been sunk large quantities of capital. This fact means that change can proceed very slowly in partly developed and developed areas and that most of the changes would involve adaptations of existing equipment to new costs for energy and labor. On the main-line facilities the design effort would be devoted to improving safety, saving labor, and reducing friction in the operating equipment. The last provision results in a direct reduction in fuel consumption. Friction can be reduced, for instance, by shipping over water routes wherever possible, or by improving the bearings and the lubrication of moving parts. On the other hand *local transport* must serve the customer and consumer more directly; therefore, convenience has tended to have priority over energy savings. Changes in this type of equipment now occurring seldom stress fuel economy even though increases in fuel costs have already begun. It is comfort, flexibility of function, and time saving that are the most important features of the new designs. Nevertheless, a few innovations are appearing that promise substantial energy savings. The Italians, for instance, are pioneering with an immensely popular line of low-powered equipment as well suited to suburban living in a pleasant climate as anything hitherto provided, but at a much lower cost. The Swiss have more recently developed a gyrobus, which converts electrical energy into the energy of rotation inherent in a spinning flywheel at passenger interchange points and operates independent of wires for some miles between these points. This would be a more suitable solution for feeder lines in more rigorous climates. Delivery vans, small boats, helicopters and small planes, automobiles, and other representatives of this group all require lighter liquid fuels, and would be dependent upon the existence of a fuel synthesis industry, either from fossil fuels or from solar energy.

Satisfactory energy sources for most main-line transport are more easily provided, even for the long-term future. The electric railway is very efficient for heavy passenger and freight movements but still a heavy current user; therefore, power-producing atomic piles can enter into the land transport picture. Similarly in the transfer of large volumes of gases, liquids, or finely dispersed solids, pipe lines with electrically operated pumping stations, provide an economical solution. In the movement of sand, crushed rock, and low-grade ores, belt lines powered by electrical motors may become the best alternative. Indeed, wherever industrial activities are intense, and the population is distributed in metropolitan densities, electrification of main-line movements appears to be advantageous.

However, many countries have yet to create this level of industrial activity and general mobility of population. For them some intermediate stage is required. In order to meet this need a diesel-electric rubber-tired train has been developed. It can go wherever there is a road or a bulldozed trail, and use any terminus with ordinary roads and streets. As traffic increases, railroads or highways may enter the picture. Here again the diesel affords the greatest energy economies for locomotives, railroads, trucks, and buses. In a developing economy, therefore, one finds economical and flexible main-line systems must depend upon liquid fuels, but generally diesel fuel rather than kerosene or gasoline as for the feeder services.

Systems for local movement and feeder lines, if planned from the beginning of the period of economic development, do not necessarily become large gasoline consumers. Costs of local movement can be much reduced by the grouping of buildings in small clusters on, or adjacent to, the main transport routes. This permits a balanced dispersal of human activities. For moving the short distances required within a cluster of structures, or between neighboring ones, the possibility of human-powered conveyances, such as bicycles, pedicabs, handcarts, and wheelbarrows should not be ignored. For a city lying on flat land in an equable climate these solutions with an Oriental flavor are more likely to be economical than any employing liquid fuels. There is another two-fold saving involved: first, the streets do not have to be constructed so as to bear heavy burdens, which means thinner surfacing with less reinforcement and maintenance, and second, the lighter vehicles require less metal and metal-working in their fabrication. The over-all savings made possible by the use of lightweight vehicles are so considerable it seems very likely that the preferred materials of construction for the vehicles would be the light metals, such as aluminum and magnesium, and reinforced plastics, expensive as this may appear at first glance.

Thus qualitative considerations alone, the sum of current technological experiences, suggest that a much wider set of alternatives are open to a society ready to begin its development soon than have ever existed before. If the fossil fuel supply for such a society is secure the preferred pattern for the evolution of transport would probably not differ greatly from what is known, but if the primary dependence is to be upon atomic power then quite a novel pattern could emerge. In either instance there would be a general tendency to use energy more efficiently, but an assessment of the specific effects will depend upon the quantitative cost relationships.

In order to measure true thermal efficiency some over-all method of energy accounting must be applied. It must start from the source, such as amine, oil pool, or sunlight, and determine the energy loss with each transfer through space and each transformation up to the point of use. The techniques of energy accounting or energy-balance estimates are well understood and often used by engineers for a single process or installation, but systems of national accounting have had to wait until the past few years to come into being. Thus they are still experimental and relatively crude. Widgery has worked out an historical analysis so as to arrive at an input-output table with six categories of input and seventeen outputs (see Ayres and Scarlott, 1952,

TABLE 17. TYPICAL ENERGY COSTS FOR TRANSPORT—1950

System and Equipment	Cal/ton-km *	Btu/ton-mile
Ship: ocean-going, 20,000 tons, bulk	22	60
Pipe line: petroleum	48	130
Pipe line: natural gas	2500	7000
Railroad: diesel locomotive, bulk	370	1000
Railroad: coal-steam, bulk	1500	4000
Highway: diesel truck—20 ton	650	1750
Highway: delivery truck—2 ton	2200	6000
Pathway: wheelbarrow—100 kg †	2000	5400

* These costs assume that the movement is over relatively flat terrain. For every hill 100-meters high the energy expenditure is roughly equal to three kilometers of movement on the level unless, as in some electric railways, energy is regenerated on the downgrade.

† Assuming 2000 extra calories of food are required per day for very heavy work and that a 100-kg burden can be delivered to a point 10 km distant. The previous items come from miscellaneous American sources.

Ch. 21), while Barnett (1952) has sought to extrapolate to 1965 using a somewhat more extensive set of outputs or end-uses for energy. Barnett demonstrates the quite interesting observation that, for the United States, the average energy expenditure per dollar of gross national product has been declining irregularly at the rate of about 1% per year since 1920. The prospects for improving thermal efficiency in railroads, power plants, and domestic heating should enable this trend to continue for at least another 20 years.

Applying these accounting methods to various means of transport, one can obtain the "energy-system efficiency" and thus have available averages for the efficiency at which each different portion of the transport system currently operates. (See Table 18.)

It is only when all the steps in extracting, processing, and using a fuel can be traced, that one can determine whether any one of several alternative transport schemes is the most efficient thermally. Some energy is spent in the course of removing a fuel from its source and bringing it to a refinery; more is lost in the course of processing to the rather narrow specifications of modern engines; upon being introduced into an engine relatively large quantities escape as low-grade heat; finally a fraction already translated to mechanical movement is lost to friction in the working of gears and bearings and the flexing of tires. Table 17 makes possible the comparison of various transport systems at their present state of development. It represents averages for a whole economy and therefore can only be used for broad long-range decisions of national policy. For any specific location engineers can follow the fuels

TABLE 18. ENERGY-SYSTEM EFFICIENCY FOR TRANSPORT (U.S., 1950)

Equipment	Process	Thermal Efficiency, %
Coal locomotive	Mine to engine to steam to motion	$96 \times 97 \times 7.5 = 7$
Gas turbine locomotive	Mine to engine to gas to motion	$96 \times 97 \times 17 = 16$
Oil-steam locomotive	Well to refinery to engine to steam to motion	$96 \times 97 \times 10 = 9$
Diesel-electric locomotive	Well to refinery to engine to current to motion	$96 \times 87 \times 97 \times 28 = 23$
Electric locomotive	Mine to station to current to motor to motion	$96 \times 87 \times 30 \times 95 \times 90 = 24$
Motor car	Well to refinery to car to engine to motion	$96 \times 87 \times 97 \times 21 \times 30 = 5$
Diesel ship	Well to refinery to bunker to engine to motion	$96 \times 87 \times 97 \times 30 = 25$
Aircraft	Well to refinery to plane to engine to motion	$96 \times 87 \times 97 \times 10 \times 90 = 7$
Pipe line	Well to station to engine to motion	$96 \times 30 \times 90 = 26$
Wheelbarrow	(Not provided for by this accounting)	Approx. 10

Principal source: Ayres and Scarlott (1952).

(The ultimate efficiency of any transport system is the product of the efficiencies of the separate stages by which the fuel is processed and consumed. Thus mining averages 96% efficient—another way of saying that 4% of the energy is used up in the course of the mining operation—while combustion averages 97% efficient. Each of the other steps has some equivalent efficiency. The ultimate efficiencies shown here are expressed in the form of a potential; it is that fraction of the total energy input which can be applied to the purposes of movement on the surface of the earth. The losses due to imperfect organization of transport are not included here. The table suggests that pipe lines and diesel ships should become much more useful as energy costs increase, and that the present coal locomotive would then very likely be scrapped.)

from source to use and determine respective energy-system efficiencies using marginal energy costs instead of average costs. In these circumstances there may be some occasions, but not very many, when steam engines or internal combustion engines are more efficient than Diesels or electric motors.

The real value of computing energy system efficiencies is quite simply stated. They suggest what specific adjustments may be expected to occur as energy becomes more expensive. Gasoline- and fuel-oil-powered vehicles would diminish rapidly in importance. Electric-powered vehicles, such as electric trains, would again be ascendant. If, as has already been anticipated, liquid fuels will become relatively more expensive than other sources of energy, then even the relatively efficient diesel would decline in importance. Electric motors, whose current was delivered from substations, and the as yet incompletely developed gas turbine, would become the prime sources of movement. The over-all increase in energy efficiency for a whole society during such revolutionary changes could be at least three-fold. But this is purely for movement, expressed as ton-miles or passenger-miles; it is the *operating* cost measured in terms of energy. A reduction in the energy cost of *manufacturing the equipment* used is problematical.

Perhaps even greater savings might be made in a region of almost invisible waste. The transport of people, it has been implicitly assumed here, should be organized so as to provide the opportunity for certain standards of convenience to all individuals at the lowest cost. Time, whether it is to be used for formal work, household chores, education, or leisure, has a value, to which may be attributed a money equivalent. The time used in movement is, for most purposes of living, a dead loss. It is a cost as much as the fare paid the conductor is a cost. Now how do the respective transport systems for the movement of passengers compare when a first approximation of the sum of these costs is made? For each society a table, such as that of Table 19, can be prepared from engineering and economic data and the relative costs can be computed.

For most societies the gross pattern revealed in Table 19 is likely to recur. The over-all costs for the bicycle and the motorscooter tend to be lower than for the other modes of movement. The urban electric railway system can become a more economical mode than any if the time lost waiting for trains can be reduced. This might be accomplished by a careful planning of routes and the use of forethought in the choice of sites for settlement and productive activities. In any society where time is valued at more than 10¢ per hour, walking becomes an expensive way of moving. Certainly an economy intent upon providing adequate comforts and conveniences cannot depend very much upon movement by foot, except for periods of leisure, because of costly reduction of availability for work. It is also evident that the cost of fuel energy (at 0.2 to 0.5¢ per 100 Cal) becomes an important share of over-all costs in only a few instances, so that doubling or trebling the costs of fuels should not seriously affect over-all cost relationships.

If one were to start afresh and devise a pattern of urban living that was both convenient for the resident and efficient in its energy con-

TABLE 19. TYPICAL COSTS FOR THE MOVEMENT OF PEOPLE

	Energy Expended, Cal/ pass.-mile *	Fares or Charges, cents/ pass.-mile	Avg. Speed, mph	Delay, % of trip	Time, $/hr †	Cost for Movement, cents/ pass.-mile ‡
Airplane	1500	5	300	30	1.00	5½
Helicopter (40 pass.)	2500	7(?)	100	30	1.00	8½
Train (inter-city)	100	4	50	10	0.80	6
Train (rapid transit)	100	2½	30	40	0.60	6
Private auto (2 pass.)	800	4½	35	20	0.60	6½
Bus (city)	100	2	20	40	0.40	5½
Motorscooter (1½ pass.)	200	1½	20	20	0.40	4
Bicycle §	25	¾	15	10	0.40	3¾
Walking §	100	1	2½	10	0.20	10

* These are bastardized units for the expression of costs, but they seem to convey meaning to a much wider audience than units more rationally contrived. The figures presented do not include energy costs for equipment and improvement of right of way.

† This is an imputed average value per hour of time lost in delay for the persons normally using the respective modes of conveyance. Because of apparent inconsistencies in human behavior the value of delay time is very difficult to measure.

‡ These totals take account of the value of time and cost of service under the conditions specified. Differences of $0.02 per mile are probably significant for decisions between alternative transport systems.

§ This is not only for the amortization of equipment, and the wearing out of shoe leather, but also for the calories of extra food consumed as shown in the first column. Starchy foods at $0.05 per 1000 Cal are adequate to meet this extra demand.

sumption, it would probably be linked by an arterial network of high-speed electric railways which hauled passengers by day and freight by night. A system of bicycles, carts, car-hire, and small delivery vans working out of each station would probably be the most effective means for local distribution. High population and commercial densities would exist around the stations while parks, gardens, and low-density residential areas would occupy the interstices. Such arrangements could match the over-all convenience of movement now enjoyed by middle-income Americans, but the cost would come to only a small fraction of that paid by Americans.

Wherever existing systems cannot be scrapped, but are overwhelmed by congestion, other arrangements may be introduced. For example, if a personal carry-around radio-telephone system existed it would become convenient to call taxis or other vehicles to whatever out of the way point persons happen to be stranded in a metropolitan area within a few minutes. By this means the special advantages provided by the private automobile can be obtained without troubling about the problems of parking or of maintenance. This is an example of the substitution of communications for transport. With long-range planning perhaps half the vehicles on the road can be eliminated—with no real reduction in living standards.

A new form of very high speed (up to 600 km/hr) transport is likely to be developed in the next two decades to substitute for aircraft. They would move in straight closed tubes, electrically powered, on air cushions. Energy expenditure per passenger-mile would probably drop somewhat but still remain comparatively high. The principal use would be the connection of urban centers in a megalopolis. [L. Lessing, *Fortune,* April 1965, 124 ff.]

8. MANUFACTURING

In order to establish the over-all effects upon industry of the using up of fossil fuels it is necessary to find a "normal pattern" for energy consumption. Because of the importance of international trade in manufactured products this is a relationship not easily discovered in the real world. Each economy has one or more specialisms; each is unique and therefore not readily classified or analyzed. This is as likely to be true in the more distant future as in the present or the immediate past.

The advantage one economy holds over another presently stems from cheap water power, mineral deposits, fertile soils, or merely the holdover of some past advantage which has not yet been obliterated by disaster. In the future foreseen here, the best deposits of fossil fuels and the richest veins will have already been exhausted, and the reservoirs behind the big dams will have filled with sediment, so that all economies will be dependent upon the low-grade resources that are quite uniformly distributed. Despite equalization of prospect on this account there remain important sources of differentiation that will very likely lead to a new distribution of specialisms. The cost of fresh water, the availability of wood, the degree of alternation between sun and shade, access to deep channels, and just plain flatness, these all provide conditions that some industries prize. Thus an unknown inhomogeneity in the distribution of industry is expected to replace one which is known.

The problem of water is a case in point. In small quantities, say a gallon or two per day, water is an absolute human necessity, but ready availability in or close to the household, where 10 to 100 gallons per day may be consumed, is a greatly appreciated convenience. Water use is more or less continuous, similar to the use of electric power, but the supply tends to be seasonal with wide random deviations. We can judge by pure inspection, with the aid of local studies, that in a few of its uses there are substitutes for fresh water; in many there exist simple ways of economizing; and in others there are possibilities for recycling and reusing water. Just how much of this is possible depends upon the place and the time. We cannot generalize about the quantities of extra water required for the areas of the world yet to be developed.

Nevertheless, water is known to be scarce in many parts of the world, even in a few places where annual rainfall is normally high. Water is scarce and expensive because energy must be supplied to move it about and important amounts of capital investment are required before it can be safely stored. For agriculture, the way it is carried on at the moment, the costs that can be borne are rather small—about 1 to 2¢ per ton. For the most intensive market gardening, and for hydroponics, perhaps as much as 5¢ per ton can be afforded in otherwise favorable circumstances. For manufacturing and household uses perhaps 10¢ per ton will not introduce excessive costs. The justification for the charges quoted is not scientific, nor is it based upon economic analysis, but the charges are cited only as an indicator of what are outer limits for important quantities of water in any part of the world today. Reviews of rainfall and topographical data suggest that many populated parts of the world will be unable to meet such targets by the customary means of storing and pumping the accumulated precipitation. What alternatives are open to these areas?

It has always been possible to "manufacture" fresh water by distillation from sea water or brine, but hitherto the processes could not be considered useful outside of the laboratory and few isolated campsites. The invention of compression distillation during the last war, and its recent improvements, have made possible large-scale installations at Aden and Kuwait in Arabia, where whole cities and large oil refineries depend upon the output.

Still in the research stage are some interesting processes that promise to be more economical in their energy consumption. Most of these processes have been reviewed very simply and in remarkable detail in a recent book *Fresh Water from the Ocean* (Ellis, 1954). It is particularly useful because it evaluates the various approaches in terms of very large-scale desalting operations, sufficient to meet the daily requirements of a city the size of New York, a feature very seldom taken up in current technical publications. The conclusions are that electrodialysis, a "sieve" process that uses ionized plastic films as charged net membranes to separate the salt from the water (employing a mode of action similar to that evolved by living cells), should be somewhat cheaper than solar stills and compression distillation in most locations. Electrodialysis is expected to require 3 to 8 kwhr per ton of fresh potable water and an estimated $150 capital investment for power and equipment for a ton-day capacity. Simple solar stills, based upon plastic membrane rather than glass, would cost of the order of $300 per ton-day of capacity but have low power requirements. Compression stills require 13 to 18 kwhr per ton of water produced, have much more severe maintenance problems, and have an over-all capital investment cost in this same range. Reasonable estimates derived from this information suggest that the 10¢ per ton target is barely feasible. A recent resurvey by Gilliland (1955) suggests that freezing and remelting sea water may lead to techniques as cheap as this but the others are more likely to run 15 to 25¢ per ton.

If domestic and industrial water costs rise to this level then important new criteria are introduced regarding the energy requirements of industry and new factors for deciding where economic activities should be located. The "manufacturing" of water is tied to the waste heat obtained from other manufacturing, accessibility to very deep water, the sunniest of the weather, and many other aspects that are very local in character, but it could easily become the single largest power-consuming industry—one that hardly exists at all today.

One over-all approach to estimating the energy requirements of manufacturing might start with adding up all other foreseeable energy expenditures in a society, including cooking, lighting, home heating, transport, etc. Then assume that this sum makes up 50 to 75% of the total energy consumption for the society. The remainder would be the energy cost of manufacturing the equipment and the supplies to keep it operating. For the year 1947 in the United States the comparable figure for energy devoted to *nonmanufacturing activities* is 72%. There is an important force at work—the trend toward improving efficiency and performance of mass-produced machines—which suggest that the proportion of energy devoted to manufacturing should increase.

This is because the economizing trend calls for more precise components and material specifications. Accordingly a bit of energy is spent in additional manufacturing in order to save much more energy elsewhere. That is why the top estimate for over-all energy consumption would assume that eventually as much as 50% of the world's energy may need to be put into manufacturing.

There is a remote possibility of a counter trend developing—if urban patterns of living can be simplified. Much familiar equipment and structures, such as furniture, vehicles for local transport, city streets, etc., could become largely superfluous. There may be spatial arrangements for distributing people that would permit dispensing with an important share of the manufactured products normally considered essential for maintaining their comfort and convenience. (A more detailed discussion of such possibilities will be found in the following chapter.) If that were the case, a more appropriate estimate of the over-all supply of energy devoted to manufacturing would come to about a quarter of the whole.

But what about the disappearance of specialized products obtained from fossil fuels? The problem of metallurgical coke has already been dealt with in the earlier discussion of materials of construction. Perhaps the next most essential substances whose supply is threatened are the "light ends" from petroleum which have become the foremost resource requirement of the rapidly expanding petrochemicals industry. The output of this industry, in the form of plastics, fibers, rubbers, soaps, solvents, paints, fertilizers, and even some food products, is now becoming essential to the efficient operation of a modern society. It is difficult to assemble a set of basic industries supplying fundamental industrial and human needs that do not require as inputs important quantities of these light hydrocarbon intermediates, and it could be done only by making important sacrifices in cost and quality. Two directions are open at the moment for resolving the difficulty, and very likely both will be used. One would emphasize the gradual evolution of a technology that converted cheap carbohydrates into chemical substances to be substituted for those now felt to be essential, as in the instance of nylon, which gradually moved from coal tar sources of raw material to petroleum chemicals and is now rapidly entering a stage where the principal dependence will be upon using the waste products of sugar and cereal processing. The other direction would lead toward the development of an efficient technical process for manufacturing acetylene, ethylene, and propylene from the methane and carbon dioxide that can be generated from solar-energy systems, as illustrated in Figures 13 and 14. Both directions are likely to develop through routine industrial research; therefore no crisis or special difficulty can be anticipated. Any product-by-product review suggests that the chemical industries will never be so firmly wedded to their raw materials as the iron and steel industry is to coke. Part of this flexibility is due to an increasing dependence upon electric power and low-pressure steam as sources of energy. Thus, if atomic power develops as expected, the gradual disappearance of the fossil fuels should not embarrass the chemical industry at all in its attempts to meet the reasonable demands of world development.

9. The Consequences of Fuel Changing

Analysis shows that contemporary fuels can be displaced for use after use, process after process, as the price increases, by new and relatively inexhaustible fuels. Thus, home heating may be one of the first applications to start undergoing such a transition, electric power may be intermediate, and cement manufacture one of the last—if we are to judge by the technology of the alternative processes and their inferred cost structures.

The research and development arms of the industry, foreseeing the inevitability of the transition, have ample time to work out a process or product design incorporating all the latest scientific achievements. The improvements are seldom worth while if fitted to old equipment that is being used up and worn out, but if new designs are expressly developed to take greatest advantage of the possible improvements, increases in efficiency at the time of transition might be quite abrupt. A spectacular example currently in progress is the substitution of Diesel-electric locomotives for steam types on American railroads where the over-all efficiency in energy use increases by more than a factor of three.

Parallel to the improvement in efficiency, when measured in terms of energy conservation, would be a several-fold increase in capital outlay. An atomic reactor, for instance, will cost from five to ten times more than the mine, boiler, and all intermediate equipment required to generate the same amount of energy from coal; a dependable solar-heating unit for a home may cost five times as much as an oil burner; mass algae culture might produce food with what is considered a reasonable capital outlay, but if the facilities were devoted instead to fuel production, then again the capital requirements would be surprisingly high as compared to present norms for natural gas. Therefore the manufacture of capital equipment and the effort required to put it in place are likely to become a much larger part of the economic activity in a future society than they are in any of the present societies.

Another predictable effect of future changes in energy sources is the marked reduction in labor requirements associated with the transition. Underground miners, most fuel distributors, and many manufacturing workers would disappear from the scene much as farm hands disappear as the mechanization of agriculture reaches the more advanced stages. Probably the major new source of employment would be in the service fields, but, in view of the large investment in capital equipment anticipated, construction would undoubtedly play a highly significant part. The kind of labor would also change, mainly from fatiguing work, such as mining, machine operation, or assembly, to machine tending and maintenance.

In the preceding pages an attempt was made to analyze the energy cost for various aspects of human comfort, and the conveniences that seem to be essential to continued comfort. This approach presupposes

TABLE 20. ENERGY COST RANGES EMPLOYING NEW TECHNOLOGIES

	Cal/yr per capita
Hot water and cooking *	1 to 5×10^5
Space heating	Up to 10^6
Light	10^5
Communications (paper & power)	10^5
Clothing, shoes, etc.	10^5
Misc. consumer goods	10^5
Water	Up to 3×10^5
Transport (persons & goods)	1 to 4×10^6
Manufacturing	0.4 to 4×10^6

* Except for space heating a good share of these energy uses are in the form of electric power, for which original calories would be almost three times as large as indicated. It appears that the *total* energy expenditure, excluding manufacturing for armaments, new investments, and most replacement of capital, would range between 3 and 8×10^6 Cal per yr per capita. This is not far different from what one would judge is now being spent for these categories in countries whose energy consumption is about 10^7 Cal per capita per yr. To be sure, the standards of comfort and convenience were set somewhat higher than is now being experienced in these countries, but this was generally in directions where the energy cost of additional comfort was small. Therefore, although changes in the efficiency of applying energy to relieving human needs are expected, the over-all effect is not spectacular. It would be quite surprising if an integrated economy could achieve this comfort status for an additional individual with less than half the expenditure of energy now used at the margin, even in parts of the tropics that may afford certain advantages in energy economy.

that, for a given society with given technics, there is a threshold (saturation) level of energy use for the achievement of the status of comfort. Beyond this threshold the expenditure of large amounts of effort and energy would yield small returns in the improvement of physiological comfort. Comfort and convenience were settled upon as measures of a minimum adequate standard of living solely because they were common properties of the human species. They constitute a quantitative denominator derived from recent scientific studies upon man which have yet to be used to any important degree in social thought. Perhaps the next step is to make complete measurements upon thousands of representative individuals in order to define the environments suited to comfort, and develop an index to denote the state of comfort for an individual at any given time. Something like this has been attempted for the subcategory encompassing thermal comfort, but some obstacles in the refined measurement were encountered (C. P. Yaglou in Newburgh, 1949). Such refinements are less significant in measuring total comfort, but then other difficulties may arise. A comfort index, combined with an attitude-survey measuring the security or insecurity felt about maintaining a satisfactory level of comfort, should be a better means of comparing standards of living than any developed to date.

Basically a standard of living can be judged only in terms of the values and traditions of a single culture. Thus in a climate where clothing is superfluous, as far as it is required for thermal comfort, it may still be a "necessity" because of the standards of decency and ritual that prevail, whereas a neighboring culture may tolerate its members' wearing any quantity or kind of clothing down to none at all. As the various societies in the world become informed about comfort and the most convenient means for achieving it, they are likely to redirect their productive effort, discarding many wasteful and unnecessary "necessities." After comfort has been achieved, energy can be expended without qualms in other directions, such as monuments, luxury, sport, the arts, etc.

This is, it must be admitted, only a materialistic view of human behavior. Psychologists will be quick to point out that masochistic behavior, where a person or group will consciously choose discomfort in order to gain honor, prestige, or some intellectual satisfaction, is also a prevalent kind of behavior. In fact, the prestige or satisfaction gained usually has its value set by the amount of pain and discomfort experienced. Such behavior, if it is not extreme, recognizes the universality and value of comfort but will reject it "for something better." The scientist and the engineer are not in a position to plan for such attitudes. Their task, at least at this point in time, is to provide the *opportunity* for all to achieve comfort, despite the exigencies of declining resources, so that each individual may have the freedom to choose between comfort, or, what is for him, some superior end.

The various subcategories of comfort and convenience have widely differing energy requirements. In order to establish a range of energy applicable to consumption on a world-wide scale, it is necessary to lay down some reasonable, but simplifying, assumptions about the organization of the societies that plan for and administrate the provision of all the basic needs and amenities. The first of these is that the population is tending to become predominantly urban in character, and that the amount of movement and communication required would therefore not be far different from what is experienced in cities today. Another is that the inefficiencies due to the retention of archaic cultural tradition have been largely discarded in the process of urbanization.

Over-all energy expectations remain much the same as before. Assessments of the information held in secrecy by governments and corporations were appraised with quite high accuracy, considering alternative arguments extant at that time. It is interesting to note that, despite the large sums spent recently in developing the desalinization technology, the prospective costs of fresh water have not improved. The lowest costs are now anticipated when such a plant is operated in concert with a large nuclear power plant located at water's edge. Waste water treatment technologies deserve much more thorough investigation than they have received.

Selected References

NEW ENERGY SOURCES

S. Fritz, "Solar Radiation on Sunny Days," *Heating and Ventilating*, **46**, p. 69 (1949).

S. Schurr and J. Marshak, *Economic Aspects of Atomic Power*, Princeton University Press, Princeton, 1949.

C. Beau and M. Nizery, "Industrial Utilization of the Differences of Temperature between the Deep and the Surface Waters of the Sea" (in French), presented at the Fourth World Power Conference, London, 1950.

T. G. N. Haldane and E. W. Golding, "Recent Developments in Large Scale Windpower Generation in Great Britain," presented at the Fourth World Power Conference, London, 1950.

H. C. Hottel, "The Engineering Utilization of Energy," *Proc. Am. Acad. Arts Sci.*, **79**, p. 319 (1951).

E. Ayres and C. A. Scarlott, *Energy Sources—The Wealth of the World*, McGraw-Hill Book Co., New York, 1952.

H. J. Barnett, "Energy Sources—Trends, Requirements," *Ind. Eng. Chem.*, **44**, p. 1228 (1952).

W. Isard and V. Whitney, *Atomic Power—An Economic and Social Analysis*, Blakiston, New York, 1952.

E. W. Golding, "Harnessing the Wind," *Discovery*, **14**, p. 373 (December 1953).

Palmer Putnam, *Energy in the Future*, D. Van Nostrand Co., New York, 1953.

——, "Power from Hot Water," *Beama J.*, **60**, p. 42 (1953).

M. L. Ghai, T. O. Bansal, and B. N. Kaul, *J. Sci. Ind. Research (India)*, **12A**, p. 165 (1953).

J. A. Lane, "Reducing Nuclear Power Costs," *Nucleonics*, **13**, p. 24 (1955).

D. M. Chapin, C. S. Fuller, and G. L. Pearson, "A New Silicon *p–n* Photocell for Converting Solar Radiation into Electrical Power," *J. Appl. Phys.*, **25**, p. 676 (1954).

S. McLain, "Nuclear Power Reactors," *Electrical Engineering*, **74**, p. 144 (1955).

H. B. Prince, "Silicon Solar Energy Converters," *J. Appl. Phys.*, **26**, p. 534 (1955).

H. B. Prince, *A Growth Survey of the Atomic Industry, 1955–1965*, Atomic Industrial Forum, New York, 1955.

DOMESTIC ENERGY UTILIZATION

E. F. DuBois and J. D. Hardy, "Basal Metabolism, Radiation, Convection and Evaporation . . . ," *J. Nutrition*, **15**, p. 477 (1938).

J. D. Hardy and G. F. Soderstrom, "Heat Loss from the Nude Body . . . ," *J. Nutrition*, **16**, p. 493 (1938).

H. C. Bazett, A. C. Burton, and A. P. Gagge, "A Practical System of Units for the Description of the Heat of Man with His Environment," *Science*, **94**, p. 428 (1941).

B. Rudofsky, *Are Clothes Modern?*, Paul Theobald, Chicago, 1947.

D. H. K. Lee and H. Lemons, "Clothing for the Global Man," *Geog. Rev.*, **39**, p. 181 (1949).

C. A. Mills, "Temperature Dominance over Human Life," *Science*, **110**, p. 267 (1949).

L. H. Newburgh, ed., *Physiology of Heat Regulation and the Science of Comfort*, Saunders, Philadelphia, 1949 (includes discussion of work of Sir Stanton Hicks, pp. 31–35).

C. E. A. Winslow and L. P. Herrington, *Temperature and Human Life*, Princeton University Press, Princeton, 1949.

H. H. Hausner, "Human Efficiency as a Function of Light and Illumination," *N.Y. Acad. Sci.*, **51**, p. 1166 (1950).

M. Telkes, "Review of Solar House Heating," *Heating and Ventilating*, **46**, p. 68 (Sept. 1949); "Low Cost Solar Heated House," *ibid.*, **47**, p. 72 (Aug. 1950).

K. Buettner, ". . . Effects of Temperature Changes on Skin . . . ," *J. Appl. Phys.*, **3**, p. 703 (1951).

G. S. Sharon, "Design Procedure for a Solar House," *Prog. Architecture*, **33**, Part I, p. 88 (Mar. 1952).

G. Conklin, "New Directions in Thermal Insulation," *Prog. Architecture*, **33**, Part I, p. 100 (May 1952).

H. L. Logan and A. W. Lange, "Evaluation of Visual Comfort Data," *Illum. Eng.,* **47,** p. 195 (1952).

C. A. Mills, ". . . Reflective Radiant Conditioning," *Heating, Piping, Air Conditioning,* **75,** p. 75 (Feb. 1952).

S. S. Stevens, item in *Science,* **121,** p. 124 (1955).

INDUSTRIAL ENERGY UTILIZATION

O. G. Specht and C. A. Zapffe, "The Low-Temperature Gaseous Reduction of Magnetite Ore to Sponge Iron," *Metals Technol.,* **13,** p. 1 (June 1946).

E. H. Atkin, "Turbojet Aircraft," *Mech. Eng.,* **73,** p. 791 (1951).

V. N. Ipatieff, G. S. Monroe and L. E. Fisher, "Low-Temperature Hydrogen Production," *Ind. Eng. Chem.,* **42,** p. 92 (1951).

R. L. Meier, "The Long-Term Prospects for Essential Minerals," *Bull. Atomic Scientists,* **7,** p. 214, see also p. 312 (1951).

W. G. Townley, "Turbojet Transports," *Mech. Eng.,* **73,** p. 787 (1951).

——, "Fluidized Reduction of Iron Ore," *Chem. Eng.,* **168** (Apr. 1952).

——, "Progress in Railway Mechanical Engineering," 1950–51, *Mech. Eng.,* **74,** p. 285 (1952).

O. L. L. Fitzwilliams, "The Giant Helicopter," *Am. Helicopter* (April–May 1952).

T. Vermeulen and N. K. Hiester, "Ion Exchange Chromatography of Trace Components—A Design by Theory," *Ind. Eng. Chem.,* **44,** p. 636 (1952).

W. F. Floyd and A. T. Welford, eds., *Fatigue,* The Ergonomics Research Society, H. K. Lewis, London, 1953.

M. Telkes, "Fresh Water from Seawater by Solar Distillation," *Ind. Eng. Chem.,* **45,** p. 1108 (1953).

H. Quastler and V. J. Wulff, "Human Performance in Information Transmission," unpublished MS, Control Systems Laboratory, University of Illinois, 1954.

W. F. Floyd and A. T. Welford, eds., *Human Factors in Equipment Design,* The Ergonomics Research Society, H. K. Lewis, London, 1954.

Economic Commission for Europe, "Some Important Developments during 1953 in Iron and Steel Technology," Geneva, 1954.

R. G. H. Watson, "Electrochemical Generation of Electricity," *Research,* **7,** p. 34 (1954).

C. B. Ellis, *Fresh Water from the Ocean,* Ronald Press, New York, 1954.

E. R. Gilliland, "Fresh Water for the Future," *Ind. Eng. Chem.,* **47,** p. 2410 (1955).

Chapter 4

NEW PATTERNS
OF LIVING

NEW FOODS and new sources of energy would, by themselves, require that a new mode of life be developed. However, there are at the same time many other important problems requiring solution, and other forces impinging upon the folkways. Some of these are related to the enigma of human reproduction; still others to the necessary relocation of people. But above all others is the task of revamping human institutions so that the opportunities presented by new technology can indeed be grasped.

These are largely social problems, since they deal primarily with interrelationships between human beings, and do not now involve materials or the man–machine interaction. Most people would instinctively exclude the scientist and the technologist in the search for solutions. Yet, in many instances, a social problem can be restated so that it is also a scientific or an engineering problem that is not only researchable, but soluble! Epidemics of some infectious diseases, for example, were once primarily such a social problem. If the analysis is accurate, the ensuing investigations successful, and the results put to use, the difficulty may disappear, just as most epidemic diseases have disappeared in the past half century.

Another more elaborate example of the restatement of a problem so that a technologist's tools become useful may be drawn from education—certainly as much a social process as any that can be imagined.

Often nowadays in a changing society, it is discovered that some rather complex information must be transferred rapidly to a large section of the population, but at the moment of crisis only a handful of persons possess this information. If the problem were to be solved by a purely social process, each of the informed persons would teach a handful. These groups would break up into individuals and they would bring together and teach new groups. This process would continue until the whole prescribed section of the population had been reached. Such a procedure is quite slow and requires a considerable amount of human effort. At the same time, garbling of the message—the so-called "rumor effect"—is probable. This could mean that the essential elements were not communicated as originally intended, but some other messages of an unpredictable nature were communicated. Prevention of garbling requires great discipline among the message carriers, and a much more involved human transmission system which incorporates several arrangements for making internal checks and corrections.

The communications technician would take a different tack. He would look for some economical means for transcribing the lesson into widely understood symbols and then use communication devices, such as printed publications, radio, film, or some other medium for conveying these symbols. The transcription would be pretested on a sample audience, so that one could have some confidence that the correct message would be conveyed. Such a system requires much less effort, and usually saves time, but one cannot be completely sure of its being understood because it is seldom feasible to provide a means for the recipients to talk back or ask questions for clarification. Nevertheless, under most conditions, this second solution would have a markedly higher probability of success. Communications technology has been developed over the past few decades to meet such social needs at lower cost, especially if the time allowed is short.

Thus the technicians can bring forward "solutions" to this and many other social problems. The real source of success, however, is in finding a formulation of the problem that permits use of some of the store of scientific knowledge that has accumulated so rapidly over the past few decades. Therefore the economic and social analysis in the pages to follow will not be along classical lines, but certain strands of argument will be picked up and followed solely because they appear to come into conjunction with some hitherto little known aspects of science and technology that may now be used for problem solving.

Educational communications have recently made extraordinary advances. Stimulated in part by national competition in the exploration of outer space (not envisaged as significant when the book went to press!), new methods of teaching mathematics and science were developed and diffused through the secondary school system. They are already transforming the educational systems of several developing countries (e.g., Formosa, Turkey, Greece), making it possible to borrow technological innovations at a much greater rate in the future.

Programmed instruction has been invented and improved. Its most significant impact has been in vocational education, but more radical changes will accompany increased access to computers. The behavioral sciences have now been firmly joined to communications technology, so that this combined domain has become the most fruitful source of "solutions" in social planning.

1. FACING THE MALTHUSIAN DILEMMA

The number of persons for whom to plan is a fundamental and inescapable factor in world development. At present it is apparent that there is more manpower available than can be successfully mobilized for developing the available resources. Thus we have the phenomenon of widespread underemployment in areas that are "underdeveloped." There are also more people living in many of these areas than can be supported at a decent level of living by applying techniques already known. This was demonstrated in Chapter 1. However, such a condition of population surplus need not be permanent—since the means for increasing food, energy, and raw materials production are already on the horizon.

How many persons can the earth sustain? One approach to determining maximum population is to complete a calculation begun earlier. It was demonstrated in Chapter 2 that the technology of microbiological food production should stretch sunlight and soil resources to the point where it is probable that they would be sufficient to feed 50 billions of persons. This would imply virtually continuous urbanization stretching over most of the flat portions of the world. A subsequent analysis of the minimum energy costs of comfortable urban living suggested that they could not fall far below an average of 10^7 Cal per person per year. If this quantity were to be drawn from sunlight at reasonable efficiencies, it turns out that one needs flat surface roughly the size of the Pacific Ocean to accommodate energy demands for 50 billion people. All the other requirements that can be put into physical terms are equally stupendous, but cannot be proved impossible. (The investment required, for instance, would be 10^2 to 10^3 times that of the U.S. today.) It is barely credible then that 50 billions can live moderately well on the planet, and that this number represents a practical saturation level.

At the current rate of growth it would not take long for the earth to become saturated with humanity. If the present 0.8 to 1.0% annual over-all increase were to be maintained, the elapsed period would only be three to four centuries. This assumes that the annual increase could be maintained in the face of regional shortages of materials and raw materials that now seem overwhelming.

Actually it is not the threat of 50 billions of persons that is so serious, because people would probably get used to the idea and its implications within a few generations, but the present *rates* at which various populations are growing. The demands of the new persons require virtually all the savings the growing society is able to muster, if even the minimum wants are to be met. Meeting these needs will bring most programs of economic improvement to a standstill, with net per capita increases in income remaining uncertain. There are likely to be many counterparts to the first Five Year Plan for India which only claimed that conditions should be no worse at the end of the period than they were in the beginning.

The present world population increase of 20 to 25 millions per year is fantastically expensive. In order to feed and clothe them we have to clear new land for crops, or improve the existing fields, and accelerate the depletion of resources. The capital required each year just to maintain these people *at the subsistence level* is estimated at close to $10 billion per year. Later it will be possible to judge what it would cost to maintain them at a minimum adequate standard of comfort and convenience, but it is already apparent that this sum is likely to exceed the total annual investment in the world today.

What these rough measures emphasize is that world development cannot proceed in an orderly fashion unless there is some form of social control over population increase. There are places in the world where this has come into being in recent times. Some societies have arrived at a population equilibrium with low birth rate and low death rate that has been maintained over several decades. Most of these are in northwestern Europe, or of that stock, so that the records of the social processes by which this stability in numbers came about have been accessible to researchers. From the investigations it is possible to draw some general conclusions about how they achieved this condition and have been able to continue it despite much local opposition stemming from religion and nationalism.

The improvement of public health and safety in these countries during the 19th century was accompanied by an acceleration of trade and manufacturing. Under these circumstances the population grew steadily, mainly because of a decline in the death rate while the birth rate remained virtually constant. The excess population, forced to migrate from overcrowded villages, went to the city or to new territory overseas. In the city new opportunities existed. The time of marriage, for many logical reasons, was advanced to a more mature age. Also children were an inconvenience in the cities of that period, and so primitive methods of contraception were brought into widespread use. Shortly after a social class became predominantly literate a gradual decrease in its birth rate was observable. This was true even of the agricultural areas that were brought into steady commercial contact with the cities. Another important factor tended to be the increasing independence, within the family unit, of the wife. It appears that wives, almost everywhere in the world, have quite consistently preferred fewer children than their husbands. Once they achieved literacy, and were permitted to hold down a responsible job, childbearing was often postponed. The depression of the '30's, with its loss of income and threat to social status, brought still more postponement of marriage and more carefully planned families.

Thus, in all cases where the new population stabilization was achieved, it was required that there be:

> Knowledge of some means of contraception
> At least one means available to each income level
> Diligent use of the method
> A high level of literacy or communication
> Opportunity for improving comfort
> A decline in the authority of the male in the family
> An urban, or urbanized, environment.

These are circumstances that can exist only if economic development has already proceeded a long way in that society. The world does not yet have an instance where a rural people with low levels of literacy, and with consumption at subsistence standards, has voluntarily taken up birth control and made a success of it.

The mass populations in Asia have expanded their villages to the saturation point without generating simultaneously a wave of education and economic opportunity in the cities with the vitality of the movements in Western Europe. One suspects that this was because they started later, the transition was more rapid, and the political dominance of the West delayed indigenous responses. However, whatever the reasons, these societies are now in a position where, in order for investment and resources development to accelerate, the drain on resources caused by population growth must be markedly reduced. Thus we are faced with a prerequisite for development that has no relevant precedent; unlike Europeans, these people need birth control before migration, before literacy, and before economic opportunity—while they are still absorbed in the tradition-directed routines of village life. China, India, Pakistan, Indonesia, Egypt, and the others cannot follow in the footsteps of Japan, because the latter's population has already exceeded the capacity of the local soils, fisheries, and mines by at least 25%. The rest of the world does not have that much surplus to spare.

It appears from this line of argument that the most useful research that would contribute to the solution of the population problem relates to the functioning of the family in various village cultures. Is there some simple inexpensive means whereby both the concept and practice of birth control can be introduced into such an imperturbable ritual-oriented institution as the rural family?

Sociologists and demographers have begun such studies (Taeuber, 1951; Chandrasekhar, 1953) in recent years. They find that the two or three child family is an ideal held by most women, and often by the men as well. These views are held privately, often in contradiction to the established mores of the culture, but they are operative only as wishes that exist without mode of fulfillment. By the time their families are complete, twice this number are likely to survive. Under such conditions the over-all numbers will increase by more than 2% per annum. Investigators have found that the idea of birth control is almost everywhere present, even in the most primitive societies. It may take the form of an herb concoction, a charm, or a vaginal plug, or lead to abortion and infanticide. None of those means is sufficiently effective in agricultural communities; indeed they are seldom applied at all until the size of the family has become impossible to support. Thus the scattered evidence available suggests that there is hope of introducing a truly worth while contraceptive into the rural family, once it became available and convenient.

Among demographers and sociologists faced with this problem there has been some wishful speculation too. The ideal solution, they felt, was a small pill that produced temporary sterility. It must be nontoxic, have no undesirable side effects, and have only trifling cost. It must not lose its potency through age, heat, humidity, or exposure to air. In other words, it should be as simple in its application as taking aspirin. Such a drug, most of them feel confident, could be rather quickly (that is, over the span of one generation) introduced into rural villages, if that were the object of a carefully planned campaign. In Puerto Rico 89% of the poorest wives said they would be willing to use such a pill (Hill, Bach, and Stycos, 1955).

Any drug that would embody such properties must be a rather unusual product. It would enable a control of human fertility by purely physiological means in contrast to the rather inconvenient and unesthetic methods available now. The nontoxic specification permits such a drug to be entrusted to a population without careful supervision and with minor demands upon scarce medically trained persons. It would not matter if news about the drug were conveyed by word of mouth, so long as it was accompanied by easily understood directions for its use.

In the pharmacopeia one finds a prodigious list of drugs, but there are very few entries that are considered to be potent, while at the same time so safe that they can be distributed openly and widely in chemist's shops, by pedlars of DDT, antimalarials, aspirin, and dextro-maltose, or even by coin-in-slot vending machines. Therefore, we might rightly enquire whether the synthesis and general availability of such compounds is not a wishful dream and whether there exist any concrete possibilities that it will come about. Why, if the birth control pill is at all feasible, hasn't some more expensive analog been already discovered that would point the way?

In the face of such questions one can only resort to the storehouses of relevant knowledge and experience, and search through them for relevant clues and suggestions. Fortunately, research of rather important dimensions has been accumulating in the area of human reproduction. The aim of these studies has been primarily that of settling questions about disease, disability, and their treatment. The physiology and biochemistry of reproduction are fields of investigation that should include the findings most relevant to the synthesis of a birth-control drug. They have advanced particularly rapidly in the past two decades and have tended to become still more relevant since much of the research has been taken up by the laboratories of the pharmaceutical companies.

If we should ask the questions of a medical scientist who is familiar with the present state of knowledge, how might he reply? He would know not only what is published, but would have contact with research groups who understand all the difficulties of acquiring knowledge and who are willing to report to a colleague the frustrations and tentative successes that never get recorded in the medical literature. His knowledge is tempered with experience, with sympathy, and with doubt. Very likely he would first outline the processes of human reproduction in such a fashion as to reveal the possible points at which such a drug may act in order to have the effect desired. He would look for steps in reproduction where a neat biochemical interposition or blockage seems possible. At certain stages there are regular transitions or changes which take place uniquely in a very few specialized cells. Then it seems quite possible that simple chemicals and simple interaction would be involved. Accordingly the incidental effects of the blocking drug upon surrounding cells would be minimal, giving rise to a real hope that its general toxicity would be low. He would very likely propose that the most vulnerable points in the human reproductive cycles are the following:

Maturation of the ovum
Ovulation
Secretion of female hormones
Action of hormones on the uterus
Early stages of embryonic development
Reduction-division of sperm progenitors
Physiological maturation of the sperm.

These points of action are not stated with precise scientific language so that for the specialist in this subject quite a bit of ambiguity remains. Besides, each specialist is likely to have a favorite to which he attributes greater promise than to the others. It is at this final stage that specialists tend to disagree. It is quite possible that the ultimate birth control drug may be a composite of several chemicals operating upon several sites simultaneously. This property would contribute to dependability of action of the pill, and thereby generate greater confidence in the users. Needless to say, the side effects should be so small that they do not modify, for physiological reasons, the sexual urge or behavior in more than a tiny fraction of the population.

Doctors and biological scientists are not the only persons who can help in the search for an adequate drug. Since the problem of unwanted children has been with the world since the race evolved, it is quite possible that, somewhere in dim history, an herb or natural product was found that had this effect. This would be the contribution of the explorer, the anthropologist, and the collector of ancient and native lore.

The contributions of social scientists and humanists have not provided any real solutions, but they have introduced the best leads that have been uncovered to date. Doctors, with their scientific training, were able to suggest administration of hormones, particularly progesterone, but this has some risk and may entail a cost of $5 to $20 per year for the raw materials alone, independent of distribution expense. The possibilities stemming from forgotten herbs and medicaments require more extensive description (Henshaw, 1953).

One very interesting line of research has been based upon the reported use of an herb called gromwell (*Lithospermum ruderale*, although the *officinale* species has also been shown to have this physiologic activity) by Shoshone squaws, apparently to prevent pregnancy during the strenuous treks from one waterhole to another in the dry season. An aqueous infusion of the carefully dried herb appeared to stop ovulation in mice with no observed ill effects. Very limited experiments upon humans suggest that there are no immediately detrimental side reactions or toxicities to deal with, but the dosage required (about 20 g of dried herb per day) is too large to be economical. Therefore the isolation and chemical identification of the active ingredient has been undertaken.

Another such herb is the field pea, *Pisum sativum*, which had had a similar reputation among some village women in India. It was found rather quickly that the active ingredient was concentrated in the oil fraction of the pea. Sanyal (1954) claims that the major effect is due to a simple chemical constituent, *m*-xylohydroquinone, which can be cheaply manufactured from petroleum chemicals. The first attempts to confirm Sanyal's scientific claims in a Western laboratory have not met with success. Nevertheless, the Western scientists feel that there is some ingredient in *Pisum sativum* that affects menstruation and, very likely, ovulation. It will take a great deal more scientific work to establish what it is and how it operates. Meanwhile Sanyal's collaborators have reported the use of *m*-xylohydroquinone pills by hundreds of native, poorly educated women in Calcutta (Ghosh and Gupta, 1954). The pills were taken at times equivalent to the 16th and 21st days of the standard menstrual cycle. Figures show that the fertility was reduced 50 to 70% in these preliminary studies. Such effectiveness, even if it were to be maintained over decades, is not sufficient. It seems very likely, for a variety of arguments, that once a contraceptive measure is used by poor people the reduction in birth should be 80 to 95%. If further experiments demonstrate that simple products from *Pisum sativum* are at all effective, then there are many suggestions in this Calcutta study for improving the effective use of the drug in an illiterate population.

Interestingly enough these two distinctly different threads of experience were shown to be rather closely related. Noble and Graham (1953) showed that chemicals like *m*-xylohydroquinone had a physiological action not unlike that obtained with *Lithospermum* extract. However, no hydroquinone ingredient could be extracted from *Lithospermum*.

These workers also obtained a slight activity with hesperidin, which recalled the controversy surrounding Sieve's paper (1952) on phosphorylated hesperidin, a natural product obtainable at low cost from processing citrus fruits. Sieve claimed a most remarkable effectiveness for pills that were already known to be nontoxic. They were to be taken with every meal as long as the woman wished to remain sterile. However Chang and Pincus (1953) tested the presumed mode of action of the drug and found that it did not hold for rabbits. In short, Sieve's claims could not be confirmed by other workers.

In quite a different direction, but still mainly in the area of applied social science, would be an exploitation of the possibilities of very cheap and easily prepared spermicides. These products might be made, for example, by fermentation of natural products to lactic acid mixtures, by making strongly saline jellies from rice flour, or by preparing foam tablets. It seems possible that a new trade could be created in the village that would be devoted primarily to the manufacture of such contraceptives. These crude preparations tend to spoil quickly in tropical conditions, and so they would have to be made afresh every few days by an artisan. The social innovation required for this approach to work at all would be the devising of a system for maintaining the quality of preparations; otherwise this method of achieving control of the size of families in the village is likely to encounter a number of failures followed by loss of confidence in the method. Quality control may involve creating an extensive inspection staff (this is the bureaucratic solution) or the confirmation of quality within the village by some spot test—this may mean that the testing procedure would be associated with the raising of small caged animals, such as rabbits, hamsters, or mice. Some relatively tradition-bound rural cultures can quite easily adopt a new craft, especially one that promises to keep family size close to historic levels, whereas they may not always look with favor upon the intrusions into family life required by other modes of birth control.

Sometimes the basic clue will not be found in old wives' tales, but in researches in quite a different area in biology. The nitrofurans, for instance, first became of interest because they had some remarkable bacteria-killing properties, but Nelson and Steinberger (1953) showed that they also induce temporary sterility in male mammals. Unpublished reports suggest that these compounds, along with others that are the object of general medical research, may halt the growth of the embryo. This particular use of drugs in birth control has very possibly been surreptitiously practised to some degree in the past few years, but they must be administered under the supervision of a medically trained person because the dose is expected to come close to the borderline of toxicity. Self-medication can very easily be harmful.

To this potential battery of pills might be added one or two more that would absolutely assure that the desired size of family was actually obtained, and unwanted children did not arrive on the scene. Drugs for bringing about early abortions are already fairly well-known. Previous objections of the medical profession to the use of abortion—based upon the possibility of infection—have recently been shown to be largely without foundation (Tietze, 1951). Abortion is safer than childbirth, both in primitive and developed areas. In Japan and Russia, and even in some Christian societies where it would on the surface appear ideologically reprehensible, abortion has been and may easily remain a preferred method of family limitation, at least as a line of secondary defense against surplus progeny. It is certainly no more drastic a solution than permanent sterilization of the wife, which has become a very popular method in Puerto Rico and parts of the Middle East.

This survey of the current state of knowledge suggests that doctors and scientists do not know very well where they stand in relation to the birth control needs of rural villages. It has not been possible to corroborate in other laboratories the most promising claims that have appeared. Controversy is rife about what has already been discovered. This is quite a common occurrence at the frontier of biological investigation. After some years of careful work the issues usually do get settled and the frontier moves on. The findings of the past few years that relate to this birth control field have been more encouraging than discouraging. An increasing amount of research is being initiated.

Let us suppose one or more such drugs were found, and investigators in various parts of the world agreed upon their physiological effectiveness. What would be the next steps? The first of these can be foreseen quite clearly. The first step would require large-scale pilot tests in typical populations which would be kept under very thorough medical scrutiny for years. These studies would be necessary in order to assure that there were no untoward physiological effects which are not detectable in short-range studies. The medical observations need to be accompanied by studies on the actual effectiveness of such drugs in reducing the number of unwanted children. Therefore statisticians and demographers will be necessary, because they have developed the techniques for measuring over-all changes in reproductive behavior. However, in order to obtain the most understanding from pilot tests of this kind, the people who are involved ought to be interviewed so that the motivations for using and not using contraceptives can be evaluated. The anthropologists, sociologists, and social psychologists all have worth while professional experience that would enable them to suggest methods for the new system of birth control that would be most reasonable for all concerned.

The shortage of social scientists and the lack of carefully detailed knowledge about the social consequences of similar innovations will make these pilot tests difficult to organize and slow to arrive at answers. There are thousands of competent doctors and biological scientists in the world, there are thousands more nurses and medical technicians, but there are only hundreds of statisticians, and only a few score sociologists, anthropologists, and social psychologists who are equally specialized and qualified. Yet the staff of such a pilot test would have to lean heavily upon social science.

The subsequent step in the introduction would lie almost wholly in the area of social science. If a given set of drugs was shown, in several independent pilot tests, to be economical, convenient, nontoxic, and otherwise acceptable, there still would remain the task of bringing the information to the attention of hundreds of millions of persons in the poorer strata of the world's population. Rapid introduction into a relatively agrarian society would require a program much more intensive and ingenious than has been applied to, say, public health activities, or nutrition, anywhere in the world.

It seems logical that the spread of birth control in some countries may best be assigned to the agencies responsible for public health. Thus, those professional workers that interfere with the equilibrium of births and deaths are encouraged to develop a professional skill in combining alternative techniques of life-saving and life-prevention in such a fashion that only moderate population disturbances occur in the course of transition, rather than the alarming four-fold to eight-fold expansions that have hitherto been experienced.

In order to acquire this knowledge and skill some rather large-scale social experiments will have to be carried out. Initially these experiments would be rather simple, and would probably be organized along the lines set forth by Ogburn (1953) for introducing the rhythm method of birth control. As the early information is accumulated, it will be apparent that the successful introduction will need to be either more rapid, or less demanding of scarce manpower and money—quite possibly all of these at once. Then, still more elaborate experiments will have to be designed and conducted that will perhaps bring the methods of disseminating effective information about birth control up to the standards required for population stabilization in backward rural areas. This process of experimentation must be repeated for each culture desiring to embark upon a program of economic improvement, just as each public health program has to be adapted to the biologic environment and cultural pattern of the region being covered.

On the whole the outlook for birth control is more cloudy and uncertain than any other element of science and technology which appears to be necessary for improving levels of living. It deserves much more attention than is being accorded it in the allocation of funds for research. The need for scientific and clinical investigations on the subject is rapidly coming to be understood, but it is seldom realized that the social researches must be on a much larger and more expensive scale than those falling within the scope of biology and medicine.

A nearly perfect "fertility valve," permitting control over exposure to conception at very low cost, has now been developed and tested. The intra-uterine device is greatly preferred over pills or other contraceptive methods, not only for reasons of cost but also convenience. Other cheap methods are being readied for the remainder. Large-scale social experiments have been conducted in Formosa, where the educational level of women was high and controls could be quite strict, and in Korea, India, Puerto Rico, etc. [*Studies in Family Planning*, No. 6, March 1965 (published by The Population Council, New York).]

2. Defining a Minimum Adequate
   Standard of Living

In some parts of the world, the preconditions to economic development will no doubt be met. The population there has not yet reached a level that prevents a steady accumulation of capital. Ways and means for meeting food and fuel needs are available. Foreign equipment and outside specialists can be imported whenever required. National integrity is secure enough so that long-range thinking is possible. Under these circumstances a systematic program for economic development can be formulated.

However, before this program can be fully outlined, some very searching questions must be asked. What is the principal aim of the effort? Whom does it intend to benefit? Will it proceed to enrich first those persons who hold economic and political power and then, by stages, allow the extra goods and services to trickle down to larger and larger classes of people? This scheme has many points in its favor, the main one being that it worked in Western Europe and North America without centralized co-ordination, and it is now working in the Soviet Union, but with strict controls and elaborate plans. Such a program might aim at maximizing output. An important fraction of the increases in output may go into armaments, or even into monuments, but economic development can still proceed.

In recent years there has been a strong reaction against this mode of thinking, so that quite a different aspiration is stressed. A new question is being asked. How can the most welfare (or the most general satisfaction or the most public benefit) be extracted from scarce resources in the least amount of time? There is another way of stating the question so that the answer can be more explicit. How can the whole population as quickly as possible reach an adequate standard of living? In practice one doesn't insist that each person reach this standard, but only that he have the choice of taking a job that pays that well or of staying with his traditional way of life.

If a feeling of adequacy can be achieved with much less resources, then, for a given expenditure, a larger number of persons can be brought up to adequate levels. This goal puts emphasis upon the conservation of resources at the point of consumption (hitherto conservation has almost always been discussed at the point of extraction or of processing). Such a formulation permits the introduction of the science of comfort and convenience, where principles of the latter, when joined to well-known principles for economizing, improve the efficiency of consumption.

What shall be considered an adequate level of living? Each society holds different ideas about what are justifiable expectations. Within each society these expectations vary greatly from one social class to another. Yet some visible, agreed-upon standard must be set so that the approximate long-run demand for goods and services can be estimated and the resources can be allocated in a reasonable fashion. Science helps in setting the standard because it offers facts as a means for settling differences in opinion concerning what is adequate; it also puts a premium upon consistency of attitudes.

The most common decisions in these matters occur by default. There is hardly ever any serious concentrated thinking on this problem. The standard is settled upon then by transferring piecemeal the patterns of consumption that have evolved in the more developed countries, rejecting those features that do not seem to fit the local way of thinking. Often it is resolved that the conspicuous benefits enjoyed by the privileged classes in the pre-industrial society are to be granted to all social classes. In this manner the modes for clothing, household furnishings, entertainment, diet, and many other aspects of the standard of living have become established.

The difficulty usually encountered in this borrowing process is that many points of view arise concerning what it is that other people have that is truly worth having oneself. It is impossible to establish, except through trial and error on a massive scale, what features of other peoples' standards are relevant to local needs and essential to the task of conserving resources. There is no simple means for achieving consistency or agreement in this domain of valuations, even among the experts, as long as such a chaotic and unsystematic approach to human ends is taken.

In an attempt at being less arbitrary, Seebohm Rowntree conducted studies in Great Britain in the years 1900, 1936, and 1950 which, among other things, attempted to establish a "poverty line." (See Fig. 21.) It is evident from his work that even the same investigator will modify his view of what constitutes a minimum adequate standard as the times change. In some cases the modification is in the direction of greater economy, e.g., the replacement of candles and oil lamps by electric lighting, or of greater convenience at no extra cost, e.g., cooking over gas instead of coal, but in a few instances there was clear gain, such as the availability of a radio set and compulsory health and unemployment insurance. He had the good fortune to make his observations during a period when the proportion of the persons living at or below the poverty line in the rather typical city of York was reduced from about 33% in 1899 to about 4% in 1950, and even less in the subsequent years. This progress may have justified his recent acceptance of

Dietary

	Breakfast	Dinner	Tea	Supper
Sunday	Tea, bacon, bread and dripping or margarine (or fried bread).	Stewed breast of mutton, with savoury balls, potatoes.	Tea, toasted teacakes, and margarine.	Hot milk (skimmed), bread and margarine or dripping, cheese.
Monday	Porridge and treacle, tea, bread and dripping or margarine, bacon.	Barley broth, boiled meat and potatoes.	Tea, bread and margarine, jam.	Brown bread and margarine or dripping, cheese, cocoa and milk (skimmed).
Tuesday	Porridge and milk (skimmed), tea, bread and dripping or margarine (or fried bread).	Broth reheated with dumplings, and bread.	Tea, brown bread and margarine, treacle.	Cocoa, bread and margarine or dripping, cheese.
Wednesday	Porridge and treacle, tea, bread and dripping or margarine, bacon.	Stewed liver, green peas (marrow-fats), mashed potatoes.	Tea, currant bread and margarine.	Cocoa, milk, bread, dripping, grilled herrings (2).
Thursday	Porridge and treacle, tea, bread and dripping (or fried bread).	Irish stew, rice and currant pudding (for children).	Tea, brown bread and margarine, treacle.	Bread and margarine or dripping, cheese, cocoa (half skimmed milk).
Friday	Tea, bread and dripping or margarine, bacon.	Lentil soup, fig pudding.	Tea, currant bread and margarine.	Cocoa, brown bread, stewed tripe and onions.
Saturday	Tea, bread and dripping or margarine, fried or baked herrings (3).	Boiled meat pudding, potatoes.	Tea, bread and margarine, jam.	Cocoa, brown bread, baked onions.

Dietary cost, at prevailing prices, family of five	15s 1d
Rent, 4½ rooms (about 900 sq ft)	6s —
Coal, 210 lb per week, yearly average	2s 6d
Clothing, for normal activities	5s —
Household sundries, candles, soap, utensils	1s 8d
Personal, newspapers, church, burial clubs, hair cuts, drugs, etc.	5s —
Total per week	35s 3d

FIG. 21

Source: B. S. Rowntree, *Human Needs of Labour*, Nelson, London, 1917.

somewhat higher standards of adequacy. He demonstrates also that the consumption levels of persons in the laboring classes do not get much above the minimum even today.

Parallel investigations were carried out in the United States in order to determine appropriate levels of public relief. The results of the Heller Committee of the University of California are representative of the more advanced thinking in the United States during the '30's. They take for granted that greater variety in diet and in personal sundries is "necessary," but do not include any charges for medical or dental service, unemployment insurance, burials, and other entries made in the Rowntree survey. It is interesting to note that the California minimum in 1936 cost $94 per month while that for the British, when converted into 1936 dollars, cost only about $30 to $35 per month for a family of five. (See Table 21.) Obviously there were considerable differences, both in price levels and in ideas regarding what was "decent," with the British valuing living space and privacy more highly but convenience, appearances, and mobility much less. Other social surveys have not served to clarify means for arriving at a consistent minimum adequate standard.

A recent book called *Standard of Living* (Pipping, 1953) tries to make this and much related material a central concept in economic theorizing. Pipping feels that it is not at all helpful to say that people maximize utility, where utility is so buried from sight it cannot be measured. What they actually appear to do is to achieve by one means or another a customary mode of living modified somewhat by new information available to them. This customary mode or standard is not necessarily that of the same social class in which the individual was reared but is very frequently associated with a somewhat higher station in life. Various components of a "standard of living" can be identified from interviews with individuals and groups (this may be carried out in much the same manner as some of the more advanced marketing research today) and indexes can be compiled purporting to measure standards of living. Pipping identifies four main elements in his standard of living:

> Activity—arrangements for working time and leisure
> Family—size, age structure, and interrelations
> Consumption—maintenance of social status and efficiency
> Saving—security and deferred consumption.

For conditions of equilibrium this synthesis of sociology and economics may not be amiss, but for conditions of economic growth and rapid cultural change it is quite inadequate. One of the strongest driving forces of economic improvement is a moral issue, that of social justice. It was this, for instance, that motivated Seebohm Rowntree to make his famous studies of poverty. In a generally accepted standard of living there is an element of "ought to be," where serious omission leads to scandal and to crusades for rapid improvement. If the situation cannot be altered the standard will be trimmed by stages to meet with reality.

In periods of rapid cultural change, standards tend to become chaotic. The customary modes of life to which individuals, groups, and classes refer tend to lose their meaning. Concepts of justice, fair play, and responsibility break down. Firm decisions cannot easily be made— today it appears as if it ought to be one way, tomorrow another. In these circumstances it seems worth while to have prepared and ready for acceptance a simply formulated standard that will stand up in the face of educated criticism and remain relatively unaffected by the waves of information about consumption which, it can be predicted, will pour into the society from outside its borders. Thus we need an approach to standards-setting in the developing society that has some stability over time and between cultures. It should be also, in conformance with ideas of justice, achievable by all citizens within a reasonable period of time.

The real contribution of the studies upon nutrition and other aspects of human physiology has been to establish what levels of consumption, sustained over a period of years, bring discomfort and impairment of function. More than that, new ways of achieving this long-run comfort at less cost are continually suggested by the results of the studies. By use of this part of natural science one is able to define what is downright excess and what is physiologically irrelevant, and can come to recognize the breadth of the boundary region that separates adequacy from inadequacy. This boundary region is the extent of uncertainty that stems both from differences between individuals, and from the unfinished state of the investigations. Advances have been made up to a point where a tentative *minimum adequate standard of living* (hereafter referred to in abbreviated form as the MASL) can be quickly prepared from scientific and technical data, and suitably adjusted to local institutions by the use of information from social and economic surveys.

But at what level of consumption should the MASL be set? Science and common sense suggest several pertinent criteria, which include:

Maintaining alertness and efficiency at industrial tasks
Providing for comfort up to the threshold
Developing sufficient conveniences to maintain that level of comfort
Using the cheapest commodities possible for meeting these requirements
Creating social services that bring awareness of available opportunities.

In effect this is comfort virtually equal to that at the American level. It is true that Americans spend profligately to advance their comfort and convenience, far more than other peoples probably could ever afford, but this spending is largely beyond the comfort threshold discussed in the foregoing chapter on new fuels, and for conveniences more imagined than real, so that there are insignificant and indeterminate additions to the totality of comfort or convenience. As will be seen, this level might be achieved, using excellent management and organization, for about 20% of the present per capita expenditures in the U.S. This desired level must be superior to that now experienced by the majority in Western Europe, because avoidable discomfort is quite apparent there, even to the extent that productive capacity is impaired.

It is only by drawing upon the body of accumulated scientific knowledge, and the objective approach, that one may hope to achieve substantial agreement about the *physical* requirements of a "good life." In the course of accepting science as an arbiter, rather than any one of the prevailing patterns of values, various disponents are forced to reassess their points of view in order to put them into verifiable from. Surveys, investigations, and experiments would then define more and more closely which commodities, and what quantities of them, need to be allocated in order to maintain a MASL. Thus the cost of the standard may be reduced, the inequities removed, and the over-all efficiency of the society employing the standard continuously advanced. It would meet more completely the needs of its members. Scientific method would then substitute in part for political compromise or strife—the only other means of resolving conflicts between values and interests.

The general aim of "at least a minimum adequate standard for all" can be much more than the goal of economic development. It can also be used as an instrument for the prevention of waste in the process of economic development. However, in order to demonstrate the strategic use of the MASL, the key factors normally limiting the growth of the poorer economies must be examined.

The most publicized difficulty of the typical underdeveloped economy is its limited capacity to accumulate capital. An annual rate of saving

TABLE 21. Minimum Adequate Budget for Five

Man Engaged in Sedentary Activities, His Wife, and Children
California, 1936

	Cost/month	% of Total Cost
Total	$94.80	100.0
Food	40.51	42.7
Man	8.75	9.2
Woman	8.75	9.2
Boy, 11 yr	8.80	9.3
Girl, 6 yr	7.19	7.6
Boy, 3 yr	7.02	7.4
Clothing	$11.81	12.5
Man, unemployed	2.24	2.4
Woman	3.14	3.3
Boy, 11 yr	2.69	2.8
Girl, 6 yr	2.07	2.2
Boy, 3 yr	1.67	1.8
Shelter	$31.37	33.1
Rent—5 rooms	22.50	23.7
House operation	6.83	7.2
Electricity	1.80	1.9
Gas—$1.72, plus $0.10 each for 5 persons	2.22	2.3
Wood and coal	1.63	1.7
Cleaning supplies—$0.26, plus $0.05 each for 5 persons	0.53	0.6
Stationery and postage	0.15	0.2
Garbage removal	0.50	0.5
Furnishings—$0.98, plus $0.20 each for 5 persons	2.04	2.2
Miscellaneous	$11.11	11.7
Care of the person	2.41	2.5
Cleaning supplies—$0.18 each for 5 persons	0.93	1.0
Shaving upkeep—man	0.08	0.1
Haircuts—2 adults @ $0.50, 1 child @ $0.40	1.40	1.5
Leisure-time activities	$4.71	5.0
Movies—2 adults @ $0.25, 2 children @ $0.11	0.72	0.8
Gifts, etc.—5 persons @ $0.08	0.41	0.4
Excursions—4 persons @ $0.20	0.80	0.8
Newspaper	0.75	0.8

TABLE 21. MINIMUM ADEQUATE BUDGET FOR FIVE (*Continued*)

Man Engaged in Sedentary Activities, His Wife, and Children
California, 1936

	Cost/month	% of Total Cost
Boy Scouts	$0.52	0.6
Spending money—2 children @ $0.22	0.44	0.5
Tobacco—man	1.07	1.1
Education—1 child @ $0.30, 1 child @ $0.08	0.39	0.4
Church—2 adults @ $0.21, 2 children @ $0.08	0.58	0.6
Carfare—mother for shopping	0.87	0.9
Incidentals—5 persons @ $0.43	2.15	2.3

Weekly food allowance for sedentary man or active woman:

	Price per Unit	Quantity	Cost
Bread	$0.083	4½ lbs	$0.374
Flour—white	0.047	¼	0.012
graham	0.064	¼	0.016
Rolled oats	0.060	¼	0.015
Macaroni	0.122	¼	0.030
Milk—evaporated	0.071	1½ cans	0.106
Potatoes—second quality	0.027	4 lbs	0.108
Beans—dried	0.075	½	0.038
Tomatoes—fresh or canned	0.045	1¾	0.079
Carrots—fresh	0.024	2	0.048
Cabbage	0.017	1	0.017
Lettuce	0.047	1 head	0.047
Other fresh vegetables	——	——	0.035
Oranges & other fresh fruit	——	1 to 1½ lbs	0.052
Prunes—small size, dried	0.066	⅛	0.008
Bacon—sliced	0.424	⅛	0.053
Butter	0.392	½	0.196
Lard and cooking oil	0.174	⅓	0.058
Sugar	0.051	1	0.051
Molasses	0.133	½	0.066
Meat	0.160	1¾	0.280
Cheese	0.265	¾	0.199
Coffee or tea	0.187 (or 0.716)	——	0.115
Sundries—add 1%			0.020

Total per week   Approx. 24 lb $2.02
    (for moderately heavy work add 4 lb of starchy foods and $0.20 per week)

Source: *Quantity and Cost Budgets, 1936*, Heller Committee for Research in Social Economics, University of California.

greater than 5% of the national income is unusual, whereas 15 to 30% would be required for a rapid rate of economic development. A large part of this difficulty is rather fundamental, because of conditions where often a majority of workers are barely making a subsistence, but an important part can be traced to inefficient consumption patterns in the upper income groups who may reasonably be expected to do most of the saving. Thus, if, from some accidental stimulus, the national income were markedly increased, it is highly probable that this would lead to an orgy of spending for land, luxury housing, automobiles, refrigerators, and other symbols of higher social status and wealth. Very little of the increment would be saved or invested. Also, whatever savings were accumulated would not be invested in enterprises and activities that would obtain the best return for the economy, but are more often committed to relatively unprofitable investments, such as gold bars, inventories of goods, or the heavy manufacturing installations that are monuments to nationalism.

In order to obtain conditions for the most rapid growth, all income beyond the necessities of life ought to be saved in order to be expended upon the capital goods and services most useful to a program for building up productivity as rapidly as possible. It is this summarizing statement of economic policy that suggests the basic usefulness of an explicitly defined minimum adequate standard of living (MASL). If the latter were to be set up as a practical wage and salary ceiling, instead of a desired wage floor as Rowntree and others had thought of it, with what remained being rationally allocated to investment, then the economic conditions required for a maximum rate of advance should be present. The problem of introducing new incentives to replace those usually depended upon will be taken up after some of the implications of this policy have been explored.

Self-denial and abstinence from luxurious consumption seem quite feasible in societies that have achieved political stability and have developed an elite group with rather puritanical standards—a not uncommon combination associated with rapid improvements in the level of living. It is very likely, however, that the general acceptance of frugality would have to be buttressed with the system of rationing and other more sophisticated measures that will be considered later. The major distinction between this approach to rapid economic development and historical methods is in income distribution, as shown in Fig. 22. It is proposed here that incomes should cluster closely around the MASL until virtually all persons have been rescued from the futility of scratch-

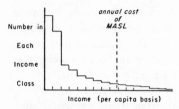

This is a typical income distribution for a very poor underdeveloped economy. A majority are living at subsistence levels. If the income beyond what it would cost to achieve the MASL were to be redistributed among the poorer classes only a very minor improvement could be obtained. If the society were to undergo a classical mode of economic development, similar to what has happened in Western countries and the U.S.S.R., income distribution would change roughly as indicated in the following diagrams:

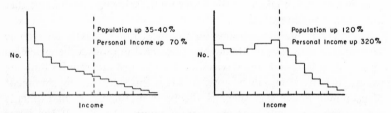

If the MASL were to be set as a virtual wage ceiling, as a part of development policy, then the mass production of "utility" goods should reduce their cost and also a new distribution of income would be brought about. The welfare position is obviously preferable.

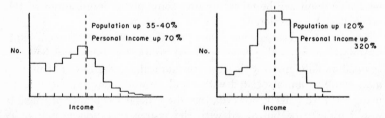

These diagrams assume strictly comparable conditions. Actually a necessary part of the new strategy would be the introduction of birth control to the areas living at subsistence levels. If this succeeds at all there should be a smaller population increase associated with any given increase in income than before, and also smaller numbers left in the lowest income classes.

Fig. 22.   Income Distributions for a New Development Strategy

ing a subsistence from a stubborn soil. When productivity has been raised to the point where all persons can participate in the new society, a more than minimum policy for consumption might be adopted.

Such policies not only appear to be efficient when judged in economic terms, but also they seem to fit quite closely to the equalitarian standards of social justice now being widely dispersed from their origins in European political theory. The callous display of wealth is deeply resented in any society that has abandoned fatalism but is still struggling with poverty; consumption to excess by a power-holding class serves as a ready target for protest and agitation. All the infectious ideologies, whether left, right, center, religio-mystic, or otherwise, take this to be one of the facts of the modern age. Therefore, the evolving political system in a developing society seems to require a "fair shares" strategy like this, if it is to survive and grow.

This discussion has left unanswered precisely how the sciences might be used to determine what should go into a minimum adequate standard. This involves assigning quantities to individuals that can be averaged over a population in a series of categories seemingly distinct but actually dependent at the periphery upon assignments to the other categories. Food for instance is a large item in the budget that has become rather simple because the study of nutrition has proceeded far enough to permit an adequate definition of requirements for almost each individual. Yet even the quantities of food made available are linked with the amount of heavy work, the dependence upon bicycle transport, and the participation in active sports. Clothing requirements are tied to weather, heating in the home, the kind of work, and other relatively objective factors. How much consumption might be modified by any factor can be the subject of factual investigation that can lead to relatively clear-cut decisions.

In the instance of shelter and permissible rents, however, an area of real controversy is encountered. The logical economic approach, from the point of view of those responsible for economic development, would be to provide just enough more living space, suitably equipped, to permit the adults to become dependable industrial workers. The Russians have shown that this aim can be achieved with roughly 3 to 4 square meters (30 to 40 sq ft) per capita, or three persons to a room, even in a harsh climate that prevents much living out of doors. The disadvantages and long-run diseconomies of this level of crowding are, however, readily apparent to their planners, and so the promise is made that the present overcrowding is a temporary condition which will be overcome in time.

Public health has been another criterion of what might determine adequate housing—a rising tuberculosis rate in the crowded parts of cities has been an index confirming suspicions derived from pure observation that the average slum dweller there had too much close contact with other humans and, therefore, very likely too little space. Unfortunately for this argument new therapies for tuberculosis and other diseases of congested areas have recently been introduced and they are bringing about a striking decline of incidence. Thus both the index and the associated arguments concerning public health must be discarded as being indecisive.

The designers of new housing usually approach the problem from the opposite direction. They have in the past adjusted their product to clients with higher than average standards of consumption and rather carefully developed esthetic sensibilities. The liberal use of space has become so much a part of their system of thought that a space allocation of much less than 20 square meters (215 sq ft) is felt to be substandard. If the designer should begin anew, starting from the demands of physiological comfort, patterns of family living, needs for contact with the larger culture (magazines, books, television, possibly telephone, bicycle, etc.), storage requirements, and other conveniences, he would develop from such data a series of most economical and suitable solutions. By going through this process of design several times for temperate and tropical climates it becomes apparent that 6 square meters per person, as a population average, ought to be sufficient living space for a home. Some of the further implications of such designs will be analyzed later.

A final group of costs in the MASL include police and fire protection, education, health, and social security. Their standards are much less subject to investigation and verification of adequacy. We know that these services are necessary to urban living, and we are quite sure that the levels of productivity required to make possible the MASL also require that a majority of the workers be urbanized. However, there are many ways of organizing an efficient city besides those that have been traditionally employed, so that it is much more difficult to arrive at reasonable figures that have general validity. Arguments based solely upon the comfort and convenience of the individuals fail to lead to any clear-cut indication of what would be reasonable. The standards suggested in Table 22 are based upon relevant experience, and appear to have internal consistency. It seems quite certain that the society implied by the standard is at least workable, but it may miscalculate what is a true minimum.

TABLE 22. A Minimum Adequate Standard of Living (MASL)

Characteristics of the Society and Area:
    Normal body weight—55 kg
    Population density—300 to 1500 per sq mile (1 to 5 persons per hectare)
    Climate—semitropical and humid
    Mineral resources—small and scattered
    Examples—Formosa, South China, South Brazil

Commodity	Quantity per Capita	Reasonable Retail Cost/ Unit, U.S. 1950	Annual Cost
Protein *	22 kg/yr	$ 1.00/kg	$ 22
Carbo-hydrate } 2500 Cal/day	Either 250 kg/yr } balanced	0.27/kg	65
Fat	or 110 kg/yr	0.55/kg	
Vegetables & fruits †	Complementary to above and according to tradition		15
Rent & furnishings ‡	6 sq meters	6.00/mo	72
Utilities			
Electric (cooking, lighting)	12 kwhr/mo	0.05/kwhr	7
Water §	2 to 3 tons/mo		2
Heat	None		—
Communications ‖	Shared telephone		5
Miscellaneous household	(flysprays, matches, utensils, bedding, etc.)		5
Apparel			
Clothing	5 kg cloth (up to 3 *clo* level)	2.50/kg	12½
Shoes	3 pairs sandals or equiv.	1.50	4½
Personal services			
Laundry	100/kg/yr	0.05/kg	5
Haircuts	15/yr	0.20	3
Local transport ¶	200 rides/yr	0.10	20
Newspapers	⅛ of 400 issues	0.03–0.05	3
Postage	30 letters	0.03	1
Misc.			3
Health			
Services **	(Enough to achieve life expectancy of 60 to 65 years)	4.00/yr	4
	(1 professional, 4 technicians, 4 common labor per 1000 persons)		
Equipment	1 bed/200 persons, etc.	50.00 investment	6
Medicinals & supplies			10
Education ††	6 to 10 years average schooling		
Teachers	7/1000 persons		3

TABLE 22.   A Minimum Adequate Standard of Living (MASL) (*Continued*)

Commodity	Quantity per Capita	Reasonable Retail Cost/ Unit, U.S. 1950	Annual Cost
Buildings & equipment		$50.00 investment	$ 6
Materials & supplies			5
Police, fire etc.	3/1000 persons		6
Social insurance	Disability, old age		20
Misc. social services	Nurseries, psychological clinics, etc.		10
Cultural activity, recreation etc.			20
Total cost ‡‡			$331

* Protein needs to be processed to a greater degree than other food stuffs in order to be made palatable and to be prevented from spoiling. This necessity leads to a much larger differential between the cost of production for protein and the retail price than for other foods.

† Fruits and vegetables would ordinarily bring the caloric level up to 2900 to 3000 Cal per day per capita. Perhaps 10% of this would be lost through spoilage, wastage, etc.

‡ The efficient use of such small amounts of living space requires that very little of the bulky type of furniture be employed. It also means that many household functions, such as baths and laundry, are carried out on a communal basis.

§ In densely populated areas, low levels of water consumption are necessary because it is difficult, or too expensive, to construct extensive water reservoirs. Some new water-conserving methods of sewage disposal will have to be worked out for these areas.

‖ Mass communications, such as radio or television, may quite possibly be necessary to rapid economic development. The power costs would be trivial, but equipment and programming costs might be considerable. The latter have been assigned to the categories of education and recreation.

¶ The level of transport expenditure presumes that most of the population is linked with interurban transport.

** The designation "professional persons" includes sanitary engineers and dentists in addition to doctors. It is now relatively inexpensive to achieve a 60 to 65 year average life span, but to go beyond this, the health services must cope with cancer and other degenerative diseases which require expensive surgery and much more hospital care.

†† This assumes two- or three-shift schooling at 3½ hours a day and eleven months a year. Children can be used for light productive activity the other half day.

‡‡ It is quite possible that some allowances have been over-liberal, and the miscellaneous or "catch-all" categories may be too small. Similar calculations made upon other populations and climates have led to costs of the MASL that are as much as 15% higher and lower than this figure.

Some warnings should be posted concerning the assumptions that lie behind the calculation of an MASL. The element of tradition cannot be ignored, particularly in the initial stages of development. This will appear on the account books as waste, or at best as a difference between what is "minimum adequate," as defined here, and what is "decent," as defined by the culture. Thus, if the MASL is to be applied as a wage ceiling, it cannot be applied too rigidly or it may meet with widespread objections.

Since very few persons are able to judge at what point their own consumption becomes excessive, an administrative mechanism must be worked out that will assure fair shares according to need. Individual eccentricities must be accommodated in a flexible fashion. The ultimate solutions may easily involve the circulation of several kinds of limited-use currency (or, in a more derogatory sense, negotiable ration-book coupons), in addition to a cash payment to cover miscellaneous items. Financial incentives can be retained through awarding increased allowances for services that require trivial expenditures of energy, capital, technical skill, or other scarce items in the economy. Thus a minor technician might spend his monthly allowance for cultural activities and services upon two sports events, several picture magazines, and a dance, while the executive's allowance might permit a play, some books, two parties, and several servants. A multiple-market system can be devised so as to give the consumer a fairly wide choice and a chance for variety in his consumption patterns. The same ends might be achieved by taxation policy, but usually such methods are less flexible (Dahl and Lindblom, 1953).

Such systems are not difficult to invent in theory, in view of the rationing experiences of the past fifteen years, but the efficient administration of an elaborate distribution system in an immature economy is far from easy. It may be necessary to begin with a rather crude system for maintaining the MASL as an effective income ceiling. An example is found in the Orient where civil servants have been given rice allowances and dwelling assignments depending upon size of family, in addition to a small stipend and some medical services. This device has often worked out very successfully. By its employment, the enforcement of the MASL as a rough maximum for consumption becomes more a matter of setting standards for shelter and community facilities and much less a procedure for controlling supplies and manipulating prices. (See Fig. 22.)

How much would the MASL cost in terms of capital investment? In order to answer this question the economist would naturally turn to the recent studies upon capital coefficients (capital per unit of output capacity), which are part of the effort leading to interindustry programming. Such figures are not very satisfactory for our purpose, however. Many of the industries represented operate on a forty-hour week, whereas in a rapidly developing economy capital equipment is too precious to be permitted to stand around idle. A two-shift or three-shift operation is far more probable, and so the capital per unit output in these industries may be reduced to about half of what it is in American industries at the moment. Continuous-flow services, such as power plants and waterworks, might average 70 to 80% of capacity instead of 50 to 60%. In many cases, too, the technology of fabrication is far more elaborate than is necessary, and so the capital coefficients would be much greater than is appropriate for a poor economy, which may in a few instances find a labor-intensive approach more suitable. On the other hand, there are some factors that tend to increase capital requirements as compared to contemporary experience. Modification of the existing American and European facilities so as to increase capacity is very often more economical than building altogether new plants as must be done in developing areas. The facilities required for producing extra food, water, and minerals in many of the poorer countries will encounter lower-grade resources, and therefore require more capital per unit of output. This, for instance, is one of the major problems facing Japan at the moment.

Great differences can be perceived between the capital investment patterns for the future and those that are used today. It is only by making a series of reasonable assumptions about the state of technology in the developed portions of an evolving society that any kind of an estimate can be made for the new pattern. This assessment is made in Table 23, where it is shown that one may expect that it will cost somewhere between $1800 and $3500 (in 1950 U.S. prices) to provide the facilities for maintaining a single person at the MASL. By using the same assumptions, the capital requirements for *subsistence* fall in the range of $250 to $500 per person. Any review of real situations in underdeveloped areas will suggest that *subsistence* ($30 to $100 per capita annual consumption, depending upon internal conditions) has marginal capital requirements over $250 per capita in most regions, and that it must be anticipated that capital requirements for bare survival

TABLE 23. CAPITAL REQUIREMENTS FOR THE MINIMUM
ADEQUATE STANDARD

	Amount per Capita	
	1953–4	1965
Food	$ 250–400 *	$ 200–300
Water	100–300	20–50
Clothing, shoes, & furnishings	50–100	30–50
Shelter	400–600 †	250–400
Community facilities	150–300 ‡	100–200
Transport	150–300 §	100–200
Communications	100–200	50–100
Energy sources & transformations	300–800 ‖	100–300
Other manufacturing & mining	300–500 ¶	100–300
	$1800–3500	$ 950–1900

* Marginal land and microbiological foods were rated at $100 to $150 invested per million original calories annual yield, and outlays for intermediate processing were rated at $1 invested per dollar of annual sales. About 10% was added to take care of fruits and low-calorie vegetables.

† Dwellings of concrete or rammed earth appear to be the most economical in tropical areas. By using careful design it appears that comfortable and convenient furnished quarters can be provided for $70 to $100 per square meter on either a mass-produced or self-built basis.

‡ Often health, educational, and recreational activities can be carried out in the same buildings. These activities may include such items as laundry and baths. As a result some rather economical solutions can be contrived.

§ This assumes that water transport would be used wherever possible, and that electric railway, small carts, and bicycles handle the bulk of the land transport. Buses and trucks would move people and goods in the intermediate distances, helicopters would work mainly in 100- to 500-mile high-priority cargo and passenger business, and planes would take on transcontinental and ocean passage.

‖ This broad range assumes that water power and fossil fuels will be exploited until their cost comes up to that of atomic power. This assumes that the MASL will require 5 to 7 $\times$ 10^5 Cal/yr.

¶ These societies will have much less heavy industry than North America, and so their outlays are accordingly much less.

ADDED FOR THE SECOND EDITION

The early figures were quite misleading since they applied the inflated capital equipment prices of the early 1950's to a relatively distant period when resource scarcities were being felt. At the time of publication many national plans were being constructed from capital-output ratios derived from traditional technologies. The figures cited above seemed much too high, and indeed they were.

Improvements in the outlook for capital savings in energy production, water processing (the discovery that nitrogen-fixing algae could be grown in seawater made a significant difference in calculations), and communications (aerospace technology helped here) were particularly marked. Thus a productivity of about $1200 per year per worker should sustain the MASL during development, a level that is about half that presently achieved in Western Europe.

will increase further. Thus roughly $1500 to $3000 additional investment must be found somewhere for the transfer of a single person from
subsistence to a minimum adequate standard.

From the calculations of capital requirements, and some feelings
about the rate of progress desired, it is possible to judge what should
be the standard of saving. The logic that can be used goes as follows:
It seems reasonable that each worker must sustain two dependents—a
not unlikely eventuality in a society where one's relatives have constituted the only social security (in Western societies with much smaller
proportions of children each worker supports one and one-half dependents). Thus the average worker must produce about $1000 worth of
goods and services, but at this level no contribution is made to the
accumulation of the capital that is used in his behalf and that of his
family. A productivity of $1200 to $1400 per year should be sufficient
to assure that the number of persons living at the MASL will double
each decade. Actually there would be a complex interaction, only
partially controllable, which may lead to further acceleration or to
dissipation of the development effort, depending upon social conditions.

At this continued rate of development it would take an impoverished,
resource-shy, densely populated country 50 to 80 years to provide the
MASL for all of its citizens—once the preconditions for economic development are met. This rate of growth of industrial production has
been experienced quite a few times in the past in the U.S., the U.S.S.R.,
Japan, and elsewhere, but seldom for more than two consecutive decades,
and usually not with the single aim of improving welfare. To complete
the transition from subsistence to adequacy in so short a period requires
that no political or economic setbacks, such as wars or worldwide depres-
sions, are experienced.

It has been demonstrated in Puerto Rico and some of the Southern
states that industries employing barely literate migrants from the rural
areas can reach these productivity levels within a year or two after starting up. Much more depends upon the quality of management than
upon the origins of the workers. It is in the entrepreneurial and managerial classes that the critical shortages and deficiencies will very likely
be most felt during the first several decades. The first generation raised
in the climate of a developing society experiencing the excitement, the
bustle, and the continuous changes, should be psychologically capable
of meeting the challenge, but until it comes of age the demands made
upon the judgment and acumen of the managers should be kept as
simple and straightforward as possible. The second generation, upon

working out the refinements, might find some means of sparking productivity up to levels not far from those exhibited in North America—when given equally good machinery.

The principle of applying practically all earnings above the MASL to capital investment programs has not been tried in practice. It has been considered here because it seems to be a psychologically sound procedure that leads to a very rapid, perhaps the most rapid, rate of development. It was chosen because it opens a method of analysis whereby scientific research on human welfare can directly and immediately affect the course of economic development. The normal processes for establishing the goals of scientific research and technical improvements and adopting the resulting innovations are much more involved and much less rational at present. They lead to large amounts of misdirected research and not inconsequential misuses of the efforts. By using the MASL as a practical ceiling for consumption, the scientists' and engineers' effort would be directed not at profits, nor at "the market" in the sense that it presently exists, but at the task of meeting human needs as efficiently as possible.

To economists, many of the foregoing arguments appear to have a "technocratic" tinge—referring to a popular movement in the '20's and '30's that adhered to rather oversimplified views of economic efficiency and distribution. But this similarity arises mainly from an attempt to find criteria of efficiency for the improvement of welfare that are meaningful for scientists. Somehow the units of utility must be translated into centimeter–gram-second units so that the scientist may grapple with them. The attempt here has centered upon a most general definition of comfort and convenience for the human organism that was translated into a "standard of living." This standard sets a production target for "necessities" which the applied scientist can work toward with quite elaborate strategies, because he can measure the *a priori* adequacy of various product substitutions (e.g., clothes for carbohydrates, bicycles for shoes, etc.). The scientist sees the more transient wants, which usually have a specific cultural orientation, as being much more in the nature of symbols representing authority, status, modernity, individuality, etc. Therefore, they seem to be more easily manipulated and, through the process of substitution, may be reduced to a minimum drain upon scarce natural resources. But how should this manipulation best occur? That is a task requiring the collaboration of economists and technologists. The idea suggested here drew upon experiences with rationing where it has been shown that the administrative techniques are workable. A dual market of this type can be used with such flexibility that the indirect costs or inefficiencies inherent in the approach are reduced. It is quite possible that better devices can be found that provide clearly formulated goals for long-range research and development aimed at the advance of human welfare, but very little study is being applied to the problem at the moment.

3. CHARACTERISTICS OF THE NEW URBANIZATION

Any formula for success for an impoverished mass society in its struggles to improve levels of living will call for a great deal of work. The necessary wealth must accumulate from decade after decade of hard productive labor. Yet such a society presently finds itself in a tight fix, even for making a start in this direction. There exists within its borders a large number of underemployed persons, while at the same time necessary tasks remain unmanned, and necessary products are not being manufactured. Some means must be found for obtaining 250 to 300 days of useful work per year out of that part of the labor force which is presently able to put in the equivalent of only a hundred or so.

The idea of "village development," a systematic program for raising community aspirations and getting people to work together to help themselves, has been originated to meet this challenge. The method has been brought to the point where it can be used as public policy (Aubrey, 1951). Nevertheless, the results that can be achieved are still far from adequate. Village development can increase over-all production by 50 to 100%, and in a few instances even more, but thus far there has been found no means for limiting the associated population increase; therefore, the net per capita improvement tends to be wiped out within two, possibly three, decades.

In the history of economic development one finds that village uplift has been followed by cottage industries, highly skilled crafts, and the exchange of specialties at the marketplace. This sequence is quite uncommon today because most of the products normally made in cottage-type industries and in village workshops are manufactured very cheaply for the world market by Western countries and Japan. A highly skilled laborer competing with the modern factory can seldom earn enough to survive. Even if he could make a living today the chances are excellent that his skill would become obsolete long before his working days were finished.

A modern counterpart to cottage industries has been developed in Japan, China, and elsewhere. There the manufacturing of such items as bicycles, electrical equipment, and toys has been sometimes organized on an extremely decentralized basis, so that each village may specialize in a single component or subassembly in addition to tending the crops in season. But then it is quality control that becomes critical. In modern times we have come to expect that each item produced should perform well wherever it can be used. This demand calls for careful design, precision, and a high standard of uniformity in the manufactured components. The market for substandard merchandise is declining. Only the Swiss have solved this problem of decentralized quality control, but even they have difficulty in maintaining quality in small village workshops.

These light and mobile industries, suitable for part-time work in the villages, are not numerous, nor will they provide a large share of the manufactured products required. Therefore, only those towns and hamlets lying along the main roads, or close to the centers of commerce, may be expected to participate in this pattern of industrialization. The remainder of the underemployed workers in the rural areas will have to move to the jobs, wherever they can be provided. If economic development is to proceed, many villages will gradually be depopulated to the point where there is enough productive work for those who remain.

The land itself needs the help of only a small fraction of those now residing upon it in order to bring forth its maximum bounty. The richer irrigated soils, capable of delivering two to three full crops per year, require perhaps 100 to 300 persons per square mile (40 to 120 per sq km). Compare this to the 500 to 1500 persons per square mile that already reside in the river delta areas of India, Indochina, Java, China, Egypt, and elsewhere. The excess will need to move—to the mines, the construction camps, and the cities. Eventually, it can be shown, 70 to 90% of the population will need to be urbanized. This movement looms in even more massive proportions when it is realized that the percentage refers not to present population, but to some future total very likely two to three times as large. Any long-range plan for development that does not recognize and deal with this tremendous redistribution of population is doomed from the start.

Is it possible to imagine the Indian subcontinent and China with 1 to 1½ billions of persons occupying each of them? The Nile valley with over 100 millions? Or tightly packed Java with an equal number? These are some of the expected consequences of economic development —even if better means of birth control are brought to the villages at the same time as public health measures. The cities, it will be readily seen, must expand and grow as cities have never expanded before. Towns, villages, and even whole provinces would be engulfed by urbanism. Any place that is flat, accessible to fresh water, and connected by rail or barge to the remainder of the economy has a good chance of being so utilized. The minimum adequate standard of living therefore must be designed primarily for the growing city, where improvement of efficiency must be the basis for all planning.

The pressure of population at some points will be so great it seems quite likely that a few of the cities will become quite huge. There are several ways of estimating their probable size; among them are (1) channeling the excess rural population along paths already well beaten by migrants and depositing them at locales already settled, (2) choosing the most suitable geographic sites for industrial and commercial activities and drawing the new workers to them, or (3) establishing a normal aggregation pattern for urban population according to city size (similar to Zipf's rank order relationship). All methods suggest a very strong pressure for at least some aggregations to become an order of magnitude greater than the metropolis—the population of the largest of these would be numbered in the tens of millions instead of mere millions. Thus, virtually continuous urbanism, extending for hundreds of miles, becomes quite a real possibility and merits careful appraisal. This is a completely neglected area in researches on urbanism. The city of the future built on a scale as grand as this will be called a megapolis.

The megapolis imposes special conditions upon the pattern of living that have never been faced before. What these are may be deduced in part from current problems facing metropolitan areas such as New York, London, Los Angeles, Tokyo, and Calcutta. Others arise from the utilization of new technology. Chief among the difficulties that can be anticipated are:

> Journey to work
> Perishable foodstuffs
> Movement of goods
> Disposal of wastes
> Water supplies
> Conflicting land use requirements
> Decay into slums
> Smog.

One of the most distressing features in the modern metropolis is the time consumed in the journey to work. Analysis shows, however, that much of this is primarily due to the archaic organization of our society.

Part of the discomfort and loss of leisure is a self-imposed price for living in a particular kind of suburban environment, and part is due to the inflexibility of our social institutions in scheduling their operations and hours. If the peaks in the flow were reduced by putting manufacturing, government services, and trade on a double shift, with perhaps a small interlocking midday shift, then the worst hardships would disappear. It would help even more if a third shift were to be devoted to the transfer of cargo. Thus the congestion which can be traced to the mixing of high-volume passenger traffic with slower-moving commercial shipments could be eliminated.

The number of intersections of paths tends to increase almost as the square of the population. Accidents, delay time, and expense are more directly related to these intersections of path than to the total passenger-miles or ton-miles moved. Thus an urban area ten times the size of Tokyo and environs might expect, other things being equal, traffic problems almost a hundred times as great—if this were physically possible. Drastic rationalizations are obviously called for; these are achieved principally by planning the occupancy of the land so that the paths can be conveniently merged into mainstreams of movement. Through locating the centers of highly organized activity, such as offices, factories, stores and schools, at the foot of the stream, and the densest concentration of dwellings of mobile residents adjacent to it, some reasonably efficient patterns can be mapped.

The most economic solution appears to be a network of electric railways. As indicated in the chapter on new fuels, the electric railway requires the least energy per passenger-mile or ton-mile. Although the first cost is high, intensive use of this equipment will lead to both minimum operating costs and the lowest over-all costs per person served.

Automotive traffic in trans-urban service should be strenuously avoided, except for unusual needs (e.g., cargoes with abnormal clearances, charter buses, ambulances, etc.). Not only are cars and trucks expensive to operate in an era of higher fuel costs, but also their routes are much more liable to become congested. Superhighways, which are often proposed to relieve automotive congestion, cost 10 to 20 times as much as a railroad of equal capacity. Thus they are far beyond the means of poorer areas.

A transport system is not complete until the provisions for getting the passenger to his door, or the goods to the consumer, have been settled. From an energy consumption point of view the bicycle is the best vehicle for local movement, but walking may often be more convenient. The capital cost is much less than for buses or automobiles, and the congestion problems are more simply dealt with. Similarly, goods may move cheaply from railway station or market to the consumer in handcarts, particularly those equipped with rubber tires and roller bearings. This solution seems at first glance a step backward rather than an improvement upon present metropolitan systems, but, as measured by performance, it can be shown to be vastly superior. Employing these simple, cheap systems for movement, along with a multiple shift system, permits one to allocate land uses for continuous urbanism that allow an average commuting time less than half that now experienced in London and New York. Twenty minutes average (one way) could be achieved and still allow for a reasonable amount of mismanagement and maldistribution.

The problem of perishable foodstuffs, particularly in the tropics, is mainly that of providing verminfree dry storage or expensive refrigeration if they cannot be consumed within a short period. The only economical solution is to insist that the large cities employ within their own boundaries all or many of the new technologies described in the previous chapter on new foods. Algal culture, hydroponics, fish farming, and very intensive gardening such as has already evolved in Japan and South China, could produce 90% of the bulk perishables (and perhaps 50 to 60% of the calories) within a few miles of the households. Cereals, fats, and sugar are easily brought in from the hinterland. The quantities involved (400 g or less than one pound per day per capita) seem quite negotiable, regardless of the scale of urbanism. The amount of food that can be produced is limited by the availability of sunlight per unit area. It is estimated at 15 to 30 tons (averaging 75% moisture content) per acre per year of marketable products. With consumption maintained close to the minimum adequate standard, one would be able to support 20,000 to 40,000 persons with a square mile devoted to the new technologies. After allowing for the land that must be allocated for dwellings, roads, services, amenities, and industries other than food, it is expected that the *top* population densities set by the need for very simple handling of perishable foodstuffs will be in the range of 15,000 to 25,000 persons per square mile averaged over a broad expanse of city.

The disposition of wastes and the supply of water bring up technical problems that are likely to set limits to the extent of continuous urbanism. Cities are prodigious water users (they use most of it to flush away human and industrial wastes) and so are often faced with creating reservoirs and collection basins hundreds of miles away. In many countries irrigation projects and the upriver cities have prior claim to the water but have grave problems in waste disposal, while the maritime cities find it difficult to acquire adequate supplies of pure water but can usually dilute their wastes in the sea.

Several kinds of solutions suggest themselves. One might be to circulate sea water for industrial cooling and waste disposal, conserving fresh water for drinking, washing, and gardening. Another might convert sea water to fresh water, particularly during dry seasons. It may often be more desirable to collect human wastes in some other manner, compost them, and return valuable nutrients to the gardens. As the city grows the costs will be determined less by the technology employed and more and more by local topography and climate. When, in the process of expansion, the costs of water and waste disposal soar far beyond the national average, then the approximate limits of that particular urbanism have been reached.

Most of the rules for an economic allocation of land in continuous urbanism are settled by choices of transport system, food distribution channels, and the solutions to problems of water supply and waste disposal. They must be adapted also to the geography and to the terrain. Other rules are set by the characteristics of the industries and will be discussed in greater detail later. Most heavy industries will want sites on navigable channels, while the somewhat lighter assembly plants will like good rail connections. Food production and processing units depending upon algal culture will prefer tidal flats or marshes. Atomic power plants and the associated power-using process industries need safe, dry central sites with a plentiful supply of cooling water.

Other recommendations are introduced by the planner, based upon past experiences with the decay of central portions of large cities. In order that orderly processes of slum clearance can quickly and effectively take hold 30 to 60 years after the initial building up, the planner will want to have some land in all parts of the urbanism committed to temporary or short-term uses. This adds flexibility to the process of growth because in a pinch the uncommitted area can be assigned, and other areas can be withdrawn from less productive activities to re-establish the strategic reserve. Then, when redevelopment is undertaken, there is some room to start the work. Redevelopment would be completed by making a series of shifts, each one opening up new space.

A hazard of large-scale urbanism that is just now coming to be understood is *smog*, a dense, choking pollution of the atmosphere combining dust, smoke, noxious gases, and fog. Whenever atmospheric conditions prevent the dispersal of airborne wastes for a few days, conditions become intensely disagreeable. Much of this trouble can be traced to inefficient combustion in auto engines, in fireplaces and furnaces, in trash burners, and in industries. The properties of the megapolis thus far outlined avoid many of the primary sources of contaminants, but the vast extent of the urbanism may call for more careful control of vapors and gases than has occurred to date. The precedents for such controls have already been set.

Into the network of intensive gardens, electric railways, and bicycle paths must be placed various foci of human activity. Some of these are interrelated complexes of heavy industry (e.g., ferrous metallurgy, light metals fabrication, inorganic chemicals, organic chemical synthesis, food processing, electrical equipment, shipbuilding, etc.); several are devoted to commerce (central shopping areas, wholesaling, raw materials allocation, warehousing, etc.); and several more are involved in governmental and private services (legislation, licensing, planning, public health, universities and trade schools, research and development, radio-television programming, insurance, credit, etc.). There are other, usually lighter, industries, such as garments, household equipment, building materials, printing, electronic assembly, and some kinds of food preservation that could be scattered throughout the urban area in a decentralized fashion. Much the same can be said for local shopping facilities, sports stadia, hospitals, and high schools.

The pattern of the megapolis begins now to take on the form of a web with several nuclei. The decentralized smaller-scale activities would be spread out along the strands. The local stations and minor intersections on the railways could be liberally sprinkled with small offices, workshops, and factories that could employ up to half the mobile workers quite close to home. Each nucleus, however, would be a metropolis in its own right, developing intense, organized politico–economic activity on the part of millions of persons. Each would come to provide large-scale employment for the white collar worker, the coverall worker, and the roustabout. These would not, except under rare circumstances, live in the nucleus itself, but ordinarily move daily between the garden areas and the place of employment. Between the nuclei, in the interstices of the web, one would expect to find concentrations of process industries or intensive agriculture.

There is a final test for a concept like continuous urbanism. It starts with a likely site and elaborates what steps must be taken over a period of time in order to establish a desirable pattern. Each step must be within the means of the society at that moment, its budget, its administrative effectiveness, and its constitutional guarantees. All scraps of information, whether they be geological, geographical, cultural, or social, must be taken into account. If, in such a step-by-step analysis of the evolution of an urban expanse, no impasse, critical difficulty, or insoluble bottleneck can be discovered, then plan-making becomes practical and worth while. This was done in a preliminary fashion for the Madras area in India, with the result that no foreseeable element of congestion arose that could not be dealt with economically. Indeed, the organizational pattern originated to meet the special problems of the very large city appears to be a remarkably satisfactory solution for cities in general in developing societies with populations of as few as a half million or so. Such cities could achieve levels of comfort and convenience superior to present Western cities with only a fraction of the investment hitherto made in facilities.

The social controls envisioned as shaping these patterns of urbanism do not differ substantially from those used in the Commonwealth of Puerto Rico. That island has a modern, democratic constitution, and is presently used by the United Nations as a training station for administrators of economic and social development.

The growth of cities has in the past also created very severe social problems. These problems cannot be solved with gadgets. They stem from the tremendous difference between the manner of living in the rural areas from which the migrants come and that in the crowded quarters in the city in which they normally congregate. The peasant and villager learned as children how to behave and what to expect of other people, but in the city these rules no longer operate consistently. The response of the migrant varies. Some of the bright and energetic ones learn how to improve their position, but without respect for the law. Thus gangsterism and petty larceny thrive. Others refuse to tolerate the difference and isolate themselves as much as possible from the life of the city. They do not learn the new language, nor do they take advantage of the various services provided to city dwellers. However, the children of such migrants cannot be isolated. They rebel, and a high juvenile delinquency rate is to be expected. Everyone becomes unhappy—children, parents, and the authorities whose duty it is to preserve law and order. Sometimes family life virtually disappears, with individuals living however they can. The majority adjust reasonably well, but almost every one of them when reviewing his experiences can recount instances of unnecessary misery, confusion, and hostility brought about by the abrupt change in environment.

Sociologists have investigated the adaptations made by migrants to the large city. They have followed many migrations, and traced the effects of city life upon family life, racial or ethnic conflict, outlawry, and the growth of slum conditions. Out of these studies no sweeping generalizations can be arrived at, but many typical patterns may be described. From their work it must be expected that continuous urbanism would suffer more intensely from these ills in the course of its growth than ordinary-sized cities have in the past, unless some measures were taken in advance to alleviate the condition.

Perhaps the simplest proposal is that of reducing the shock to the migrant, that institutional arrangements should be made which introduce him gradually into the life of the city, and make available useful niches for those who don't fully succeed in making the adjustment. It can be arranged that the ordinary migrant be settled in a neighborhood that spoke his own dialect, that made available familiar foodstuffs, and permitted him to organize his household along lines he already understands.

If, as asserted earlier, the new technology makes possible cities which grow most of their own food, then intensive gardening, which requires a large amount of labor, is a very suitable occupation for migrants. Equally effective employment for strangers to the city may be found in the less skilled aspects of construction work. The demand for artisan skills, however, is expected to decline precipitately, because distribution systems in an urban area are so much more efficient (they make available cheap manufactured goods that displace the products of the artisan). Among the young immigrants there is less commitment to the trade learned in the home village, and therefore less shock if this source of livelihood is lost. Nevertheless, the establishment of light industries close to his neighborhood might make use of the discipline associated with the practice of a trade, while the skill itself is abandoned.

The answer to this assortment of human problems associated with mass urbanization is to decant the waves of migrants from the rural hinterland into communities, which shall be called here "urban villages." They would be located along the transport lines leading into the growing metropolis. The clumps of these communities, located from 15 to 50 miles from the center of things, would serve as satellites initially but would finally merge with one another, and with the "old city," to form the web of urbanism previously labeled the *megapolis*.

As it can now be perceived, the urban village would start as a piece of scarred, flattened ground stretching away from a railway platform. The previous inhabitants were bought out so that at that time there would exist only the empty land, the marks for the location of streets, dwellings, schools, and bazaars, the half-buried water line, and the stationmaster's hut. At the station are left the first migrants (all of one language and principally from one locale) and the building-block molds with bags of cement by their side. The migrants, some of them with families and some without, live in makeshift shelters until their walls are up and the insulated roofing has also been dropped onto the platform. They are sustained by the regular flow of bags of rice and the first quick crops of vegetables which can be extracted from the open land. They are directed by a group of specialist technicians who show them how to lay a solid foundation, build up a neat reliable wall, cultivate a garden that uses water and sunlight to best advantage, dig sewerage, elect a responsible council, and a host of other activities essential to the development of the new community. With the first full-scale harvest comes a necessity for marketing, and therewith contacts with other urban villages and the urban nucleus nearby.

After the schools are built, the other social services installed, the techniques of gardening perfected, and some industrial and white-collar skills acquired, the productive basis for the minimum adequate standard of living will have been achieved. If the planning had been carefully done, the productivity of the community should be high enough to permit them to exchange their services on equal terms for what they consume. From that time on the main concern of the urban village is expected to be that of filling out its stock of domestic and community equipment. This would involve reorganization and reconstruction of facilities so as to achieve a higher productivity. Much of the resulting increase in production would go into the national exchequer for purposes of resource development, but a part would be used to increase the density of settlement up to whatever levels seem to be most economic in a highly organized society. This plan permits taking in a second wave of migrants from the country.

The urban village, as described here, serves a special economic purpose. It introduces the ambitious landless migrant to city life in such a manner that he would not get in the way of orderly circulation and physical growth of the urban area. At the same time he could quickly reach satisfactory levels of productivity. It is a device aimed at reducing the painful uncertainties associated with moving from a more or less stabilized folk culture to a terribly complex and confusing city. It should be a middle station between the rural village and the city which, it is hoped, would reduce the social costs of urbanization. Because of the vast rural-urban migration anticipated, most of the urban villages would have similar origins and developmental histories. Some of them, however, may be built more quickly with the existing pool of construction labor in order to provide decent shelter for minor civil servants and the more skilled industrial workers. For the exceptional cases, quite different patterns of development are to be expected—because their residents are mature enough to choose their own methods and, within a limited budget, create a community more suited to their special needs. An experiment in the direction of creating some of these more specialized communities is to be found in the new capital of Punjab, Chandigarh, in which plans were made for fifteen self-built subcommunities and ten others constructed for various income and status levels (Le Corbusier, 1953).

Initiating the redevelopment of the middle-aged urban village would coincide with the elaboration of metropolitan-type services in the urban nuclei. In the stages of most rapid growth and settlement such services can exist in only a skeletal condition, with many half-trained persons trying to serve as teachers, administrators, technicians, and organizers. Then a period ensues when quality becomes as important for the overall society as quantity. Each element of the hastily built structure is subjected to rationalizing procedures for the improvement of performance. Communications channels are perfected so that every literate individual shall be granted the opportunity to participate in the principal activities of the society. Over this rationalizing period the tempo of intellectual life quickens, taste change, and the long-range goals may be modified. It is useless to make plans now that extend beyond this period.

Within this setting of the urban village, it is possible to trace the implications of the minimum adequate standard of living as it affects the dwelling and the average (or standardized) family. It is the adequacy of the physiological comforts and convenience, in terms of time and effort required, that must be judged in conjunction with the respective costs of various alternative proposals for providing comfort and convenience. Here one encounters strong predispositions and points of view which reflect one's own experience and culture. They are not easily abandoned because this is a part of culture which is seldom challenged on rational grounds—they have been incorporated into our standards of decency and our esthetic sensibilities.

When considering the organization of shelter, the Western man must thoroughly divest himself from a middle class set of "ought-to-haves." Why, for instance, should roughly 20 square feet be allocated solely for one person's bed? If the bed were not so ponderous the space could be used for other purposes at least fifteen hours per day. Scientists have yet to make measurements determining whether reed mats, a most common Oriental solution, come up to the threshold of comfort. Most likely it will depend largely upon what one has become accustomed to. Foam rubber and similar vermin-resistant synthetic materials are potentially quite cheap. Pallets can be as comfortable as beds, but their cost runs to only a small fraction of what beds cost. If the floor tends to be drafty, then a hammock may be the solution. By using a bit of storage space one gains almost all of the 20 square feet for living space! There have been many improvisations in this direction, but a variety of well designed solutions that would suggest one or more approaches suited to any climate or culture has not yet appeared. It remains a challenge to the young architect and interior designer who is able to work with and use the findings of the physiologists.

Equally vexatious are chairs, divans, and tables. At the present time less than half the world sits on chairs as a matter of habit, and the dining table custom is still less common. Nothing in the physiology of man demands this equipment in order to achieve conveniently a comfortable relaxed state. Nevertheless if an advanced furniture-saving pattern of living has been achieved anywhere it would be by pure chance and not a matter of intent. The present trend in poorer areas is to discard elements of culture incompatible with popular Western standards. To become civilized is commonly felt to mean that one must be encumbered with such impedimenta. Yet it is quite possible to conceive of replacing these major furnishings by a low table with floor cushions or rugs in the Oriental fashion, again releasing much immobilized volume for multi-purpose living space (the table might be designed to be up-ended to keep the center of the room clear most of the time).

Such planning for the organization of interiors makes certain that the small rooms ordinarily associated with living at minimum standards are no longer a liability. The cluttered, cramped effect given to a modest house or apartment by cheap ramshackle furniture gives place to a simple, almost puritan dignity.

Among the most wasteful ideas invading the world today are the American concepts of the ideal kitchen and bathroom. They are dangerously wasteful because they lead to a squandering of energy and water resources that can only be sustained in North America. They are also highly prestigious—especially when propagated as "modern" culture in Hollywood films and the international editions of American magazines. The moneyed classes in most of the underdeveloped areas are already installing enamelled monstrosities. Soon the demand, whether achievable or not, will be found among the poorer classes. Unless something is done fairly soon they will come to feel deprived of the best things in life until they, too, can have a shiny all-electric kitchen and a pastel-colored plastic-tiled bathroom.

Convenient and economical substitutes depend upon the mode of cooking. A pattern based mainly upon the solar cooker, filling in with kerosene or charcoal on cloudy days, will differ in important respects from one based upon an electric hotplate. However, all the more complex kitchen functions, such as baking, roasting, and refrigeration, would be removed to a central point in the neighborhood in either case. It is probable that, for $100 to $150 cost, using mass-produced items, time-saving and effort-saving features can be at least as satisfactory as are obtained in any $1000 factory-made American kitchen.

The bathroom needs similar treatment. Many cultures presently have communal bathing traditions. When they are so economical such traditions are worth maintaining and reinforcing. Wherever water is scarce bathing facilities might best be combined at the neighborhood or community level with laundry facilities. The water closet needs redesign so that it uses less water, no water, or seawater, whichever is most economical in the locality. The washing and cleaning that remain to be carried out in the dwelling will probably center around the kitchen sink.

Very likely some new functions will have to be added to the dwelling which are only now beginning to be recognized. One of these might be a "communications nook," designed to meet the greater informational requirements of the societies of the future, particularly for the managers, scientists, civil servants, teachers, artists, skilled workers, technicians, and persons of similar responsibility. At the moment it is visualized as built around a cheap, yet-to-be-manufactured television set that is able to handle magnetic tapes that store messages and programs broadcast at inconvenient hours. Intercommunications provisions could probably be built in that would obviate the need for a private telephone. This sounds absurdly expensive now, but information-handling equipment is still in an era of rapidly declining costs and engineers are confident solutions can be found.

Such detailed considerations of what might go into a suitable design for the MASL can lead to radically different views about what a proper dwelling should be like. Designs based upon building blocks, which stem from the need for self-built housing for new migrants, have already been mentioned. Many experiments with this mode of community building are being carried out at the moment. As indicated earlier, such designs are likely to be predominant during the period of maximum growth. The descriptions of designs for colder climates using solar heating were presented earlier in the chapter on new fuels. They are more complicated and will require either some prefabrication or a fair amount of skilled construction labor.

Efficient housing for the skilled workers and professional classes will have a higher priority, and therefore much of it is likely to be constructed at an early stage using the pool of skilled construction labor. Some architects who have worked in the tropics, and have recognized the need there for ventilation and protection from solar radiation, might design for family living between horizontal concrete slabs with no walls separating the units from the out-of-doors or from each other. Privacy comes with carefully separated screens, and by pulling night shades up to head height from the floor. All surfaces would, of course, be sound absorbing in order to reduce the noisiness of open living at such close quarters. Other architects might go to another extreme and design air-conditioned concrete shell igloos in various sizes. These could be equally cheap to build and maintain if windows are eliminated and high efficiency fluorescent enamels were available for continuous illumination. (Presumably this would be justified on the theory that so large a proportion of the time will be spent at fluorescent screens it might be best to keep the eyes close to adjustment required!) It appears that any of these designs for dwellings, and of course many others equally diverse (even some styles approximating European and American traditions), may be acceptable solutions to the problems of economizing imposed by the minimum adequate standard of living. The basic point to be made is that, for purposes of design, the restraints imposed by accepting a minimum adequate standard of living still permit as astonishing a variety of solutions as are exhibited in world housing today. Both the mansion and the single-family bungalow would be out of place, but there remain sufficient alternative designs to prevent monotony in the cityscape. In the long run, if history is any guide, many will become esthetically acceptable, and even pointed to with pride and appreciation. But there are very few, if any, completed designs available now that fully satisfy the requirements.

Very likely a new international design esthetic is needed. It must provide variety with economy and extract beauty from simplicity. It would be applied to tasks ranging from the shaping of the smallest kitchen utensil to the layout of a billion-dollar urban center. Such a system for expression, which must grant equal value to beauty, utility, and cost, would have quite different emphases from those that operate today. The change can be stated as follows: rules for economizing, and for scientific and technical appropriateness, become criteria not subsidiary to, but equal with those of form, color, the flow of lines, and the use of space.

This mode of creation will take time to mature—probably several decades at a minimum. It is a challenge for serious, socially responsible artists, those who are willing to perceive and comprehend sets of ideas never before encompassed. Innovation in design and esthetics is normally subsidized to a much smaller degree than innovation in science or technology, so that it is here that a real deficiency may arise in the ensemble of techniques necessary to world development. The extra support and stimulus indicated should not be restricted to industrial and commercial design, although the criteria suggested are far more relevant for such activities, because experimentation might as easily take place in the purely decorative arts. From there the transition into interior design, apparel arts, architecture, film making, and verbal communication should be smooth and continuous so that conceptualizations in one field should quickly introduce new opportunities for pleasing variations into others.

ADDED FOR THE SECOND EDITION

The advances suggested above have been extended in later publications. [R. L. Meier, *India's Urban Future*, R. Turner, ed., University of California Press, Berkeley, 1962; and A *Communications Theory of Urban Growth*, The M.I.T. Press, Cambridge, 1962, Ch. 9.] In both instances solutions were proposed to foreseeable social problems of urbanization through the use of new systems of communications.

Very little new has been contributed to the long term issues of city-building through a direct attack on the problems. Developing cities can rarely afford even minimum systems of essential utilities, so that housing becomes ever more chaotic and decrepit due to overcrowding and neglect. The Puerto Rican formula now has several equivalents among partly developed countries, but the remainder cannot afford such standards.

Urbanizable space will be a serious problem in densely populated locales. Beginning in 1964 it became increasingly evident that floating structures (buoys of special design) were likely to become economic platforms for urban settlement. Therefore, some of the cities might well spill out into protected waters and even the high seas. The implications are very much worth exploring.

4. The New Industries

Because of the lack of sufficient resources, the industrialization of the remaining two thirds of the world cannot proceed in the same pattern as that which held for the first third. It has already been pointed out that quite new industries would be required, if an adequate standard of living is to be achieved everywhere on the globe.

The most significant of the industrial innovations which appear to be both ripe for development and essential for sustained progress are:

> Microbiological food
> Atomic power
> Steel by hydrogen reduction
> Fresh water from sea water
> Cheaper communications systems
> Fully rationalized construction methods.

Each of these has yet to come into existence, but it is possible already to discover, by imaginatively expanding upon experimental findings and current technical data, some outlines of the future.

Probably none of these can be more fascinating in its implications than the industrial complex that should eventually surround the microbiological food installations. In the beginning, an algae culture unit would occupy only a few hundred acres. In such sizes the by-products are of trivial value, and so little is likely to be done to conserve them. As demand increases and production experience is accumulated, the installations will expand to thousands of acres in extent and become almost fully automatic. The major material inputs are expected to be cooling water, perhaps fresh water, carbon dioxide, phosphates, and potash. The major output would be a wet protein-rich foodstuff, but there would also be important quantities of fertilizer solution ideal for hydroponics or irrigated market gardening, some electric energy during sunny days, natural gas, some sulfur and, in the long run, liquid fuels.

It is easy to see that several food-processing industries, especially those that shrink the weight or volume of the product while preparing it for consumption, are likely to settle down in the immediate vicinity. The intensive gardening going on alongside is likely to encourage still a wider variety of food-processing operations. Then, to service the food industries, container manufacturing would start. In order to use waste substrates from all the producers, as well as the high quality biological services created for them, antibiotics plants would open up. Alongside them, utilizing other wastes, might be ponds for the intensive culture of fish. In order to be close to the users of their product, spice and preservative specialists would set up shop in the neighborhood. Food machinery fabricators might do the same. The present day "stockyards complex" presents not too different a pattern, but it has been enveloped completely by the metropolis as an undesired, but necessary, means of supplying its own food needs and of making a livelihood. The new aggregation, based upon algae protein, is part farm, part factory, and part something that is still undefined. It is admirably suited to the kind of extensive urbanism described a few pages earlier.

Atomic power is likely to initiate quite different patterns. It is most efficiently produced in very large quantities and should therefore be located close to the load center in large urban areas. The requirements of safety, however, suggest a location carefully isolated from human habitation. Thus, heavy power-using industries, which at the same time require only small amounts of labor, are likely to become associated with atomic power. They would help isolate it from the residential areas. Chemical and metallurgical processes, including the new methods of steel making, fall into this category. Thus, in urban areas we must look forward to huge billion-dollar reservations of process industry with an atomic power plant holding the central position and iron, aluminum, magnesium, chlorine, caustic soda, nitrogen, phosphate, acetylene, and allied industries nestled around it. The connecting maze of pipe lines that permit such industries to feed upon each other's services and wastes would no doubt justify the term "complex," yet it will appear quite different from present day experience with aggregations of heavy industry. (See Fig. 23.) The forests of chimneys would not be in evidence here but in their place against the horizon would be scores of condensers ("upturned goblets of the gods," an anonymous poet recently called the most popular modern design in England), Horton spheres, and steel frameworks for the support of large units of equipment. The maze of rails and roads would be displaced by a few arterial lines integrated with a system of conveyor belts and pipe lines. The familiar overhanging smoke pall would, of course, never put in an appearance.

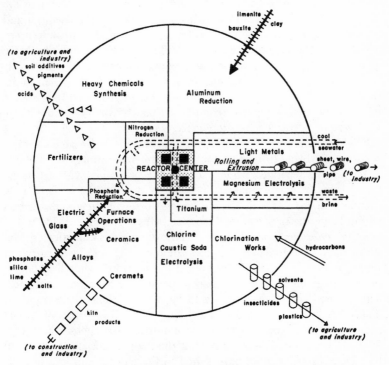

FIG. 23. TYPICAL INDUSTRIAL COMPLEX TO BE LINKED WITH A LARGE ATOMIC POWER PLANT

This is a hypothetical map of an industrial estate that might naturally grow up around a million-kilowatt nuclear reactor. The cluster of industries represented here would use the off-peak power to advantage. The processes integrate very nicely with each other so that marked savings can be made in freight costs and waste disposal as well as line losses for power transmission. The manufacturing methods are almost fully automatic so there is little danger to humans in case of reactor failure. Although there may be only a few thousand workers regularly employed in this billion-dollar complex, the fabrication and handling of the products should provide productive work for hundreds of thousands of workers in construction, other manufacturing, agriculture and services.

The development of multiproduct metallurgical extraction systems that employ very low-grade ores has already been hinted at. Atomic power plants will, no doubt, become an integral part of most such installations that were envisioned as chewing away at the accessible edges of large shale and other sedimentary deposits and later turning to granite mountain ranges. The extremely large volumes of rock, water, chemicals, and wastes to be handled suggest a highly mechanized installation and a small labor force residing nearby. Such operations are not suited to cities. This means that a fair share of the chemical and metallurgical facilities will be located away from the urban centers. The bulk chemicals produced will be brought in to the cities by barge and pipe line to supply the consumer goods industries, and the ingots would move in by rail for milling and fabrication. This division of activity occurs because it is in the latter stages of manufacturing that a relatively high labor input is required, a characteristic that shows every sign of being as true a generation hence as today.

The manufacture of fresh water from inland brackish waters, or from sea water, is likely to employ four quite different principles. Potable water may be separated by solar or compression stills, with a concentrated brine as a by-product. Such brines may be the basis of bulk chemicals industries. The Claude process, involving vacuum distillation and utilizing the temperature difference between warm and cold water, permits the generation of some electric energy also, particularly on sunny days. Electrodialysis requires some electric current to carry out the separation (3 to 5 kwhr per ton); it has no worth while by-products but will probably need less investment per unit of fresh water obtained. The ion exchange resins promise to be most efficient in desalting ordinary brackish waters, and may be designed to yield brines of special chemical composition. Water-using industries will choose those that fit their over-all needs most aptly, but the domestic needs of cities will be met by those methods most suited to the climate and location. If this calls for a large production of salts, the city may find itself specializing in heavy chemicals, although even in the long run it appears that the demand for such chemicals will never catch up with the potential supply.

The developments leading to much cheaper communications are largely those involved in the transition from paper records, manual bookkeeping, and semiskilled human manipulators of levers and controls to the fully electronic systems now being developed. This is a very broad conceptualizaiton that includes as a special case the anticipated integration of radio, television, telephone, and films previously introduced.

The full implications of rationalized communications are so tremendous that it is still quite possible that its most important contributions will be missed. For example, many unlettered rural migrants to the cities in the United States have been consciously accelerating their adaptation to city life through the purchase of television sets. At another level we see that the standardized commodity markets, the security markets, the checking accounts in banks, and consumer purchases can all be interlinked into a communications net that works in as fully an automatic fashion as the modern telephone exchange and would be more efficient than older methods for most of the same reasons. Thus, we can begin to see that many of the familiar historic functions of cities are likely to go underground; most transactions will no longer be face-to-face but will be carried out through interposed underground cables and windowless buildings.

The focus or "nodal point" in a communications network has become the center of effective political and economic power. Geographically these foci are associated with top administrative offices in government and business, as well as security markets, advertising, cultural innovations (theater, publishing, radio and television programming, etc.), and technical libraries. Nearby will be large hotels, institutions of higher education, research and development organizations, consultant groups, and related services. Even in countries where this complex of activities is less developed it is recognized that the radio-TV stations, the cable offices, the telephone exchanges, and the universities are the key points that must be taken quickly if a revolution is to succeed.

With the expected expansion of communications channels, still greater numbers of persons (mainly "white-collar" workers) will be needed to collect data on the everyday events and transactions and feed them into the network. Fortunately not many of these extra communications-oriented workers need to work in the congested core of the city, because in most cases it is cheaper to move lower-priority information to the worker somewhere on the periphery than the worker to the information at the focus. The costs of short-range decentralization appear to be reduced as communications systems improve.

There is some doubt that "fully rationalized construction methods" belong to a series of industrial innovations. The construction industries have not generated any strong research and development organization. This may be due partly to the effect of business cycles—construction thrives when the economy grows, falls flat when the economy falters—where firms with low overhead costs have the best chance of surviving.

The element of traditionalism, in the businesses themselves and their clients, is at least as important. A glance at the architecture of under-developed countries shows that wherever traditional building is even more archaic it is possible to establish a very modern construction indus-try. However, the modern sector of the industry cannot serve the mass needs unless it employs standardized designs, components, modules, and specifications, and establishes agencies for improving and perfecting the standards. This would make possible routinized construction requiring a minimum of experience and skill on the site while still obtaining good quality structures. Adhering to a minimum adequate standard in hous-ing and urban services would create a mass market even in a very poor society and therefore advance standardization of construction methods. The problem of a rationalized construction industry turns out to re-quire much more a perfection of social organization than a series of technical innovations. Its solution hinges upon the capacity to know one to three years in advance what shall be constructed and where. In other words, the organizations involved must be given a chance to plan. Since construction represents the commitment of capital, and capital is scarce and must be allocated according to schedule in a developing economy, the opportunity to plan is not an unusual or unreasonable requirement. It should be remembered, too, that in the rapidly grow-ing modern sector of the economy, which doubles in size each decade, employment in construction is likely to equal or exceed employment in manufacturing.

There is much that may be learned about the new industries by view-ing modes of organizing manufacturing activities. A study of history provides us with a progression of such modes, of which the following can be identified:

> Household manufactures
> Village handicrafts
> Artisan's workshops
> Primitive factories
> Integrated "assembly lines"
> Continuous-flow processes
> "Automatic factory."

Each one of these approaches to production requires different inputs of capital and labor. Each one, as we move down the list, assumes increasing organization of the production process.

Experience tells us it is no longer safe to depend upon any of the first three for the rapid improvement of levels of living. Productivity and quality are consistently low for products manufactured by those methods today. In addition, wherever they may be used, these methods of production are extremely vulnerable to technological change. Minimum adequate standards of living probably cannot be achieved in densely populated areas that depend heavily upon village development and the fostering of the arts and crafts.

The alternative forms of the primitive factory (the batch process, the machine shop, the mill, etc.) and the basic principles of the assembly line are largely innovations of the nineteenth century. They depend for their efficiency upon the application of increasing amounts of power and a greater division of labor. Their history and stages of evolution have been very interestingly portrayed by Giedion (1948). These kinds of technology have passed their zenith and are now showing relatively few spurts of progress.

By far the most modern techniques for organizing industry, and also the most interesting, are the last two on the list. A continuous-flow process refers to a production system where the inputs, outputs, and intermediates are handled internally as streams. A power plant is such a continuous-flow process when powdered coal is screw-fed into a furnace, the heat produced boils the water, the steam created is piped to the turbine, and the rotational energy so generated is converted to electric power. Thus there are set up three flows which are maintained: coal to ash, water to steam to condensate, and energy to electric current. A modern oil refinery employs an intricate web of such streams constantly moving through the equipment. The key to the success of the continuous-flow process is the instrumentation. The instruments ceaselessly measure such properties of the streams as temperature, pressure, composition, density, rate of flow, color, etc. In many cases they can be set so as to operate valves and switches, thus keeping the process functioning smoothly. The plant operators seldom need to interfere. When all of the regulation has been taken over by instruments, and the only important task for the worker is that of repairing and maintaining the equipment, then the transition to the automatic factory has been achieved. The most recent electric power stations are nearly perfect examples of this development, but the chemical industry has probably pushed the art of designing fully instrumented plants the furthest.

Some of the newest and most striking automatic factories have evolved from the assembly line. In them the machines not only carry out operations upon articles-in-process formerly guided by hand, but other machines will also transfer the article-in-process to the next machine in a manner that permits it to perform its task. An example can be drawn from the large metropolitan bakeries where the flour and other ingredients are mixed, kneaded, divided into portions, kneaded again, set into pans, proofed, baked, cooled, sliced, and packaged, not only without being touched by a human hand, but also without a single repetitive human task in the line. Similarly an aluminum casting can be passed from lathe to drill press to milling machine and so on for thirty or more separate machining operations and come out a piston. Such a factory design has been virtually accomplished over the past few years in both the United States and the U.S.S.R. (Diebold, 1953; Meier, 1956.)

Once an automatic design is achieved, progress does not stop. Technological improvements continue to be introduced. In the communications industries, for instance, a great deal of effort is spent redesigning automatic equipment so that it becomes "fully electronic," and thereafter requires less maintenance and repair. In chemicals and petroleum the tendency is to develop smaller-sized "packaged units" that might be installed wherever only a moderate demand for the product existed. In electric power production the tendency is to develop larger and more elaborate turbine installations that extract a few more kilowatt-hours from the fuel. In machine shops the trend for further development is toward greater flexibility of the individual tools and machines so that orders involving intermediate numbers of replicas (from 100 to 10,000) can be handled. More than that, the successful automation of any stage in a production sequence puts pressure upon the preceding and succeeding stages. One gets a smoother production flow, with fewer jamups, shutdowns, and substandard jobs if they too are reduced to automatic control. Therefore, once begun, the advanced techniques are gradually extended both in depth and breadth.

Economists, when confronted with developments such as these, quickly identify one important feature. They think of the automatic factory as an instance of the substitution of tremendous quantities of capital for labor. They point out that the capital investment in a primitive (partially mechanized) factory ranges up to $8000 per worker, for the operation of assembly lines up to $20,000 per worker, for the manually operated continuous-flow process up to $100,000, whereas for the automatic factory it may reach occasionally to $1,000,00 per employee. The *average* capital invested per new job will be much less than the top of the range, but the averages too will show a steeply rising capital input as automation is achieved.

The engineer sees the automatic factory in a different light. He is perpetually seeking a product that will give a better performance at reasonable cost. He finds that machines will make better standardized products than artisans, and that automatic machines will permit better quality control than manually operated machines. This is important because almost always the products of one factory must be used in conjunction with the products of the others. The specifications for each part must mesh closely with the others. In an engine, for example, not only must the tolerances of the component parts be as small as feasible, but the fuel and lubricants must be prepared with characteristics which closely fit the needs of the engine. Failure to meet quality standards at any of a hundred or more points would lead to engine failure or drastically lowered efficiency. The motivation that leads the engineer to accept automation with enthusiasm is the realization that by this means quality can be improved, occasionally to such an extent that hitherto impossible jobs become feasible. The economist's tools for the measuring of quality are very poor, and so this factor is usually left out of his calculation.

Engineers hasten to point out that, despite the large quantities of capital required per worker, the application of more automatic methods has quite consistently reduced the capital cost per unit of annual capacity. This has been strikingly true when applied to the introduction and improvement of continuous-flow processes. Therefore, from the point of view of the consumer and the man who saves part of his earnings for investment, an industrialization program that uses the most advanced methods of organization as soon as possible is to be preferred over one that develops gradually in this direction. The returns on capital are greater.

The principal price one has to pay for the ultimate in mechanization is a kind of inflexibility—most such plants have larger capacities and are less able to adjust to changes in demand. If the market is miscalculated, or the problems of maintenance and repair are neglected, the losses will be much greater than for the other alternatives. Facilities of advanced design are not so suitable for economies that experience recurrent dips in production as a feature of the business cycle, or for those subject to wide seasonal fluctuations in demand. They are most useful where the economy is large, is quite standardized in its consumption patterns, and exhibits steady growth. These newest methods for organizing industry are most suited to Japan, China, India, Pakistan, Java, Burma, the Philippines, Korea, Egypt, Brazil, Argentina, Mexico, Italy, Nigeria, the Congo, etc. It will be a long time, however, before the Central American republics, the West Indies, or the South Sea islands can profit directly from the trend to automatic factories; their assured markets are too small to justify much beyond medium-sized power plants, and a few factories linked to their natural resources (e.g., instant coffee, fermentation chemicals, etc.).

The planners and administrators of an economic development program in the larger countries will also find the most advanced forms of industrial organization advantageous. They are trying to find ways for making progress in the face of many simultaneous shortages; that of capital has already been mentioned, but the scarcities of hard currency, engineers, managers, and skilled industrial workers are just as severe in most areas. Often the conditions for rapidly creating semiskilled industrial workers do not exist. They will find upon careful investigation that the most automatic designs for factories, as elaborated by European or American engineering firms, would consistently use fewer engineers, managers, and skilled workers than the alternatives available to them. Those that are needed will require predominantly Western ideas and training to carry out their jobs, so that education obtained in foreign universities and experience with international firms can be applied at once. So often in underdeveloped areas the technical skills acquired in European and American universities are largely irrelevant to the problems encountered in the native countryside, and even in the primitive factories that may be proposed.

Very early in the course of development, in most of the larger economies, decisions will have to be made regarding the methods for organizing electric power, cement, fertilizers, liquid fuels, heavy chemicals, sugar, paper, printing, and telecommunications networks. For each of these there is a continuous-flow process or virtually automatic solution already available (for others, such as mining, forestry, housebuilding, and roadmaking, solutions are not yet ready, and for some may never be suitable). A choice for each of these industries must be made between:

A program for stimulating scattered small-scale entrepreneurs using makeshift equipment and methods

A program of decentralized government sponsored factories with local participation and some centralized regulation

The construction of large, modern industrial units with strong initial government participation.

The argument against the first is that it is too unpredictable and slow, and that the accumulated profits may be invested in properties that do not reinforce economic development. The second program could be designed to evade the inadequacies of the first, but it encounters the scarcity of competent managers in underdeveloped societies. Embarrassing instances of mismanagement and waste of capital are likely to wreck the program and bring about the fall of the government. The third procedure gets around these difficulties, and it has additional advantages in that it can best use foreign skills and leads to more efficient industrial establishment as judged by competition in the world market.

The third procedure is no panacea since there are still many opportunities for missteps, but it can be so administered that the severest problems may be identified and dealt with in advance. The risks that remain are those necessarily associated with any kind of large enterprise that must continually struggle for its place in the sun against the vicissitudes presented by the future. Besides, it is a formula that can be used for only an estimated 20 to 40% of all capital investment required for a balanced program. For the remainder, which may use to best advantage the primitive factory or the ordinary assembly line (garments, shoes, larger units of household equipment, and bicycles are representative examples), more decentralized services to industry, promotional devices, and controls are appropriate.

Most readers will have experienced increasing disquietude as they progressed over the previous twenty or thirty pages. Thus far there has been exhibited a preoccupation with the technical solutions to the problems posed by the new technology. This has been quite necessary. The new industries needed for economic development will set off a series of waves and ripples whose consequences for the society are much broader than can be traced to the products of the new factories. Some of these show up when we speculate upon the location of industrial aggregations, communications centers, urbanism, water supplies, and other resource developments. Some major consequences can be traced to the forms of organization that are required to deal successfully with the new technology. But the role of the individual, his aspirations and fears, his work and play, his opportunities and constraints, has been largely omitted up to this point. Where, for example, will the jobs come from, if so much automation is to be used? What happens to the traditional ethical systems, to the family, and to the existing social institutions when a huge planning-minded bureaucracy is created?

At this point only the question of jobs and the security of employment will be taken up. The other problems will be considered later. Employment is critical because an apparent paradox has been revealed. Industrialization was introduced as a means for providing useful employment for millions of underemployed rural workers, yet a more careful inspection of the strategies for industrialization led to the conclusion that automatic factories, i.e., virtually workerless installations, were to be preferred whenever technically feasible.

The resolution of the paradox may be approached from several standpoints. One of them is the pattern of consumption that has been predicated as desirable for a rapidly developing society, another is drawn from the features of the expected growth of urbanization, and still a third may be deduced from current trends in developed societies in the allocation of the labor force. All of these point to the same outcome, but they are based upon different lines of conjecture.

The pattern of consumption conforming more or less to the minimum adequate standard of living, as depicted in Table 22 and the last diagram in Fig. 22, offers a clue to the kinds of work that would need to be done. The fraction required to produce food for the market would be only 5 to 10% of the labor force if it was as productive as the urban sector. Because the productivity of rural labor is almost certain to be less than that of urban labor for a very long time to come, the fraction working in agriculture will be larger than 5 to 10%, but it may decline toward that figure in the long run. Jobs in manufacturing will depend upon how much of the heavy capital goods can be imported, because there is a very small volume of manufactured items consumed in the minimum adequate standard of living itself. If the productivity of labor in manufacturing is equalized with labor productivity elsewhere in the city, then 10 to 15% of the labor force would be required, much of it employed in producing the capital goods required for a growing economy. Construction activity could easily reach 20% of the productive effort. The remainder of the work force, which might exceed half of the urban labor available, would be needed to provide education, health, personal services, municipal services, and other social services. A few more might engage in sports, drama, music, scientific research, and other cultural activities on a full-time professional level.

In rapidly growing cities one finds several qualities of labor available.

A small fraction is made up of old settlers who will operate many of the more stable businesses, move into the professions, and take over most of the jobs where a higher degree of skill is required. They will also share the clerical work with the better educated migrants. Normally the migrants crowd into the slums, accept employment in unskilled service work or manufacturing, and move out of slums as they acquire skills and their incomes rise sufficiently to pay higher rents and greater transportation costs. In the pattern for growth suggested here, however, the overcrowding of the slums would be forestalled; but this means that reasonably adequate dwellings and services must be provided simultaneously elsewhere in the city. Migrants are normally used for construction labor, but a slum prevention plan would mean that a larger share of them would be engaged in such work. The extra demand for construction and related services would compensate for the smaller demand for industrial labor when relatively automatic factories were used for economic development. This strategy appears to make possible the most efficient use of capital for industrial investment at the same time that it reduces the diseconomies associated with the long-run strangulation of the core of the city by slums.

The decline in employment in the food and fiber producing sector and the short, quick rise followed by a long decline in the manufacturing sector are already well-known phenomena associated with economic development. The Western countries have followed this pattern, and the plans published by the U.S.S.R. suggest that the same thing will happen there. If we try to deduce from current trends what the labor force allocation will be a generation hence in these advanced countries, most experts would propose that agriculture would take up less than 10% of the labor force, that manufacturing would require 10 to 15%, construction about 5%, and the remainder would be engaged in services. There are good reasons for believing that political leaders of rapidly developing countries would aim at an economy with that kind of structure rather than the kind exhibited by Western countries at the turn of the century. Since they now have technologies available that enable them to by-pass the labor-intensive-industry phase, it seems quite logical that much of the pattern considered normal for an advanced economy would emerge quite early in the urban sector of the developing economy. The incoming male labor, used mainly in construction in order to speed up the pace toward the goal of a modern productive society, would then constitute the main deviation from the advanced pattern. The construction effort would be greatly facilitated by those industries where it is expected that capital as well as labor would be saved by choosing the automatic technology (cement, glass, chemicals, plastics, refined metals, sheet, wire, pipe, machine components, communications services, data processing, etc.). Thus, when it is considered in some detail, the strategy for industrialization that employs many of the very newest technologies seems to reinforce the strategies proposed for rapid improvement of welfare and the orderly growth of cities. In general the jobs would be less monotonous and less routine than they have been in the past; they would still tend to become specialized, but more tasks would be oriented to understanding the behavior of people in various institutional settings and contexts. The assembly lines employing human operators could become a minor feature of industrialization.

This manpower distribution is expected to have special psychological consequences. If twice as much effort can be allocated to construction as has been permissible in developing economies in the past, and more effort allowed for social services, then the effects of the development are visible much sooner to the ordinary citizen. In the past, development has depended largely upon the sacrifices of one generation, resulting in benefits to be reaped by succeeding generations; these are rather ineffective incentives for extra effort or for saving from income. However, if the sacrifices of five to ten years earlier appear to lead to substantial gains, then the next appeals for extraordinary exertion are regarded with less skepticism. On psychological grounds it would be easier to maintain a high rate of progress with the new technology than it has ever been with the labor-intensive technologies employed in the past.

ADDED FOR THE SECOND EDITION

The term *automation* was already becoming ambiguous and imprecise more than a decade ago, so it was avoided. Now it is giving way to *cybernation*, a degree of instrumentation which allows production equipment to be operated by an automaton which may be connected to other automata. The pace with which this stage of industrialization is proceeding in North America is more rapid than expected. Indeed, the demand for inter-city channel capacity is expected to exceed the total human demand for long distance calls about 1965; provision of such channel capacity for computers and other equipment using telecommunications must increase to a level more than thirty times a growing human demand by about 1985. [W. S. Litchman, *Inst. Electric. Electron. Eng. Trans. on Communications Systems* CS-11, p. 149 (1963).]

Thus the demand for manufacturing labor in a modernizing economy should be even less than previously imagined. However, the need for good quality information about people, and the conditions under which they live, should generate a heightened demand for white-collar skills. Also more attention must be paid to investments in education.

5. THE DEVELOPMENTAL SOCIETY

Once a society begins the long and hard road to better conditions of living, it only gradually discovers that it is also trying to escape the limitations of its own culture and tradition. At first the leaders fervently believe that only a moderate reform of the indigenous cultural pattern is necessary for economic development to proceed. Certain archaic institutions, like the system of land tenure or the temporal prerogatives of the established Church, obviously stand in the way at the beginning. Once these preliminary road blocks are removed by strong internal reform, the preconditions for rapid economic development can be completed.

Very soon, however, many new difficulties appear. These, too, can be solved, but the keys to the solution are drawn from experience outside the culture, frequently from the accumulated body of scientific and technical knowledge possessed by the world at large. Perhaps just as important is the recorded experience with constitutions, political philosophies, and cultural institutions. This process of looking beyond one's boundaries for answers to problems that the society has not before encountered becomes quite common as development accelerates.

Gradually there evolves in the society a new element that gains its prestige from introducing and reducing to practice the useful ideas and information originating outside. At the start of the rapid phase of economic development this element will be quite unbalanced as to specialization, skill, and training. There will be some serious gaps where no one at all has been trained, so that essential aspects of world knowledge are known to exist, but cannot be utilized. It is like finding a wonderfully rich oil field when no one knows how to drill a well. This frustrating condition will be most common in some of the very newest technical specialties. The existence of such gaps will mean that some technical assistance from outside countries is needed to help with the planning and the installation of the new physical equipment. The natives that work along with the visiting experts are likely to become members of this new element, along with those who have been sent out to educational institutions in other parts of the world so as to acquire the new insights and skills. Many more, who learn from lectures, correspondence courses, or the study of foreign journals, may come to belong to the element without ever achieving direct contact with outsiders. Where praise and recognition from the outside are obtained, the quality of performance goes up rapidly, but where there is rejection and strong criticism—even for valid reasons—personal goals are changed. The establishment of an outward-looking elite is thus replete with hazards.

These carriers and interpreters of world culture are the doctors and dentists, the engineers, the top administrators, the educators, the enterprisers, and many of the technicians. It is readily understood why such men will tend to become attached almost as much to the world at large as to their own people and their own culture. Success at one's own appointed job, and professional status in general, depend upon understanding the international idiom. Sometimes a new idea will be carried beyond this group and sweep through the whole society, but many unnecessary imports will be popularly accepted along with the high priority items—often in a way that would amuse the more sophisticated observer and intrigue the scholar.

This stratum becomes marginal to its native society but, nevertheless, wholly dedicated to its improvement. The people in it would feel uncomfortable and restricted when conforming to the accepted modes of behavior, and yet there is no other place in the world where they can develop roots. Thus there develops a split in the society between the "modern" way of life and the traditional.

The changes in personality that seem to accompany economic development have always interested sociologists. Probably the most complete and insightful exposition, based upon historical patterns of development, is given by Riesman (1950). He postulates an initial tradition-directed character that is created under conditions of cultural equilibrium. Under such conditions virtually all decisions faced by individuals have been faced before by people in the society, and some appropriate behavior has been formulated. The variations in tradition and the cultural behavior associated with it may, of course, be tremendous. The equilibrium is often upset by persons living at boundaries between cultures, or responsible for relations with neighboring peoples, who might know of several ways of behaving in a given circumstance; this disturbance leads to uncertainty and doubt as to the "rightness" of one's own decisions concerning the way of life. Such torturing doubts, combined with increasing knowledge about the outside world, often have led to the acceptance of new religions and new systems of ethics, to heresies and reformations. In this manner a new way of life was developed that inculcated more generalized rules for making moral decisions, in other words, a conscience. This Riesman called the "inner-directed" character. A society employing such means of moral stabilization can accommodate much higher rates of social change than can the traditional culture, but it is seldom able to cope with the changes implied by large-scale rural to urban migration. Then the alterations in the way of life become so extensive that the inculcated rules, more often than not, do not fit. In such a quandary it is common sense for a person to look around him to see how other people behave in similar circumstances. Thus develops an imitative, or "other-directed," character. In developed countries people will not belong exclusively to one or another character type, but will tend to blend them in different degrees according to personal experiences.

In the future the pace of development must be much more rapid than in the past; therefore, the accompanying social changes must be greater. Little opportunity is provided for the propagation of "inner-directed" characters. A much more direct transition is to be expected from traditional behavior to modern ways of life. A youth may within a few years break with the old and commit himself fully to the new.

The "modern" person will wear Western or factory-made clothing, prefer to live in new-style or European houses, familiarize himself with films, advertisements, and other popular art coming in from Western countries. He will become a competent user of telephones, typewriters, contraceptives, and the other essential paraphernalia of civilization. He will very frequently become an active nationalist in politics.

Yet upon closer analysis it will be recognized that some features of the traditional society were retained, and that exceedingly few persons can liberate themselves completely from the traditional culture. Very commonly, such items as the "at home" aspects of rearing children, the seasoning and flavors in the diet, the symbols of reverence and obeisance, and many other particular characteristics of the old culture will be retained and persist quite uniformly throughout the society long after development has begun. Thus, although a distinction between modern and traditional can be established for each aspect of behavior, we expect to find characters distributed in a continuum ranging from the most advanced to the most archaic. We would find most people clustered around a point predominantly traditional and another point predominantly modern. The people in between have not found a permanent halfway station—it is much too uncomfortable to continue to sit on the fence—but are mainly in transition. They are in the process of changing their minds about the preferred way of life. (See Fig. 24.)

In the course of development the modern sector must grow at the expense of the traditional. This has happened in all past instances of economic development, but only as the result of the interplay of impersonal, undirected social and economic forces. Henceforth the transfer will be premeditated. Bright, promising youngsters will be found within the traditional society, brought to town, made literate, trained for a productive specialization, and co-opted at some intermediate status into

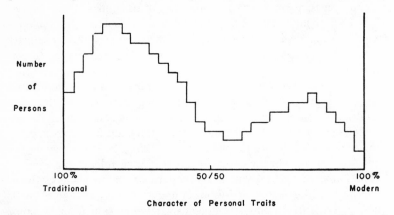

FIG. 24. THE DEVELOPMENTAL SOCIETY: DISCRIMINATING BETWEEN "MODERN" AND "TRADITIONAL" SECTORS

If one should select a set of behavioral traits, chosen to be indicative of typically modern or typically traditional orientation, it would be found that very few persons were wholly traditional or wholly modern in their actions. However, there tends to be a clustering around a pattern which is predominantly traditional and another which is predominantly modern. The traditional group would be extremely strong in the countryside, but important numbers might be found in enclaves in the cities. The modern group would be concentrated in cities, but important elements, such as school teachers, would be distributed throughout the territory. The persons in between are not there as a matter of choice, but are in transition, mainly from the traditional to the modern way of life.

Developmental societies seldom stay this simple very long. Frequently a part of the traditional sector, upon realizing that its system of values is crumbling, will follow one or more reorientations (sects) which attempt to establish a new and more stable tradition. A primitive resynthesis of this kind will borrow some elements from the modern but will usually strongly resist the remainder. Gandhism is a typical reinterpretation of tradition of the kind meant here, but there are many that are less well known in Africa and Latin America.

the modern sector of the society. (See Fig. 25.) Growth can be much more rapid when the best brains are sought out and put to work solving the most critical problems as they appear. This is an approach that can be made more immediately responsive to the personnel requirements for development than can the older methods of waiting for the news of opportunity to filter out into the countryside. In the history of economic development, it is true, the handbill and the recruiting agent played an important role in attracting the adventurous and the romantically inclined youths, along with the desperate and the malcontent, to key construction projects and enterprises, but these devices are not very selective. The transition was made at too late a date for them to acquire much more formal education. In many instances the promising

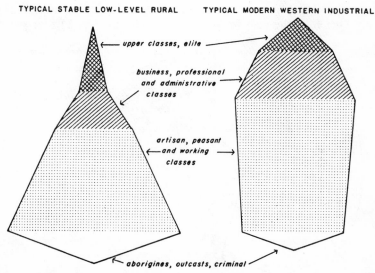

TYPICAL STABLE LOW-LEVEL RURAL   TYPICAL MODERN WESTERN INDUSTRIAL

← upper classes, elite →

business, professional and administrative classes →

artisan, peasant ← and working → classes

aborigines, outcasts, criminal

FIG. 25. THE DEVELOPMENTAL SOCIETY: SOCIAL CHANGES AS ILLUSTRATED BY STATUS DIAGRAMS

Status "pyramids" may be used to describe at a glance crude differences in the social make-up of societies. Areas are proportional to numbers of persons in the respective social classes. Each inhabitant is thus represented by some point within the diagram. Relative heights of each give some indication of the degree of status differentiation within the class. The elite of the society on the left, for example, has many more recognizable gradations than the one on the right. The upper classes are more highly organized than the middle classes, and the latter have more social contacts than ordinary workers; these characteristics are emphasized by degrees of cross-hatching.

migrants were trapped by the necessity of making a living with a low order of skill. Their ambitions and aspirations were then passed on to their children, but a whole two decades were lost. The historical process has been wasteful from almost every point of view.

The traditional sector must be thought of as a resource in more ways than one. As hinted at earlier in another context, many of these people can be useful in the hinterland carrying on activities that may be speeded up with some machinery or tools, but cannot be automatized. The majority of them, who are in most cases initially *under*employed in agricultural pursuits, could do the mining, the forestry, dambuilding, roadmaking, etc. Others, mainly women, could engage in those light industries that can be decentralized economically to the accessible villages. Still others may be drawn into new agricultural pursuits, especially labor-intensive market produce like tubers, vegetables, fruits, eggs, etc. Therefore, the plan for development will bring social change to

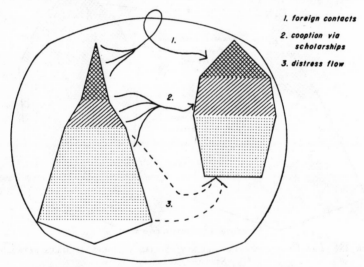

FIG. 25. THE DEVELOPMENTAL SOCIETY (*Cont'd*)

In a developmental society both of these structural types exist side by side. When the modern grows at the expense of the traditional three major streams may be detected. The children of the old elite may study abroad, or merely read about modern ways, so that many move into the modern milieu and become leaders. Other youngsters will be transformed through the educational system, mainly to professional and sub-professional strata. Lower class migrants are pushed to the cities by regional or family disasters. In urban surroundings many of these will tend to accept modern ways of life.

the village but not in such a way that it causes a breakdown in social structure. Some novelty, adventure, and movement would be introduced, but the principal effect would be to alleviate the boredom that oppresses so many of the people attached to the traditional culture. The basic pattern of life would be unchanged, but new interests and awarenesses would arise out of the new activities. After two generations or so they might be expected to accept without resistance the full set of urban services and standards, from electrification to child-rearing practices, that might be offered them out of the surpluses accumulated by the modern, mostly urbanized, productive sector of the society during that period.

Thus far the analysis of the developmental society has been limited to mass shifts of the type that would be readily detected in countryside travels by an observant reporter trained in sociology and the history of economic development. Fully as striking a change would be observed by a political reporter stationed in any of the principal cities watching the decision-making groups. He would have seen the displacement of the landholding aristocracy and the established old-line mercantile groups from the centers of power. In many countries these advocates of the *status quo* are removed by revolutionary means, but in some they remain in closer contact with reality and adjust more readily; then their power is usurped in easy stages. Next to take hold of the reins is a coalition group, made up of such people as lawyers, poets, philosophers, and practical *politicos*. The lawyers are needed to frame the necessary changes in laws and constitutions that are intended to satisfy popular measures, the poets discover the inner aspirations of the people and find for them phrases which pass with evident relish from mouth to mouth ending up as political catchwords, the philosophers mobilize the students into crusades for reform, while the practical politician tries to weld the elements favoring the coalition into a "machine" that will continue to deliver the necessary votes. Often military officers are also members of the coalition; their function is that of maintaining public order during the transfer of power and forestalling the use of military force by the traditional elite.

The coalition, however, is unable to complete the job it sets out to do. Its chief virtue is that of inspired advocacy of change, but usually many more promises are made than can be fulfilled. As a government, it rides off in many directions at once, spends more than it can take in, and starts many projects which it has neither the resources nor the skill to complete. This is usually the undoing of the coalition—it succumbs to dissident forces, leaving the net welfare position of the society no better than before—but we are interested here in those which *do* find a way out of their difficulties and seriously embark on a program of economic development. A few such *juntas* are sincere and wise enough to start the planning process.

The first concrete plan to be adopted must be primarily the work of the professional civil servant. When serious planning begins, this cadre needs to be reinforced at every turn—its powers increased, its skill extended, and its counsel expedited. The civil servant finds that a most useful ally is the promoter-type person, the man who can juggle personalities, technologies, and organizations in such a way as to construct from them a new enterprise engaged in new productive activities. The promoters are necessary to execute the most ticklish parts of the plan. Such men are quite frequently found and developed nowadays in public corporations, but historically they have operated almost exclusively in the private sector where the means used to achieve an end are scrutinized less carefully. The plan is executed therefore by handing over a very large amount of power to the civil servants and the promoters. Once launched and in a relatively secure position, the promoters move on to expansions or to new promotions, and the civil servants become occupied with new crises, so that the enterprise is left in the hands of professional managers. Their decisions are less spectacular and more specialized, but soon, perhaps toward the end of the second decade, their influence is strongly felt. It is in the managers' interest to make sure that what has been accumulated and accomplished is not lost in the process of reaching for more.

Thus far this description of changes in leadership has many historic and contemporary parallels. A sophisticated political reporter, conversant with world trends, would find little to be surprised about in these apparently necessary stages of evolution exhibited by the developmental society. However, continuing expansion will bring into play forces that suggest that the dominance of the manager-bureaucrat-promoter alliance will not last. When information relevant to the most important commitments becomes voluminous, statistical, and technically involved, and when success depends much more upon selecting the best technics than upon choosing the right man for the job, then the critical decisions must devolve upon a new group—the energetic highly placed scientists and engineers. These are not scientists and engineers narrowly interpreted, but persons with professional training in natural science, economics, sociology, statistics, and technology. They are persons whose career is tied to the recognition, use, and extension of technical innovations that must be the basis for rapid growth in the latter stages of development. Taking over a measure of real political power would require careful organization and some striving on the part of the technical clique. For such an eventuality there is no close parallel; the condition would be quite novel.

The contemporary, run-of-the-mill Western technical man is not a political animal. He does not have the self-assertive qualities required of a governing class. He defines his competence rather narrowly, and in general refuses to look at total problems in all their socio-political complexities. He intends to keep his discipline free from compromises with extraneous ideologies. No doubt this type will be faithfully reproduced in developing societies, but will not the new environment encourage some deviations from international norms? What is being suggested here is that, in the presence of a pressing need to maintain the pace of economic development, a mutant type of scientist and engineer may achieve dominance.

But then what? What kind of a society would the scientist-executive create? Such a possibility invites a nightmare for the classical humanist, and stimulates visions of Utopia in the breast of the technocrat. Certainly the clique should be competent enough, with the aid of their calculators and automatic control systems, to advance the process of economic development. With the new possibilities in technology and social redistribution discussed earlier, there should be little doubt of their capacity to manipulate men, money, and materials in such a manner as to achieve an eventual surplus, after providing at least a minimum adequate standard of living for all the population. What the surplus might be spent upon is, at this point, idle speculation. The same problems would be eventually encountered if the leadership remained nontechnical, but they would exist in less exaggerated form. However all this deals with the future, and what comes after world development, and therefore does not concern us here.

There is a third kind of reporter who could be assigned to observe another facet of the developmental society. His job would be to interpret the art, esthetics, and philosophy of values as they evolve. Many underdeveloped countries have rich cultural traditions; it would take a diligent reporter some years merely to establish a reasonable familiarity with such a past. In the course of development he would note that the old and the new are alternatively rejected and resuscitated, with various hybrids and compromises also being proposed. In historic instances of economic development, the arts suffered from an undisciplined eclecticism during the period of maximum growth. However, in the future it seems possible that worth-while and lasting contributions can be made. Mexico is an example of a rapidly developing society whose art has developed even more rapidly, while in Brazil recent architecture has been outstanding.

If a strategy of development employing the minimum adequate standard of living as a virtual income ceiling is chosen, several other important implications for esthetics and the practice of the arts would logically follow. It was pointed out earlier that incentive bonuses for extra productive effort could be granted in the form of extra claims upon services but not goods, especially not goods that required substantial quantities of scarce resources. Thus a successful manager would not be able to obtain a grand house, or a luxurious car, or a refrigerator, but he could have servants, decorate his home, eat at restaurants, attend various entertainments, and subsidize the arts. That is because an event like a grand opera, with stars and stage hands paid off at the MASL, can be quite economical. Sports events can be equally cheap. When conspicuous consumption is diverted almost exclusively into directions such as these, one can expect more practiced and expert publics to appreciate the arts. There would also be greater prestige for the successful artist.

Earlier, in the discussion on the characteristics of the new urbanization, another challenge of the MASL was introduced. The problem of designing new housing, new furniture, new vehicles, new office equipment, and new mass media for living most economically while at the same time achieving balanced dimensions and beauty in the form these products may take has never yet really been faced. Good design with utmost economy is a rarity in any part of the world. It calls for the kinds of skill which the Japanese, to cite one instance, ought to excel at quickly, since they have a highly appropriate tradition upon which to build. However, each culture would have to refashion such designs many times to suit itself.

The neat, esthetic solution will certainly meet with desecration in a society where most of the dwellings are self-built by migrants, and the majority of the community structures can be no more elaborate. The first designs must, it seems, be aimed at the minority in the white collar classes and the managerial posts. The new designs would be calculated to hold down their consumption of scarce materials. Later, at a time when redevelopment of the older self-built communities is undertaken, people can become mass consumers of the new designs.

The *planned* process of vulgarization (using this term in its narrower, more precise meaning) of design may be little different from what occurs today in the free play of the market.

Still other reporters could analyze the prospective developmental society from quite different viewpoints. However, what they would have to say, beyond what has been said, will have fewer surprises. The main outlines, as far as they can be deduced, have already been presented. It is a society which must bring about a metamorphosis of national character, must exhibit a succession of leadership classes, and could sponsor some remarkably ingenious schools in the field of esthetics. These are aspects that developmental societies have in common. For any single society, with specified institutions, resources, and politics, a much more coherent—and perhaps more satisfying—picture could be prepared.

It was the purpose of this discussion to avoid the gratuities of the writer on economic development who asserts that the society engaging in development must be "dynamic." This is a word that means something different for each reader. The attempts at explication have up till now seldom gone beyond this. But in the foregoing analysis some of the mechanisms of interaction were revealed, and the structure in the "dynamics" becomes evident. It is useful because a businessman with the help of such insights would be better able to choose the right enterprise, and the ambitious politician would pick the correct social connections.

ADDED FOR THE SECOND EDITION

An up-to-date prescription of the procedures needed for development—social, cultural, and political, as well as economic—based upon what has been learned from the handful of successes recorded in the past two decades, has now been prepared. It reviews the newest concepts in development strategy, including those to be inferred from McClelland's motivational theory (D. C. McClelland, *The Achieving Society*, D. Van Nostrand Co., Princeton, 1961). Institution-building that accelerates the flow of social communications is emphasized, together with efforts for balancing the investment in industrialization with that in human resources. [R. L. Meier, *Developmental Planning*, McGraw-Hill Book Co., New York, 1965.]

6. SOCIAL ORGANIZATION FOR NEW TECHNOLOGY

Although the changes in a society can be illustrated in terms of masses, classes, and personality types, and the over-all strategy of development can be plotted in those terms, none of these inferences tells how the work gets done. Productive effort must be systematized, and as many features as possible reduced to routines that can be handled by people with little training. Finally, perhaps, the more repetitious of them may be taken over by machines. The routines set for people are determined to a striking degree by the characteristics of the technologies that they employ. Behavior is regularized in such a way that the most reward is extracted from the effort. These constant elements of behavior in work, and often also in play, are set by an institution—a framework of tolerances and sanctions arranged for a complement of continuing activities. It is under the auspices of an interlocking set of institutions that an effort is planned, executed, and co-ordinated with other efforts. In order to carry out economic development, many new institutions must be created. They may take the form of corporations, universities, markets, neighborhood clubs, etc., all of which are familiar to us, but there may also be created totally new forms of organization based upon more recent developments in technology, particularly in communications. Each of these institutions gains a reputation and structure of its own. Each will take on a task or purpose, set its intermediate and long term goals, and systematize the effort for achieving them. This often becomes quite explicit, so that one well-organized team might see to it that a set of basic industries gets established, another might handle the problems of training an increasing number of engineers, and another might establish a library system suited to continuous growth.

All this sounds purposeful and progressive. Actually the period when many new institutions are being simultaneously created is both the most decisive and the most confusing period of economic development. At that time in the beginnings of the modern sector of the society, nothing seems set or dependable, no one is able to look far into the future and have any clear idea of where the detectable trends would take the society. Almost everything needs to be done at once, but in many instances the basic tools for doing needful things are not available. At this time unifying symbols of leadership—a man, a program, and a party—are virtually essential in order to prevent social chaos.

These conditions of society are well known to historians. They have frequently been the aftermath of revolutions and disasters. Modernization of institutions in historical instances generally led to the adoption of such innovations as a natural language suited to the new methods of printing and publishing, uniform weights and measures to promote standardization of goods, limitations upon landholding so as to introduce better forms of agriculture, new schemes for building cities so as to increase accessibility to work and to the new services, a more realistic system of education that emphasizes problem-solving rather than a comprehensive review of tradition, and others. To generalize, one might claim that many of the new and significant institutions that came into being during these periods of relative chaos were tailored to the task of utilizing the advanced science and technics at that time as well as channelling the emerging ethos.

The future process of economic development, which makes use of knowledge and technology already accumulated and presently being studied, must create new institutions that operate on quite different levels. Those functioning within neighborhoods and in local government will no doubt be adaptations of institutions already found in the native culture. At this level there is so much diversity of pattern no generalizations will be attempted. Some light, however, can be shed on the requirements put upon institutions operating at less parochial levels. These include first, the special kinds of organizations required for utilizing the new and the known technologies; second, the set of institutions servicing and reinforcing those that are more immediately responsible for production; third, the agency whose duty it is to plot the strategy of the development while supervising its execution; and fourth, the international institutions that provide information, encouragement, technical assistance, and financial support from the outside. The analysis that follows will proceed from the first to the last in a loosely connected discussion.

At this point the survey of new technology in Chapters 2 and 3 again becomes useful. One can foresee what kind of innovations the bright youngsters of the newly developing society will have to borrow, initiate, and perfect. From this evaluation can be deduced the nature of the institutions that appear to be indispensable, first to foster innovations, and then to make the most of the opportunities they present. Some highly original institutions and organizational devices are certainly needed for the following list:

> The continuous harvest of photosynthetic products
> The synthesis of foods based upon new foodstuffs
> The establishment of birth control in rural populations
> The economic operation of atomic power stations
> The exploitation of very low-grade ores
> The extension of instrumentation and automation
> The economic conversion of sea water into fresh water
> The construction of efficient networks for communications.

This set of eight new directions for the founding of institutions is very likely a minimum. Certain locales, for instance, will require other novel developments, such as the integration of new vehicles into a modern transportation system, or procedures for obtaining a sustained yield from a tropical rain forest.

This need for innovation brings up a fundamental issue. Without such innovations economic development cannot be completed in most areas of the world, but how does a people (or an economy, or a state) knowingly exploit innovations to its best advantage.

The underdeveloped countries are in a different position from the Western countries. The latter were forced to build up fundamental science and to explore blindly the hidden qualities of phenomena which some day may be useful; they have learned how to find promising personnel for this work and they have brought some system into the process of invention. Each Western country has elaborated a complex apparatus for the advancement of science and the improvement of technology. However the underdeveloped country, coming later on the scene and recognizing that it cannot afford to gamble its tiny corps of scientists and technologists upon nebulous explorations, must restrict itself mainly to extracting what is useful from what is already recorded. The underdeveloped economy draws upon the experience of its predecessors in this regard as in many others. The Western methods for stimulating discovery and invention should be used only for filling the gaps that were left in the course of earlier explorations elsewhere. This means that research and development institutions in underdeveloped countries must aim at adaptation, and even a good deal of imitation, of ideas that have already been verified and tested.

There is being created now, in India and elsewhere, a set of institutions that promise to do the job rather effectively. The logic employed for their organization is straightforward. The need for technological advance was established in a dozen or so conveniently defined areas of economic activity, such as mining, forestry, fisheries, food processing, river development, etc. For each of these, one or more laboratories of applied science is established with facilities for constructing models, pilot plants, and field studies. If an economic prospectus shows that a new development incubated in such a laboratory is ready, then an existing enterprise, or one newly created for the purpose, takes on the exploitation. The laboratory assists in getting the first production operations started and then retires to the role of technical consultant. A typical example of the scientific approach best used in underdeveloped areas is the genesis of the solar cooker in the National Physical Laboratory of India (Ghai, 1953). The administrative features are still far from perfect, but the value of the successes scored by this approach already far outweighs the cost of failures.

Most of the enterprises engaged in the exploitation of innovations are likely to be corporations. In many respects they are likely to be modeled after the international American firms. The latter organizations have grown up in a period of great technical and social change and have incorporated mechanisms within their structure which elicit continual reorganization and adaptation to new developments as they arise. The large international firms have reduced the lag between the original discovery and its application from almost half a century to 5 to 15 years—depending somewhat on the nature of the industry. They refashion their internal organization in the light of these innovations within a few years after the first large-scale application occurs. Such characteristics are most appropriate in a society aiming at a maximum rate of economic development.

Careful imitation does not necessarily imply that corporate enterprise must be privately owned. The TVA, the Export-Import Bank, and the Rubber Reserve have shown that public enterprise can be as quick acting and adaptive as any of the private firms. Public enterprise in general must be more scrupulous in its dealings with citizens than must the private firm. This requirement detracts from its economic efficiency occasionally, but at the same time it can afford to take a longer-run point of view and thus make fewer impulsive mistakes. The question of who owns the capital is nowadays almost irrelevant, because the managerial techniques that must be employed for large enterprises are very much the same whether they be public, private, or mixed.

It is worth some space to pursue this subject in greater detail, so as to reveal the variety of organizations suggested by the technical properties of the innovations.

ALGAL CULTURE. Initially these facilities will require the investment of only a few million dollars for an economic unit. Later, when the techniques for quality control have been perfected, there will be a need for the large process-minded corporation which sells only a dozen or so co-products, and deals almost entirely with other manufacturing firms. In the long run, algal culture is likely to be carried out in strings of virtually automatic factories operated by a few large organizations, but a few smaller firms operating limited acreage for special markets may stay in business.

FOOD SYNTHESIS. This requires market-oriented manufacturing with thousands of different products and continually increasing variety. Free competition, especially freedom of entry for new enterprises, can be very useful in this sector. The imagination required to create a new food has not been reduced to a science, and the capital required for getting into business on a small scale is not large. On the other hand staples and other large-volume items may be closely regulated by the government—owned and rationed by it if necessary. Most organizations would be restricted to a locale or region or subculture for reasons of distributive efficiency.

BIRTH CONTROL. Both education and volition are required here. It is an appropriate new activity for the government health department, but just how these bureaucrats can make themselves effective is not clear. A great deal more applied social science research must be carried out before the organizational methods become explicit.

ATOMIC POWER. The government-regulated utility, operating a regional grid as a monopoly, seems to be the present standard and such organizations appear to be perfectly competent to take over the running of nuclear reactors. Electrical equipment companies, manufacturing in either the reactor, generation, or distribution fields within underdeveloped nations, would do well to tie up with one or another of the dozen large international corporations because of the latter's fund of unpublished experience and accumulated skill.

MINING. The utilization of low-grade ores forces most of the future operations into a pattern now exhibited by the chemical process industries. This means large, virtually automatic installations with engineering-centered management and highly capitalized firms.

INSTRUMENTATION AND AUTOMATION. This will become an important section of the industry producing capital equipment. Some instruments and control systems are coming to have many general applications. These can be mass produced in the same manner as thermometers and television sets are handled at present. The organizational requirements for this component of the technology are readily understood. However, most products in this class will require a high proportion of research and development. It would be adapted carefully to whatever problems required solution. In this area, the large international firms have been acquiring important experience at an accelerated pace. Therefore, connections with such firms will save time and effort. However, they are equipped to solve only a part of the problems that will be encountered. The needs of automation are remarkably varied, requiring many unique experiences and points of view. There is room here for young men with ideas, the application of which does not fit the methods of the large corporation. They tend to function best as independent consultants and in small to medium-sized firms. Some governments might find it advisable to fit them into some loosely affiliated organization, a variation on the "group practice" scheme for medical specialists, in order to assure the survival of the enterprises. It is more important to assure freedom of entry in these activities than in any other foreseeable new technology. The problems of automation are so varied, requiring so many unique experiences and points of view, that it is obvious that large corporations with their emphasis upon standardized procedure could deal with only a fraction of them. There is room here for many small and medium-sized firms carrying out rather specialized functions.

WATER. Current studies upon the conservation of water, both as a resource and as a commodity, emphasize recommendations that there be water authorities for each independent basin. Such an authority is expected to play a skillful game against the weather, saving up for droughts while keeping storage capacity open to diminish the destructive effects of floods, and co-ordinating the use and re-use of the water as it flows downstream. Such organizations have limited effectiveness in Western countries because sewers and sanitary districts began life as separate organizations from the waterworks and are still mostly independent; control over vegetation and runoff in the upper watersheds is also only just beginning. The facilities proposed for extracting fresh water from sea water will fit quite well into the scope of activities attributed to an efficient water authority. The manufacture of fresh water provides a welcome stabilizing operation wherever it becomes feasible.

COMMUNICATIONS NETWORKS. The possibilities here are most remarkable because the new technologies offer at least 10 to 100 times greater flow of information at less than present average unit costs. Great savings are possible in the integration of such elements as radio, television, telephone, newspaper, magazines, books, libraries, postal systems, retailing, banking, files, and archives. Introducing new equipment, and new channels for connecting them, will lead to new ways of making decisions and quite new characteristics of organizations. The content or "programming" that fills these channels must be carefully managed so that it reinforces rather than impedes economic development. The bases for judging the value of communications are now, for the first time, being investigated seriously in applied social science, so that we have little insight as yet into the form the solutions will take.

It will be seen from the foregoing descriptions that, where the new organizations use technical data to a large extent and make decisions about predominantly material factors, one can be moderately confident that by taking the best of what is known today the problems can be solved. However, as soon as one needs to depend upon social behavior, as in birth control and communications, doubt and indecision as to the proper mode of organization become serious. This is partly because underdeveloped countries have no vested interest in the most technical areas—there are no important existing institutions that need to be displaced or modified. The new organizations move into a near vacuum of economic activity. But, when we deal in new technical aids for social interaction, older patterns must be overcome as the new take hold. The incoming institution here must be designed not only for long-run efficiency but also for the struggle for survival in the face of resistance or obstinacy from the time of inception to the time it achieves dominance. A persuasive case must be made from the start. Social scientists can provide the basis for such a case with studies of popular attitudes and the sampling of reactions of the public to the alternative procedures open to the organization. They would thus be able to point out many pitfalls in advance, and help guide the new organizations and administrations through their troubled infancies. It must be remembered, however, that social science is everywhere subsidized to a much smaller degree than natural science and engineering (usually less than 5% of the latter) and that sound research practice is even less evident in underdeveloped areas than in the applied natural sciences. Therefore, the most logical approach to these critical problems of new organizations will fail very often for sheer lack of qualified personnel.

The shortage of trained people will be painfully evident in many of the more technical organizations as well. One characteristic of an underdeveloped area is an imbalance of technical skills. There may be an abundance of theoretical chemists because very few are needed, but a dearth of analytical chemists, who seem to be a prerequisite for starting up many of these new technologies. There may be a respectable number of electrical engineers specializing in power, but virtually none in electronics (because that is too new an item in the regular engineering curriculum to have found its way to local universities!) or in mechanical engineering (because it requires getting one's hands dirty!). Agricultural engineers are known to avoid farm jobs, and mining engineers refuse to work underground, because such behavior is beneath their dignity. These inequalities and misunderstandings must be reduced somewhat in the gestation period that precedes the rapid phase of economic development, but to overcome them altogether will take much longer. The gaps in the ranks of qualified personnel needed for these organizations are another source of uncertainty affecting eventual success. This potential embarrassment is a strong reason for the proposal made earlier for setting up programs as soon as possible for going to the villages and seeking out the brightest youngsters who, after training, are to be co-opted into the professions and skilled trades where reinforcements are necessary. The training might not be adequate at first, but it is hoped that this deficiency would be made by the application of superior intelligence and by inculcating a personal philosophy that is both co-operative and opportunistic.

Earlier, in discussions of the evolving leadership classes observed and anticipated for the developmental society, it was suggested that conditions were likely to be created in some societies that would lead to the emergence of a scientist-executive class. The reasons given were two-fold. One was that many crucial decisions would depend upon the intelligent use of elaborate technical systems for processing relevant information. Another was that a large share of the burden of achieving adequate living standards rested upon the new industries which might be expected to find and develop competent scientist-executives. Persons with scientific training are likely to achieve key posts when the principal problems are related to the growth of technology. Much the same patterns for promotion may be expected in the government agencies developing the procedures for adapting complex statistical data to decisions.

It is in times of crisis, when the completion of the development program depends upon manipulating the remainder of the economy, that the scientist-executives may be impelled to accept the full responsibilities of political decision. Then it becomes a matter of saving the programs to which they have committed almost a lifetime of work. Everything about the social organization suited to the new technologies seems to be either neutral or confirmatory to such deductions. If the other strong socio-political forces, unrelated to the development effort, aid as much as they oppose the emergence of such an elite, this possibility remains one of the special outcomes that may be traced to this procedure for economic development. Many persons view the possibility of a scientist-dominated governing elite with strong misgivings—they trust professional politicians much more—and so would consider these implications to be an important liability associated with the proposals for using the most advanced science and technology.

Much will depend upon the second wave of organizations that are created in the wake of the new industries. By this is meant the professional societies, the institutions of higher learning, the social clubs, the political parties, the neighborhood organizations, the chambers of commerce, the philosophical circles, the bohemian art-centered cliques, and so on. These organizations establish an environment that permits identification of imbalance and malfunction brought about by the production-oriented organizations, and will often work out the preferred paths to reform, even to the extent of stimulating crusades. By means of this second wave of institutions, a cohesiveness is developed among the leaders in the culture that gives it a chance to reformulate its goals in the light of its current position and to take into account new forces unleashed in the rest of the world. The splitting up of personal loyalties among several nonfamily, noncommunal organizations makes it easier to experiment as well as to compromise. It is within these organizations that one should be able to observe the strongest interaction between the science-minded materialistic representatives from technological activities with cultural tradition and with the forces generated by social change in a developmental society. Political influence would be exerted indirectly by the roles played in one or another of these second-wave organizations.

At this point again a description of the anticipated effects of specific new technologies begins to break down. Nor can the picture be clarified by a resort to techniques found highly useful elsewhere in this evaluation of new patterns of living, i.e., by deducing what appear to be prerequisites to successful economic development within a given framework. In the later stages of economic development a variety of strategies begins to open up. Even societies with similar heritage and resources may move in quite different directions. Each must originate its own compromises; therefore its future history will be unique and only the vaguest of generalizations about strategy are appropriate at this time.

Considering the alternative strategies for organizing economic development is part of the planning process. Wherever resources are scarce, and a long-range social goal has been set which requires the employment of such resources, planning is necessary. Very few, if any, of the poorer societies need to be convinced of this. Nevertheless, very few of them understand what the planning process implies, or how to go about setting up an effective planning organization that would be expected to knit together the expansions of the other new organizations described earlier. It must make sure that they do not work at cross-purposes when committing the future.

The planning agency, if it is to succeed, cannot be created by fiat. It must start from small beginnings and carve out a key place for itself in the course of the development of the political system. This role is likely to differ markedly from country to country, even among those belonging to the same cultural grouping (e.g., the Arabic-speaking countries, or the Latin American bloc). At first it may only be a staff agency preparing policy for the long run, working like any other staff agency. However as time goes on, and maintaining the *pace* of the development becomes critical, then at least some form of veto power, either formal or informal, must come to reside in the agency. The veto would be used to prevent the misapplication of resources which would slow down progress later on. In order to justify such actions, and show that it was not being arbitrary, the agency would have to prepare a working plan, or master plan, to fit the objectives embodied in a long-term development plan. (See Fig. 26.)

One feature of an effective planning organization has already been made abundantly clear in the contemporary experience with this kind of development effort. It is no longer possible to divide responsibility between town and country planning on one hand, and economic and social planning on the regional and national scale on the other. The very large-scale urbanization that must be created in most cases, simultaneous with a continuing demand for raising the productivity of both capital and labor, requires that the plans be all of one framework. Delivering the responsibility to two independent agencies, as is done in most of Europe today, is out of the question.

In order to describe more clearly what the character of this integrating organization should be, it is necessary first to describe what it should do. The immediate task is to examine the goals of the society of which it is a part and for which it is expected to serve. What is the level of living sought? What are the degrees and kinds of personal freedom insisted upon? How much security from attack is demanded? What are the relations desired with other peoples in the world? In each society there are other questions equally significant. If such ends are contradictory, and the conflicts between ends are not likely to resolve themselves in the passage of time, then very likely the first program must be to get consensus upon a consistent set of ends that can be reformulated as concrete goals. With consensus of the decision-makers (in many cases this means a majority of the voters, but it can also mean a preponderance of the intelligentsia, or the institutions controlling political behavior—sometimes called "vested interests"), it is possible to

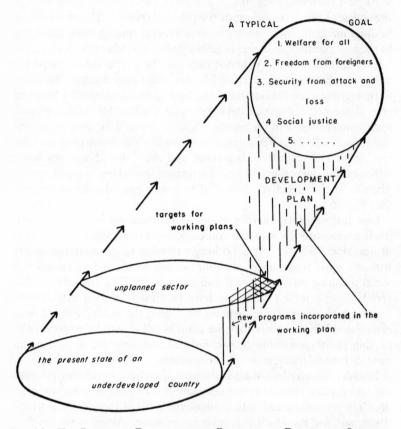

FIG. 26. THE PROCESS OF DEVELOPMENTAL PLANNING FOR DEMOCRATIC SOCIETIES

The development plan employs the available resources for transforming the society from its present undesirable state to that described by the goal. The ends mentioned in this goal are subscribed to by the literate element in virtually all underdeveloped areas, but the order of importance will vary according to circumstances. The working plans (often called master plans) incorporate a series of programs aimed at achieving intermediate targets set some 5 to 15 years in advance. Subsequent plans introduce new programs and are subject to many revisions. It is anticipated that the respective priorities will need to be occasionally revised during the development.

outline the course of development of the following half century or so that will have a real chance of being accepted and used.

In this development plan resources, manpower, and technics are marshaled, scheduled, and applied on paper in such a manner as would appear to achieve the long-range goals. In order to arrive at such a plan alternative strategies must be considered, and from these possibilities one direction must be chosen. Then, within the framework of the development plan outlined, a more explicit plan of action must be worked out. Such a working plan will cover only the next five years or so, because it takes two to three years to get a major piece of capital equipment into operation, once the commitment has been made, and because it is not possible to see clearly more than two or three successive steps into the future.

Planning requires the highest technical and political competence because the decisions have to be worked out under conditions of uncertainty and executed in an environment over which there is only partial control. These are conditions that apply also for the enterprising businessman. It is not surprising therefore that some of the best examples of planning technique to date will be found in growing firms. Firms, however, are specialists; in almost all cases they are concerned with the minor fraction of the economy that is linked in some manner to their own operations. Their problems are still simple as compared to the regional or national planning organizations which must deal with the total complex of interactions.

In planning, as elsewhere, it is easier to imitate than innovate, but where will the developmental society find models worth copying? Western Europe is a poor place to start, not only because the planning there is adapted to mature, slow growing societies, but also because the agencies for town and country planning are divorced from those responsible for social and economic planning. Nor have they completely outgrown the doctrines of nineteenth-century socialism, even where the ideologies lead to abnormally expensive administrative costs. As noted before, some of the most competent planning is done in the United States, where the word itself is under a cloud, but never on a comprehensive basis. In some of the large corporations, production planning has been developed to a fine art. In the TVA and in Puerto Rico, the principles and practice of regional planning have been developed. Comprehensive national planning has evolved in the U.S.S.R.; it has acquired a great deal of prestige in underdeveloped parts of the world mainly because it appears to be successful. Detailed analysis by British and American scholars (Bergson, 1953) suggests that much of this respect is based upon illusion, but they are the first to admit that Russian experiences, if the true facts were to be made available, could contribute a great deal to the understanding of the workings of a comprehensive planning organization during economic development.

An important element in such planning is the provision for changing tactics, or even strategies, in the face of exigencies. The best examples for this technique will be found in military planning. This may mean allocating scarce manpower to the working out of plans that will never again be pulled out of the files, but it will also mean that there will be few occasions where decisions must be made without previous study and programming. The military organizations are also pioneering in the field of linear programming, a mathematical technique that may be useful for routinizing the scheduling element in planning.

It will be seen that the task of describing the planning organization and how it functions in a developmental society has been largely evaded. Instead, the places where fragments of relevant contemporary experience reside have been enumerated and, it is asserted, each country will have to make its own synthesis from these sources. Very likely, if it is to be done at all well, the effort must be a co-operative one between scholars in developed countries and civil servants from the respective underdeveloped areas. A body of relevant theory would be most helpful—if it is at all feasible—for compressing this experience in such a way that the whole can be comprehended as well as the interrelationships between the parts. This is a field that has been badly neglected by Western universities in recent times; therefore several promising leads have been lying about in the literature unnoticed, and not followed up.

Throughout this discussion it has been presumed that each country would set its own course. Deutsch (1953) has shown that a wave of nationalism must be expected as social communications increase in the underdeveloped areas. This extension of the "belonging" feeling from the family or community to the nation brings with it a need to demonstrate independence from the influence of alien authority. The emotional drive associated with increasing nationalism is possibly a necessary element for the evolution of the developmental society, but it does not encourage the rapid expansion of world organization. International agencies will be welcome only when it is almost unanimously agreed that they will not upset the internal power structure. Such a xenophobic period may be modified if real progress is achieved over the period of a generation, and some self-assurance is generated. Therefore, truly close political and economic co-operation at the international level may come into being but only toward the end of the world development period.

This means, too, that external capital can be expected to move to underdeveloped areas only in very limited amounts. It must be obtained for the developing economies on terms their own nationalists will accept, a fact that means that Western nations and corporations are likely to invest in such areas only when they have little choice, e.g., when all the alternative sites for investment have been exploited. These sums are still quite large as compared to the present rate of investment. The McGraw-Hill economists have estimated that an investment of roughly 60 billions of dollars outside of North America would be required to implement the recommendations of the President's Materials Policy Commission by 1975, and it is apparent that the investment rate must accelerate after that date if the American economy continues to expand (Business Week, Oct. 31, 1953). The normal development of tourism, and the attendant expansion of transport and communications services, should bring some additional billions of dollars in investment over this period. Other programs, such as those dealing with international health and education, may contribute a bit more. However, the investments anticipated are still small as compared to the needs for capital in underdeveloped regions; moreover, a major proportion of the funds seem destined to go to the resource-rich and less densely populated areas. Such considerations, which are essentially economic, reinforce those based upon political judgments. Close co-operation between developed and underdeveloped countries will not flow from presently anticipated relationships.

These arguments appear to be incompatible with an advocacy of automation and a full complement of capital-intensive industries for the early stages of development; they assert that it will be neither economic nor politic, according to existing modes of thinking, to invest significant quantities of capital in densely populated resource-shy areas. Thus, if the underdeveloped countries are left to struggle individually (or collectively in regional associations) to conserve and assemble their own capital, it will take a long time to acquire the nest egg needed to initiate a development program worthy of the name.

However, the world has been overmuch impressed by the tales of capital shortages in underdeveloped areas. It should be emphasized that the world *has* the industrial capacity to produce this equipment, and it has institutions for accumulating savings in the quantities required.

That is more than can be said for the supply of technical specialists needed to install such capital equipment and get it to producing efficiently, just to give one example where true shortages exist. The principal embarrassment is that the savings are available in North America, Western Europe, and the U.S.S.R., while the most critical needs are to be found in distant and independent regions. The circumstances call for some arrangement whereby capital-accumulating countries get some significant return, whether psychological (such as the increased sense of security associated with the implementation of the Marshall Plan) or otherwise, for the use of their capital. Such an accounting device would no doubt turn out to be one of the most rewarding innovations in the domain of world development.

It seems that a device of this sort is prerequisite to economic development in many parts of the world. If it is to be accepted, the arrangement should be tied in some manner, as yet unspecified, to new or existing international organizations. This would keep the transfer from appearing to be straightforward economic imperialism. Yet, if the temper and evolution of both the donors and the recipients are judged rightly, these international agencies cannot be permitted to generate authority. They can be organized to deal with a community of independent "open societies," they can "co-ordinate" or "assist," but they cannot rule. Such co-ordination can occur most easily at a technical level, but there is no hint as yet that the expansion of the interchange of technical services or the use of the new technologies for economic development should introduce a form of world government. The activities required do not go very far beyond the present work of the United Nations.

Perhaps much later, when several major countries are making a supreme effort to reach welfare goals, and the leaders are no longer concerned about their status vis-à-vis the foreigners, some new demands will be made upon international organizations. They should be based upon very careful calculations showing how the separate societies would tend to gain more than they lose. It will be remembered that this is the same phase of economic development where it seems possible that a technical elite may become part of the leadership class.

It may be concluded from this discussion of social organization that, if technological problems can be solved as envisioned, the overwhelming task of development will be found in the internal organization of the developmental society. The task does not appear to be spectacularly difficult when the requirements are put into words because we have little comprehension of the work entailed in a massive break with tradition, nor is it easy to visualize the amount of knowledge and effort required to transform a "vicious circle" into a slowly rising spiral. Our ignorance of the social relationships in each of the underdeveloped societies is so abysmal we do not even know how to measure the dimensions of the developmental effort. Here is the supreme challenge for social science and the administrative arts for the coming half century. The need for a planning agency and a body of planning theory, to bring the engineering features together with the socio-economic aspects, is equally evident. Beyond this there must be found some mutually satisfactory formula for transferring credit, capital equipment, and technical experts from the developed to the underdeveloped areas via an international organization.

ADDED FOR THE SECOND EDITION

Some of the necessary institutions have been established and are working reasonably smoothly (e.g., IBRD, UNICEF, SUNFED, and various bilateral or regional programs). The international credits system remains shaky, to say the least, and is now being vigorously debated. An international body on planning and urbanization has yet to be formed. Problems of conflict resolution among nations are still very much with us. The exchange of technical expertise has been very much accelerated, however, by the entry of a surprisingly large number of national corporations upon the international scene.

The mathematical programming techniques of planning that were much discussed after 1954 turned out to be premature. For a long time to come the first task of a planning agency will be that of setting up procedures for obtaining dependable data regarding conditions in the society. Most of the action that needs to be undertaken thereafter will not require sophisticated techniques of optimization.

7. OTHER HORIZONS

Now it is time to back off and look at organization for technology in a new perspective. Up till now, in the search for some means of solving critical problems of supply, demand, or growth, only the easiest, the cheapest, or the most popular solutions were accepted and explored. From the solutions to individual problems, optimal patterns or strategies for development were assembled. This procedure leads to a somewhat incomplete formula (the remainder depends upon the employment of economic, social, and political institutions that are not directly affected by the anticipated changes in technology—presumably quite stable over

a span of several decades—and therefore beyond the scope of this book)
for improving the level of living up to a satisfactory scale at minimum
social cost.

However, a large component of the influential classes in present underdeveloped countries do not seem to be so worried about social costs.
There is an undercurrent of feeling, which often comes to the surface
in the form of some ancient adage or parable, that anything truly worth
while is achieved only through suffering and struggle. Thus, the easiest
way out is automatically regarded with suspicion. For such people, the
foregoing strategy of development, which would be considered to be still
difficult and fraught with risk by experienced Western critics, might be
regarded as too simple and too easy. Remember, too, that it is this elite,
and others within the society, which makes the decision, and not the
outside expert. Therefore, this exercise in ingenuity, using science and
technology for synthesizing new tools for economic development while
permitting moderate rates of social change, may be quite unrealistic for
many underdeveloped areas. Much more radical strategies might be
more readily accepted.

There are, of course, other highly original proposals for world development that go beyond the one that has been outlined here. Unfortunately they have not yet been explored as total systems. It would be
extremely useful to see them elaborated to the point where the technical
solutions to the food, fuel, population, and other problems were apparent, and the new patterns of living resulting from them were traced
at least as far as has been attempted in this study. It is a task for the
scientific generalist, those rare scientists who move from discipline to
discipline, and problem to problem, seeking intellectual gratification, or
for a team of imaginative specialists capably led. Once each of these
radical proposals has been thoroughly explored and analyzed by proponents and critics it might be possible to make less blind choices.

Another system, for example, might start from the position that Jean
Rostand (1950) has taken. "There can be no doubt that, from now on,
humanity will be able to control, to a great extent, its own organic
destiny. It need not be objected that we do not know enough about
heredity to act decisively on man. If humanity were to find itself
manipulated by a superior being who knew no more than is known
about genetics, but in whose interest it would be to make the race
evolve, mankind would soon be making perceptible progress. Today,
therefore, the question is not one of knowing or being able, but of
desiring and daring. . . . Encouraged by our successes in zootechnics

and phytotechnics, are we to go forward courageously to anthropotechnics? Are we to submit ourselves to those same techniques that are so astonishingly successful when applied to our livestock and our poultry?" He goes on to point out that this is a moral problem, a matter of social choice, which scientists may speculate about but are not permitted to resolve by themselves.

Rostand appears to be interested in the individual capacities and achievements of man. His strategy for development would presumably concentrate upon improving the potential for individual performance in future generations. The problems of improving level of living still exist, but, extending his argument, they would become easier to solve because a larger contingent would be more adaptable and more intelligent. However, no proposals have been made for setting such a society into motion, or to reduce its vulnerability to schism and other hazards. No suggestions have been made as to where novel procedures and organizations need to be grafted upon contemporary traditions or, in other words, how much of the accumulated experience of the world is to be used and what part is to be substituted.

Other people seem to be interested in communal societies where individual expression is reinforced and extended in a group by persons with equivalent or complementary interests before the contribution is even identified as the product of an individual. By a skillful structuring of groups, one might get the necessary work done for improving the level of living. However, in order to get markedly greater efficiency and accountability, many forms of groups, and hierarchies of groups, would have to be rejected. One of them that may be rejected is the family. The extended family, which includes grandparents and less fortunate relatives, ordinarily found in lower economic strata everywhere, is likely to be abandoned in the course of most patterns of economic development, but the nuclear biological family evolved in recent times mainly in Western countries is not the only alternative. Perhaps four or five different primary groups may be invented, each substituting in part for the family.

However, such a fundamentally different society requires converts and, in order to attract the kinds of disaffected persons that are potential converts, a fully developed ideology must be prepared. From recent experience with communism, fascism, and nazism we know that some of these new groups can be formed, and that they will often become the basis for a powerful society in the short run. We know, too, that such ideologies may be virulent, resulting in bloodshed, conflict, and oppression, and lead to no economic progress at all in the long run.

Can a viable ideology, and associated social system, be constructed which encourages progress and tolerates deviants? The need for using natural science effectively already provides many fixed points and invariants, both for the ideology and the social system. The social psychology of groups provides quite a few more. The presently developing theories of organization will tie things down elsewhere at a few spots. Incorporating a system for economizing is necessary. Exploiting contemporary social science to the fullest extent would still leave quite a few parts of the social system indeterminate, but for these gaps the ideology should provide a faith, a commonly accepted set of criteria for making decisions in the absence of experience.

Such an approach should yield not one scheme but perhaps a half dozen or more distinctly different alternatives. The careful spelling out of such alternatives would be quite useful materials for the intelligentsia of underdeveloped areas. This work is, unfortunately, speculation, and the kind of speculation that is in disfavor in almost all academic circles today. Natural scientists and social scientists alike have had, in a dimly remembered past, bad experiences with speculation. It led to polemics that could not be resolved, to a condition of nonaccumulation of operational concepts, and to an inability to discover and exclude crackpots. The only accepted means for discussing in public speculations about the implications of rather extensive modifications in the structure of society is in the form of fiction. But fiction, thus far at least, is insufficiently disciplined; it searches for effect, and will conveniently disregard facts if they stand in the way. What is needed now is a scholarly environment that encourages serious analysis of the future. This means not only the establishment of risks and trends, but also the formulation of new utopias that are consonant with the resources at the disposal of the society. Such a discipline would be necessary, too, to plot the conjunctural evolution of the various societies toward a single world society, but that is a task for the long run, rather than today.

In closing, it must be pointed out that all these new tools for economic development, the new organizations which put them to work, and the social systems that employ them, are intended only to improve the state of man so that he is granted the opportunity to choose for himself. Nothing fundamental is really decided upon in reaching for a minimum adequate standard of living. Man's destiny, his relationship to society, and his means for choosing intimates remain an open and unsettled question. Economic improvement on a world scale means that instead of some 300,000,000 people participating in the critical decisions with their votes and opinions, as is true today, there will be perhaps ten times that number. Thus world development, as it is depicted here, would be a liberating effort; it would permit many more persons to choose a pattern of living for themselves and to become sufficiently informed to enter into the settling of social and political issues. This means that a new freedom could be created, which has been aptly called "freedom from want," in order that other values may be cultivated.

Selected References

CONTROL OF POPULATION GROWTH

C. Tietze, "Therapeutic Abortions in New York City," *Am. J. Obstet. Gynecol.*, **60**, p. 146 (1950).

C. Tietze, S. R. Poliakoff, and R. Rock, "The Clinical Effectiveness of the Rhythm Method of Contraception," *Fertility and Sterility*, **2**, p. 444 (1951).

I. B. Taeuber, "Family, Migration, and Industrialization in Japan," *American Social. Rev.*, **16**, p. 149 (1951).

G. G. Hartman, ed., *World Population Problems and Birth Control*, Ann. N. Y. Acad. Sci., **54**, art. 4, pp. 729–868 (1952).

P. K. Hatt, ed., *World Population and Future Resources*, American Book Company, New York, 1952.

B. F. Sieve, "A New Anti-Fertility Factor," *Science*, **116**, p. 373 (1952).

B. P. Wiesner and J. Yudkin, "Inhibition of Oestrus by Cultivated Gromwell," *Nature*, **170**, p. 274 (1952).

M. Bronfenbrenner, "The High Cost of Economic Development," *J. Land Econ.*, **29**, p. 93 (1953).

S. Chandrasekhar, "The Prospect of Planned Parenthood," *Pacific Affairs*, **26**, p. 318 (1953).

M. C. Chang and G. Pincus, "Does Phosphorylated Hesperidin Affect Fertility?" *Science*, **117**, p. 274 (1953).

G. J. Martin, "Phosphorylated Hesperidin," *Science*, **117**, p. 363 (1953).

W. O. Nelson and E. Steinberger, "Effects of Nitrofuran Compounds on the Testis of the Rat," *Federation Proc.*, **12**, p. 103 (March 1953).

W. F. Ogburn, "A Design for Some Experiments in the Limitation of Population Growth in India," *Econ. Development and Cultural Change*, **5**, p. 376 (1953); "Social Aspects of Population Change," *Brit. J. of Sociol.*, **4**, p. 25 (1953).

B. Ryan, "Institutional Factors in Sinhalese Fertility," *Milbank Mem. Fund Quart.*, **30**, p. 359 (1953).

P. S. Henshaw, "Physiologic Control of Fertility," *Science*, **117**, p. 572 (1953).

R. L. Noble and R. C. B. Graham, "Lithosperm-like Action of Certain Quinones and Related Compounds," *J. Can. Med. Assoc.*, **69**, 576–81 (1953).

F. Lorimer, *Culture and Human Fertility*, UNESCO, Paris, 1954.

S. N. Sanyal, "Temporary Sterility Effect of *Pisum Sativum*," *Int. Med. Abstr. Revs.*, **16**, pp. 91–93 (1954); see also S. Ghosh and A. Gupta, *ibid.*, pp. 89–90.

N. Millman and C. G. Hartman, "Oral Control of Conception: A Contemporary Survey," *Fertility and Sterility*, **7**, pp. 110–122 (1956).

SOCIAL CHANGE AND ORGANIZATION

G. K. Zipf, *National Unity and Disunity*, Principia, Bloomington, Ind., pp. 1–87 (1941).

J. Q. Stewart, "Empirical Mathematical Rules Concerning the Distribution and Equilibrium of Population," *Geogr. Rev.*, **37**, pp. 461–485 (1947).

S. Giedion, *Mechanization Takes Command*, Oxford University Press, New York, 1948.

J. Rostand, "The Future of Biology," *Impact*, **2**, p. 88 (1951).

D. Riesman, *The Lonely Crowd*, Yale University Press, New Haven, 1950.

H. G. Aubrey, "Small Industry in Economic Development," *Social Res.*, **18**, p. 269 (1951).

E. W. Zimmerman, *World Resources and Industry*, Harper and Brothers, New York, 1951.

W. Isard and V. Whitney, *Atomic Power*, Blakiston Co., New York, 1952.

United Nations Housing in the Tropics, *Housing and Town and Country Planning, No. 6*, 1952.

K. W. Deutsch, *Nationalism and Social Communications*, Technology Press and John Wiley & Sons, New York, 1953.

J. Diebold, *Automation*, D. Van Nostrand Co., New York, 1953.

Le Corbusier, *Complete Works 1946–1952*, W. Boesiger, Zurich, 1953.

D. Lerner, "Communication Networks, Media Exposure, and Concomitant Responses," *Sociometry*, **16**, p. 266 (1953).

Philipps Ruopp, ed., *Approaches to Community Development*, van Hoeve, The Hague, 1953.

A. Bergson, ed., *Soviet Economic Growth*, Row, Peterson & Co., Evanston, Ill., 1953.

Dept. of Scientific and Industrial Research, *Colonial Building Notes*, Building Research Station, Watford, Herts, England, 1950 to 1955.

E. Staley, *The Future of Underdeveloped Countries*, Council on Foreign Relations, New York, 1954.

R. L. Meier, "Automatic and Economic Development," *Bull. Atomic Scientists*, **10**, p. 129 (1954).

M. Nash, "Notes on Village Industrialization in South and East Asia," *Econ. Development and Cultural Change*, **3**, p. 271 (1955).

R. L. Meier, "Biological Cycles in the Transformation of Solar Energy into Useful Fuels," in *Solar Energy Research*, F. Daniels and J. A. Duffie, eds., University of Wisconsin Press, Madison, 1955.

R. Hill, K. W. Back, and J. M. Stycos, "Family Structure and Fertility in Puerto Rico," *Social Problems*, **3**, p. 82 (1955).

J. Froomkin, "Fiscal Management of Municipalities and Economic Development," *Econ. Development and Cultural Change*, **3**, p. 309 (1955).

A. K. Biswas and M. K. Mueller, "Population Growth and Economic Development in India," *Indian Econ. J.*, **2**, p. 238 (1955).

R. L. Meier, "Automatism in the American Society," *Journal of Business*, **29**, p. 14 (1956).

STANDARDS OF LIVING

B. Seebohm Rowntree, *The Human Needs of Labour*, T. Nelson and Sons, London, 1918; *Poverty and Progress*, Longmans, Green and Co., London, 1941; with G. R.

Lavers, *Poverty and the Welfare State*, Longmans, 1951.

——, *Quantity and Cost Budgets*, 1936, Heller Committee for Research in Social Economics, University of California (mimeographed).

M. G. Luck and A. B. Cummings, *Standards of Relief in California, 1940*, University of California Press, Berkeley, 1945.

R. A. Dahl and C. E. Lindblom, *Politics, Economics, and Welfare*, Harper & Brothers, New York, 1953.

H. E. Pipping, *Standard of Living: The Concept and its Place in Economics*, Societas Scientarum Fennica, Helsinki, 1953.

B. R. Rairikar, "Welfare Economics and Welfare Criteria," *Indian J. Econ.*, **34**, p. 1 (1953).

RECAPITULATION

1

In order that the problem of world development may be seen as a whole, some readily communicated quantitative framework must be assembled. At the foundation of such a structure there will always be simplifying assumptions upon which the argument, and the conclusions, will ultimately rest. The key assumptions, beyond those implied by the term *development*, employed in an assessment of the present world predicament were:

1. Some agreement can exist as to what constitutes an adequate level of living or need. (This implies that conflicts of opinion regarding physical welfare are compromisable, and the area of compromise can be predicted.)

2. Common commodity types for summarizing *needs* and expressing them in quantitative terms include energy, protein, water, materials of construction, metals, fibers, and paper. (This implies that a variety of inputs can be usefully consolidated.)

3. Current estimates as to "probable reserves" of minerals can be *economically* exploited in the long run. (This assumes that new discoveries will just balance out the very familiar overoptimism surrounding known strikes.)

4. All new resource developments will have applied to them the best of the proved techniques known today. (This implies nearly ideal resource management and exploitation.)

5. Trends in population will continue more or less in the direction they are now moving. The over-all death rate should continue to drop off rapidly, with the birth

rate following after some lag; thus, a considerable increase in world population should be anticipated.

It can be deduced from current statistics, using the principles noted here, that energy needs fall into the range of 1 to 4×10^7 Cal/yr per capita. Equable climate and heavy population density provide typical conditions for the lower end of the range. The consumption data suggested for other categories of need have even wider variations.

The number making such claims upon resources in the future depends upon the present world population, its current rate of growth, the conditions affecting the "maturation" of a population of a given culture, and the absence of worldwide calamity. Upon weighing these factors, world population is expected to expand from $2\frac{1}{2}$ billions at the moment to 3 to $3\frac{3}{4}$ billions by the year 2000 A.D. Present trends suggest that world population is not likely to stop its growth this side of 5 billions, but this takes the extrapolation much further than the amount of decent demographic experience we have had up to the present.

The resources available for meeting food, fiber, and paper needs are almost entirely renewable in character, but the seasonal capacity of the earth has both absolute limits and also limits set by the state of technics. The practical capacity for food production is around 6×10^{15} Cal/yr, while that of the forests comes to about 16×10^{15} Cal/yr.

The fossil fuel resources are nonrenewable because there is only an insignificant rate of replenishment. Probable reserves are estimated at 2 to 3×10^{19} Cal. Other mineral reserves cannot be estimated so well, but it is apparent that higher-grade deposits are disappearing rapidly. Increasing costs of various metals, especially nickel and lead, will bring into use many partial substitutes and provide added incentive for scrap collection. Therefore, minerals other than fossil fuels (and fissile materials) have properties that give them a more renewable character as time passes. They are not destroyed, but merely diluted or mixed up.

With needs added up on one side of the ledger, and capacity to supply these needs on the other—with technics held constant but applied as well as we know how—it is possible to mark off critical points in the future when specific needs will begin to exceed potential supply. For protein foods this date is about 1960, whereas for fruits and vegetables it is about 1970, and for the carbohydrate foods some time after 2000. Fiber and paper supplies seem adequate. For the area outside of North America, fossil fuel use must start declining about 2050, long before the needs for energy are provided for all the population anticipated then, even if "low-waste" exploitation patterns are used. In North America, however, energy prospects are much better and may easily last several centuries. The availability of other minerals will be mainly a matter of price, or energy cost. Common metals like aluminum, titanium, and magnesium are greatly dependent upon the availability of energy.

For the future, energy-conserving innovations will become more important than energy-using developments. Technical progress can no longer be measured in terms of horsepower per employee but only with some less direct index which gets closer to welfare or productivity.

II

An over-all improvement in diet depends upon the modification of tastes so that new and more available foods will be accepted, and also upon measures for increasing the total amount of food produced. Measures for the improvement of agriculture through research and farmer education are important, but they do not seem to be adequate to meet global needs. A large portion of the research under way is concerned with luxury foods, while only a very small part is aimed at increasing yields of plant proteins and other highest-priority shortages. World problems thus suggest quite a different research emphasis from that which exists.

If we continue to apply only known and well-understood technics, critical shortages of protein must be anticipated. Already, even the poorest quality proteins are several times more expensive than low-quality fats and carbohydrates. Only about 15% of the (caloric) content of an adequate diet need be protein, but this may easily account for half the over-all cost at the moment and the proportion seems likely to increase.

How are proteins produced in nature? Recent investigations show that protein synthesis begins in the leaf, in the immediate neighborhood of the chloroplast. By a circuitous process, involving considerable loss, this protein may later be concentrated in the seeds. This suggests the possibility of harvesting leaves before this translocation occurs and extracting the protein directly from the leaves. A study has been made exploring the possibilities of such a process. In practice it turns out that it is difficult to remove all the protein from the leaf directly, and that the indirect methods available lead to unexpected losses and extra expenses. Crude protein from the leaf appears to be edible, but its flavor does not generate enthusiasm.

The best large-volume agricultural sources of cheap proteins have been found to be the seeds of the legumes—soybeans, peanuts, beans, gram, etc. Improvement in their availability depends upon the opening up of new climates and new soils for their cropping. However, this advance is slow because it depends upon the evolution of an effective agricultural extension system to promote a special strain of soybeans (or peanuts) in the tropics. The capital costs were estimated to be in the range of $500 to $1500 per annual ton of crude protein, with the higher part of the range applying to densely populated areas in the tropics.

Will the sea offer any better chance for providing protein? Present technics for exploiting the accessible parts of the sea are coming close to their natural limits. Many of the fishing areas are yielding declining catches. The possibility of growing fish like livestock, in fertilized ponds or rice paddies, has been looked into and found to be quite useful. The yields can be quite good for persons skilled in the art, but the costs are cheap only when compared to the cost of meat. Because of the problems of preserving fish, the costs to the consumer may be double or treble those for plant proteins. The marine equivalent to the leaf, where the proteins are originally synthesized, are the phytoplankton. Attempts have been made to harvest these plankton, but the costs of separation from sea water are so large, and the product is of such low value, that it seems quite unlikely such an approach will be feasible. A small but not fully established possibility that there exists a layer of shrimps, laying quite deep in the open oceans, may be exploited.

Quite a different approach is open, if microorganisms are used to manufacture protein. Then the unused capacity to grow carbohydrates, such as sugar, starch, and cellulose, may be combined with fertilizer-grade nitrogen and phosphorus as a food for the microorganisms. Microorganisms can convert these materials, when cultured in large-scale facilities, into cell-substance (principally protein). Several commercial plants have been constructed for the production of food yeast; therefore, the costs can be established. Initially the capital required per annual ton of protein in yeast may be somewhat less than $500, but this sum would increase greatly as marginal resources for carbohydrate production are brought into use. If the food yeast were accepted generally by humans, it would make a significant contribution toward eliminating the protein shortage, but it is still far from satisfying the total needs. Instead of yeast, other microorganisms may be grown whose flavor and nutritional values are different, but none of these is as economical, except possibly those which manufacture their own carbohydrates via photosynthesis.

The study of algae, which are of this last group, has been brought thus far to a pilot plant stage for one species—*Chlorella pyrenoidosa*. The algae have roughly the same protein composition as food yeast or soybean protein. Their cultures may be spread over flat unproductive land or protected lagoons and are expected to be enclosed in thin-film plastic tubing. For the *Chlorella*, the inputs to the process are fresh water, soluble fertilizer chemicals, carbon dioxide, and sunlight, while the outputs are oxygen and *Chlorella* cells. Costs should be close to those of yeast, but there is a good chance of reducing them by (1) growing algae that prefer a warm environment, (2) culturing those species which fix all their own nitrogen from the atmosphere, and (3) finding strains that also do well in sea water. If these developments are accomplished, it should be possible to produce plant proteins for no more cost than present day carbohydrates (5 to 15¢ per lb) and with a capital requirement per annual ton of protein of $300 to $600.

Fats and carbohydrates may also be obtained by these mass culture techniques, but the conditions that are required in order to produce predominant fat, or carbohydrate, also seem to ensure a reduction in the efficiency of photosynthesis. Therefore, this analysis of the long-run potentialities of world food production suggests that protein and vitamins (microorganisms are very rich in most vitamins) should have declining costs, although we may anticipate relatively constant prices for fats and gently rising costs for carbohydrates.

These recent scientific advances offer means for producing sufficient foodstuffs to care for at least twenty times the present world population, but there has been exceedingly little study of the procedures for converting the new products into food. Most people are quite conservative about what they choose to eat and, short of absolute starvation, the poorer the culture, the more resistant to change they tend to be. Therefore, the rate at which new foodstuffs can be introduced to satisfy needs will depend much more upon progress in the psychology and sociology of food acceptance than upon advances in technology. Many of the problems affecting the acceptance of new foods can be solved by imaginative people without the benefit of extensive scientific training.

III

Energy for the future depends not only upon improving the long-run supply through introducing new fuels, but also upon modifying present energy consumption patterns. The world must continue the search for economical energy sources, while at the same time it reduces the amount required to maintain an adequate level of living.

There are some long-known sources of energy, now unused, that appear to be low enough in cost to warrant commercial development in the near future. The most promising of these is wind power. Others, somewhat more distant, are tide power, and thermal difference situations. All of these would yield energy in the form of electric current, but in very restricted locales and in trivial quantities as compared to world needs. They also encounter a problem of energy storage—needed to carry the consumers through the slack periods.

Solar energy is more promising. Cooking units that operate by day or by night appear quite feasible for towns and villages in the tropics. For some climates even sun-powered air conditioning appears practicable. Solar sources for house heating and hot water heating are also possible, but the costs seem reasonable only for areas with sunny winters. Perhaps most promising in the long run is a biological cycle which includes algal culture linked with methane or hydrogen fermentation. These energy-rich gaseous products can be used for electric power generation, or they can be converted to liquid fuels, or they can be applied directly to industrial operations. A major by-product could be the fixed nitrogen that some blue-green species can synthesize from the nitrogen in air. There may be other salable by-products if the process is carried to its logical conclusion. This biological means of converting solar energy into conventional forms of energy can, without added expense, smooth out the daily cycle, but it remains somewhat vulnerable to weather and seasonal cycles. The prospective energy efficiency ranges from 5 to 17% of the solar input at the most favorable sites. This means from 5 to 9 tons of hydrocarbon fuels per acre per year.

Atomic power is equally hopeful, but further advanced technically. It is realized now that atomic power will be most useful for cities, because large power plants are more economical. Even then, anticipated costs are not low, but are more or less equal to present costs of energy in populous centers farthest from the sources of fossil fuels. Requirements of public safety are likely to prohibit atomic-powered transport except for large units. However, small low-powered decentralized atomic reactors can be useful for heating in the more densely built-up portions of cities. The reserve of fissile fuels is roughly 1000 times as great as that of the fossil fuels, if very low-grade deposits are taken into account.

These two major energy sources are quite complementary in character. Atomic power comes in large blocks from a point source, whereas solar energy comes in smaller units from extensive surfaces. Atomic power is not effectively transformed into liquid fuels for transport purposes, whereas solar energy is apparently most efficient when converted into hydrocarbons.

These new energy sources can provide large amounts of energy almost in perpetuity, but at a cost very likely higher than is ordinarily paid today. Poorer parts of the world must still look for methods of conserving energy if they are ever to achieve an adequate level of comforts and conveniences. The scientific analysis of comfort shows quite clearly that by carefully fitting together the clothing worn with the equipment for heating (or cooling in some rarer instances), much energy can be conserved—in the home, in the community activities, and in the workplace. If convenience is defined as an economizing upon time in order to carry out the necessary tasks of living, then the principal expenditures of energy for convenience tend to be in transport, communications, lighting, and other household equipment. In transport it was found that for larger urbanized areas in temperate to tropical climates, a system of electric railways, human-powered equipment such as bicycles, handcarts, etc., and low-powered motor vehicles can give satisfactory convenience at the lowest cost whether it be measured in time, energy, or money. Communications actually use very little power, and so communications devices may become an inherent part of energy-saving systems in transport and in household equipment.

A potential difficulty that cannot be neglected is whether there is some quality in the fossil fuels that renders them unique in the processing of raw materials into useful artifacts. The most important instance is that of coking coal. The best known substitute, charcoal, is not likely to be available in sufficient quantities to meet iron and steel needs. However in this instance there appears to be another technology, involving hydrogen-reduction and electric furnaces, that can be brought into operation at costs very little higher than presently experienced. Suppliers of materials may be forced into the exploitation of very low-grade deposits, and a greater re-use of scrap, but fuel-changing does not threaten any embarrassing deficiency for centuries or even millennia to come.

In manufacturing, a series of conflicting trends are encountered. The tendency to use lower-grade resources calls for more capital equipment per unit output, which requires heavy energy inputs for its manufacture. On the other hand a more co-ordinated approach to comfort and convenience should mean lighter equipment, much reduced materials use per capita, and therefore less energy per capita.

The energy requirements for maintaining comfort and convenience by re-equipment are thus quite uncertain, the estimates falling into a very broad range.

The total energy cost of comfort and convenience, when the knowledge now in the laboratories and pilot plants is applied, is expected to fall into the range of 2 to 8×10^6 Cal per year per capita. It would be in the lower part of the range in the tropics and also where the population has access to deep water transport.

IV

Simple calculations show that the Earth can probably provide comfort and convenience for upwards of fifty billions of persons—if the surface of the tropical oceans were to be exploited. Such a possibility does not suggest that this is a desirable pattern for the future, nor does it say anything about the feasibility of getting from where we are now to a general worldwide state of adequacy, regardless of ultimate numbers. A procedure or strategy for development has therefore been sought that attempts to introduce these new technologies to best advantage. From this exercise it appears that even the promised, but as yet unproved, technological achievements are likely to be insufficient. However, they miss the mark by much less than any known alternative approach.

The most critical problem encountered is that an initial improvement in welfare wherever it is most needed leads now to a very rapid drop in the death rate, particularly infant mortality. The birth rate often rises for a while before it begins to decline. The increase in population comes to 1½ to 3% per year. Since extra capital must simultaneously be accumulated to meet increased food and shelter needs, the society requires 2 to 5% annual increases in production just to maintain, with no further gain, the initial improvement. This is a good rate of gain for any society, even those with ample resources. It seems impossible to maintain such a continued increase in production if people experience no further gain in welfare as a result of the extra effort. Therefore, much higher initial rates of gain must be established that will overshadow the associated population increases. However, this would require impossible quantities of investment capital, organizing capacities, technical skills, food, and other items. Thus, the present dynamics of population make it impossible to get the developmental process going in all but a few isolated parts of the underdeveloped areas, unless there were either (1) a major catastrophe with large loss of life in subsistence areas, or (2) a way of effecting a rapid drop in birth rate coincident with the earliest stages of development.

Several attempts have been made to introduce Western methods of birth control into poor rural areas. They have met with little or no success until women were given greater freedom, and had become literate. The costs were much too high and the reductions in birth rate achieved are not dependable even a generation after the improvements in welfare have begun. A possible solution lies in the synthesis of cheap new drugs that provide temporary sterility. A variety of such drugs are believed to be technically feasible, but the scientific work is going slowly. The social studies which suggest how to go about introducing new contraceptive techniques are even more retarded. All further elaboration of a new strategy for economic development rests upon the premise that some such solution will be found for an important share of the underdeveloped areas.

A fundamental question was asked, "How much more production is enough?" The relevant criteria seem to be (1) the needs for achieving the threshold of comfort and convenience, (2) the requirements for efficiency in productive activity, and (3) the more tradition-bound and subjective description of the boundary of adequacy or the "poverty line." They all seem to converge upon approximately the same consumption level. An estimate of this level, in terms of physical quantities of convenient commodity types, was prepared for urban conditions in a typical tropical environment. If converted into current dollars it comes to a total of roughly $330 per capita per annum. The capital requirements for this standard of living were estimated at $1800 to $3500 per capita.

If the minimum adequate standard of living were to be established as a virtual ceiling as well as a floor for consumption, it is reasonable to believe that capital accumulation could be at a maximum. Incentives might be retained through granting allowances for the purchase of nonessential services and cultural activities that make no appreciable drain upon scarce resources. Elementary social justice would insist that all extra output be applied to the expansion of the productive apparatus until all persons in the society had an opportunity to live at the minimum adequate standard. If the standard were so defined that scientific evidence could be used to justify proposed improvements, then not only could the standard itself gradually become more workable, but also a new means would be introduced by which science could contribute to socio-economic advance.

A pattern of living aimed at providing work for all able-bodied adults, as well as economical consumption, will require a rapid urbanization of 70 to 95% of the eventual population. The growth of cities is expected to proceed at many times the rate experienced up to the present—even if as much manufacturing as possible is decentralized to the villages. There are many difficulties to be overcome, but most problematic of all is that of congestion of movement. The only solution which was found required the prohibition of the free movement of automobiles and trucks in the cities along with the following provisions: (1) the basic transport net be made up of electric railways, pipe lines, belts, bicycles, and carts, (2) public facilities and manufacturing be operated at least two shifts per day, permitting the transfer of freight in the odd shift, (3) the perishable fruits and vegetables be grown within walking distance of the points of consumption, (4) industrial and commercial centers be distributed at advantageous points throughout the urbanism, and (5) part of the land remain uncommitted during the period of settlement as a form of reserve for emergency uses.

In order to minimize the social costs of urbanization it was felt that most of the settlers could be accommodated in "urban villages," which permit the migrant to adjust at his own pace. Large cities were envisioned as becoming a web of transport facilities, with subcenters at the intersections, relatively self-sufficient urban villages strung along the routes between them, and intensive gardening or industry filling in the interstices. The urban villages, in order to be economical enough for the resources available, need to be organized on quite different principles than are presently employed in Western countries, and much more economical designs for housing and household equipment need to be developed.

The most efficient pattern of industrialization now available to large societies emphasizes the use of continuous-flow processes and automation as much as may be economic in any developed part of the world. Fewer factory workers are required for this mode of production; therefore, a larger proportion can be allocated to new construction and social services. This drastically alters the strategy of industrialization and urbanization. Formerly, urban migrants were initiated to work disciplines in rather primitive manufacturing establishments and assembly plants, but in this new scheme they would learn mainly through construction effort. (Most of the industrial work available in the future would require a well developed sense of responsibility or advanced skills.) This mode of initiation helps delay the influx and makes more manageable the migration into the manufacturing zones that has hitherto led to terrible overcrowding and congestion. Labor-intensive construction, especially of housing and service facilities, may be expected to provide a psychological satisfaction generating necessary public support for the development program.

Vast social changes must be expected as the economy progresses. A modern element, dependent upon world-wide sources of information for its success in meeting problems of development, but still wholeheartedly committed to internal improvement, tends to differentiate itself from the traditional stock. This modern, largely urban element must increase its strength by selecting the bright youngsters from the villages, educating them, and adopting them. The way of life of the modern stratum must grow at the expense of the traditional element. Many new societies, based upon a fusion of world-wide with local values, are likely to be created if a feasible development process can be found.

Within this changing milieu the productive effort is given meaning and continuity through social institutions. Each society needs an interlocking set through which the new technologies, along with the contemporary, are enabled to serve. Fortunately, known modes of organization seem to be appropriate in all but one, possibly two, instances. That one would deal with birth control, as mentioned before. The other dubious one reflects uncertainties surrounding the latest developments in communications systems. They are much too new for their implications to be understood.

Working out the over-all strategy of the development, and supervising the performance of the other organizations, seems to require an effective planning agency. At the moment only a few fragmentary prototypes exist for such an organization which permit it to function in an open society without the display of force. The planning agency can even function as an instrument of a democratic government, since the social controls required for developmental planning seem to fit well within the most recently formulated democratic constitutions. Much of the pioneering in administrative techniques of developmental planning will have to be done in the underdeveloped areas themselves.

At the international level, the present institutions as they are evolving seem to fit the needs for development as envisioned here, except that some formula must be found for the transfer of substantial quantities of capital in the form of equipment from those areas that can already produce it to those that need it for a running start.

There are other possible proposals for world development that emphasize other aspects of science and technology. In general they seem to require more difficult development paths than that chosen here, but they merit careful investigation.

It is recognized that world development, if and when it should be achieved, does not solve any fundamental human problems about what to do with space and time and life. However, it would ensure that many more persons, through their votes and opinions, could participate in those decisions. Thus development, as discussed here, is aimed at providing freedom—the freedom to choose whatever seems worth while.

Appendix

PROBLEMS IN FUNDAMENTAL SCIENCE

Once a body of interrelated knowledge, such as exists in natural science today, has been built up, it becomes more and more difficult to predict the direction from which will come the key datum that opens up totally new vistas. Therefore it is rather presumptuous to assign high priorities to a series of problems which are amenable to attack by theoretical or very generalized approaches. Progress is desirable at all points on the frontier of knowledge. However, some human requirements will be much more difficult to meet than others; therefore, certain research directions in fundamental science are more likely to generate opportunities for solving these practical difficulties than others. It is no more difficult to explore in these potentially useful directions than in the directions that have already been chosen, but hitherto potential usefulness for world development has not been a criterion for choice. Generally, subjects and materials for experimentation were chosen purely for reasons of convenience to the investigator, but here a new criterion, that of making more explicit the possible modes of action leading to economic development, is suggested.

Some of these useful areas are, for one reason or another, already heavily favored by scientists. Photosynthesis is one example and human nutrition seems to be another. Therefore, what will be emphasized are those subjects which attract insufficient attention at the moment and are hence undermanned. The following list exhibits no order of priority but merely an incomplete record of significant problems:

1. All questions of protein supplies for the long term eventually trace back to the sources of economical fixed nitrogen, where the best hope seems to lie in microbiological fixation. What is the full mechanism of nitrogen fixation in microorganisms? Does the overcoming of the astonishingly high activation energy for this process introduce any special limitations? This may become a dual problem since it is becoming apparent that a great many types of organisms can fix nitrogen to a small degree, but a very limited number of species are capable of fixing it 10^3 times as rapidly. Thus there may be two distinctly different mechanisms, or several which are associated.

2. Among the thousands of different algae it is expected that only a few species and strains will have optimum mass culture characteristics, but practically nothing is known about their genetic relationships and variations. Green and blue-green unicellular algae reproduce very much like simple

bacteria. Can bacterial genetics be applied to these organisms, or do new phenomena come into view?

3. Somewhat related to this is the desirability of knowing much more about the physiology of photosynthetic microorganisms, especially the structure and properties of the enzyme systems by which starch and cellulose are synthesized. This information, when combined with background in algal genetics, may eventually lead to a system whereby even carbohydrates may be synthesized most economically through mass culture.

4. What are the constituents of the deep scattering layer in the oceans? We should know how these species feed, what feeds upon them, the regional fluctuations, etc. Why does the layer remain at 200 to 400 meters depth during daytime? What are the responses of the chief organisms to light, to chemical gradients, to shapes and forms, and so on? In a more abstract sense, how do they communicate with each other? It seems quite possible that somewhere in this mass of observations information will be turned up leading to an economical harvesting technique.

5. What are the biochemical mechanisms by which methane fermentation occurs? Although a great deal has been done with this process already, there remain serious gaps in the state of knowledge, especially in the presence of protein substrates.

6. Much the same questions may be asked about hydrogen fermentation. This is a more recent discovery and has thus been very incompletely explored. Success could lead to larger supplies of a valuable reducing agent, and perhaps to new technologies for metals extraction.

7. How can one measure and record human attitudes to various food types and flavors? What are the mechanisms by which such attitudes are modified?

8. A great deal more thorough investigation is required for understanding the sensations pain–discomfort–comfort–sleep. At present the data remain in a most unintegrated state. If an index of physiological well-being cannot be formulated, we should not only want to know the reasons why, but also what are the best alternatives.

9. What are the effects upon personality of a ten-fold or even a hundred-fold increase in communications channel capacity made available to an individual? (This would be equivalent to putting a Stone Age child into a school which is equipped with a library containing many colored pictures and a TV set.) We are interested here mainly in children who accept the challenge and become adept at communication, although the patterns of rejection may also be significant. Such studies might attempt to discern whether any general phenomena of a surprising and unexpected nature exist when primitives suddenly come face to face with the ultramodern and attempt to cope with it.

10. Much more study and experimentation is needed in the physiology of human reproduction. Most of this will lead merely to the accumulation of specific, detailed observation, a small part of which is almost certain to fit into successful techniques of birth control, if and when they are developed, for the poorest peoples.

11. What are the characteristics of a developmental society whose high-

est goal is the generation of highly superior individuals? This study requires a synthesis of what is already known about human organization.

12. What appear to be the optimal characteristics of a developmental society in which one's greatest responsibility is to one or another classes of small group (such as the family, the team, the cell, or the clique)? It is not too difficult to describe static societies in such terms, but the requirement that they be "developmental" adds a new and perplexing dimension to such speculative investigations.

13. One thread runs through all these rather specific areas for exploration. We need a theory of organization, a metric for structure and order, that is superior to anything available today. One feels that it should comprehend a system of categories, a system of levels, a definition of "freedom to act," entropy, communication theory, learning theory, and very likely others equally important. Such a theory, if it should ever be formulated, would greatly extend our knowledge-acquiring capacity.

ADDED FOR THE SECOND EDITION

Perhaps it is not astonishing that these thirteen fundamental queries remain unresolved after more than a decade of research. They were not framed so that a single experiment could produce an answer. It is more surprising that meaningfulness has been retained despite the outpouring of scientific publication.

I would add another now, however, which is derived from the last:

14. It has been noted by several observers in the past few years that voluntary increases in the flow of social communications lead directly to an increase in the likelihood of stable, representative, legitimate government in most cases. Why should this be so? Expediting social communications seems to reduce violence arising from internal conflicts and introduce much more consultation between interest-groups. What intervening institutions must exist between message transmission and the affairs of state? Why do certain countries (e.g., Argentina, Ghana) fail to fit the generalization?

PROBLEMS IN APPLIED RESEARCH

A great deal of applied research is already under way in the world's laboratories. We have only to look at their agenda to discover what problems are believed to be important. Contrary to many impressions, these agenda *are* available, because where research and development projects are not public, as in some industrial and national defense laboratories, they can be readily deduced after a while from their locations, publications, and the kinds of experts who are hired. This is an area of publication that is rather comprehensively digested, abstracted, and catalogued, so that the chances of missing a significant line of development for more than a few years are small. Therefore, it is quite possible to make some over-all appraisals of applied research, assessing where it is now and where it is going.

Most of the applied research now in process seeks to exploit pint-sized opportunities. Even if such a project were completely successful it would have no further implications than turning out a neat, temporary profit for a selected set of enterprises. This work lacks general and widespread applications since it is capable of bringing about only very minor social and economic adjustments. There is no immediate value in it for world development.

Some research is applied to efforts that have but a slight possibility of being successful, but would lead to a large payoff. Because the chances are remote one should not lay out full strategies of world development dependent upon them, but the existence of such research means that whatever strategy is chosen must be flexible enough to adjust to surprise contributions, if and when they should occur.

There are also a few areas of applied research that seem to play a crucial role in at least the program for development that is advocated here, and perhaps a good many others. These problems are researchable, since some of the relevant unintegrated information is available, more can easily be acquired, and fruitful hypotheses can be put forward. Nevertheless, the effort presently allocated to them is far from enough.

What follows is an incomplete list drawn from the last category. Further study of the requirements for world development would make extensive additions to it.

1. How can one extract the "yeasty flavor" from food yeast in an economical fashion? This distinctive flavor retards the widespread introduction of food yeast protein, but a good portion of it appears to have fat-soluble characteristics and may thus be removed. Much more needs to be known of the biochemical characteristics of this flavorant. Once it has been collected, the information will aid not only the processors, but also the specialists in the organoleptic qualities of foods, and an immediate increase in the supply of cheap protein would result.

2. A series of imaginative experiments ought to be initiated in representative societies aimed at discovering what kinds of new and nutritious foods are easily accepted, and what social institutions will stand in the way of introduction. Further than that, what appear to be the optimum strategies for evading the limitations of these institutions? Because societies are so different (and imaginations too!) very few generalizations can be expected from such studies, but the skills needed for contacting strange cultures can be acquired so that the time required to obtain positive results should be rapidly reduced.

3. The design of temperature-difference plants ought to be further developed and refined, especially the types that include turbines or other means for generating power from the small pressure difference that exists within the unit. The ultimate efficiency of large-scale solar energy processes appears to depend upon the operability of these plants with small temperature differences. Supplies of fresh water in many parts of the world will also depend upon such a process.

4. The elaboration of the continuous flow hydrogen-reduction process for the production of steel seems to be quite essential. Adequate studies of procedures for ferrous alloy manufacture seem to be particularly called for, because these alloys are themselves great metal-savers and are normally produced in small enough lots to reduce the developmental risk by accumulating experience with special purpose small scale plants using the process.

Large general purpose facilities might be built economically from this experience.

5. The procedures for extracting many products, including fissile materials, from very low-grade mineralized deposits should be investigated. Chemical treatments are likely to become dominant in such separations, but it would be useful to know what chemicals and what chemical processes so that one could carry a study of the implications much further.

6. Transport systems that require investments by easy stages, installing extra capacity just one jump ahead of development, would be a highly desirable project for intensive engineering research and development. Roads and railroads require a very heavy initial outlay, from which the returns do not really come in until a decade or two later. In other words, rails and roads tend to be under-used in their early life, and become embarrassingly rigid and inflexible in middle age. What is needed is an orderly sequence of stages in transport lines which will, in the beginning, carry economically only a few tons and a few passengers per day, but can be expanded by increments to thousands of tons and thousands of passengers per day. The Swiss Gyrobus and the American Tourna-Train are examples of possible intermediate stages, but more links are needed as well as a careful integration of the respective specifications.

7. There needs to be large-scale research on a series of contraceptive and birth control measures tied to clinical and field tests. The important problem here seems to be bringing together the doctors in public health service with the practical research men in the biological development laboratories and the sociologist-demographer groups. These professions, and their responsible institutions, have found it very difficult to work closely together, even in the United States where interdisciplinary collaboration is much more encouraged. There should exist as soon as possible a structure of institutions that can quickly translate new findings in science and in social studies into improved procedures for bringing birth control to those underdeveloped countries that desire it.

8. There is an aspect of consumer economics that has been neglected. It is increasingly possible to apply technical and scientific criteria (welfare requirements) to establish the efficiency of consumption. By this means it is possible to state what quantities of what commodities are necessary to provide adequacy, but no more than adequacy for each spending unit. Thus certain important forms of waste can be detected that would otherwise escape the accountant's eye. It is possible to devise distribution systems, resembling the more advanced rationing procedures, for the important goods and services, which are rather efficient in terms of all these criteria—technical, economic, and scientific. Not all the consumer needs can be so standardized and served, and so it seems necessary to introduce a market for the remainder as the best means of mediating between supply and demand. How should these markets be permitted to interact with the other distribution system so as to provide continually improving consumer choice in a developing economy? The question posed here is not just economics, but implies an application of the principle of economizing to social organization for the distribution of goods and services.

9. The form that industrial and commercial design may take can be a powerful influence in the culture, aiding and reinforcing economic development. Design traditions and approaches that emphasize *over-all* economy and efficiency have never been consciously fostered. Such a program of design deserves serious study and experiment in all parts of the world. There are at least several themes that such design may take up, so there is no threat here of world-wide uniformity.

10. Self-built housing and neighborhood development seems to be a necessary means of accumulating social capital in the earlier stages of economic development. The experience from scattered experiments in this area since the Second World War needs to be tied together so that the features of specific programs for the building of villages, towns, and cities by this technique are as well understood as the procedures for organizing and operating a construction firm or a factory. Efficient use of part-time untrained labor is apparently the key problem; this can be accomplished only through careful planning and organization. Very likely there will have to be associated with the effort some form of prefabrication, the exact type depending upon climate and the building materials available, and certain kinds of manufacturing. We need an administrative formula for building towns and cities by self-help.

11. When a social system is changing rapidly in a developmental sense many more alert and intelligent people must be recruited than would otherwise be necessary. Tradition-directed behavior will not solve the problems being faced. Increasing numbers of bright youngsters will need to be found among the lower classes if the posts are to be filled. Therefore it would be extremely useful if an effective means for selecting such exceptional youngsters from within a partly literate peasant society were to be developed. The technique would have to identify promising individuals in such surroundings at as early an age as ten years, because if they are found too late the training process is hindered. This problem cannot be solved merely by the building up of a battery of tests and examinations, but requires constructing a channel for the acquisition of status. Such channels do not exist even in embryonic form in most of these societies today.

12. What structures of corporate organization will be most appropriate to the new technologies? The issue here is not public versus private operation, as Americans might imagine, but in what manner a hierarchy or team can function so as to deal successfully with risk as it is expected to be encountered. The decisions to be made could hardly be more complex than those encountered at present, but they will require more of the highly technical considerations that are only rarely taken into account at the moment.

13. Any society engaged in a program of economic development must establish a strategy, mobilize its resources, plot a definite course of action for the immediate future, and continue to work out better allocations of resources. At present, the experience of various parts of the world has not been assembled in any form in which it can be used. The same mistakes are repeated over and over again. In political systems subject to majority rule this is excusable, because the essential information diffuses slowly through the less educated classes, but from professional civil servants much

more is expected. At the moment they too must be forgiven because the world lacks a systematic presentation of the *how* of developmental planning. This will require more than a distillation of contemporary experience; it calls for a synthesis from many fragments in order to construct several alternative models for development. These models, which are really frameworks for making decisions about the long-range future, must be sufficiently explicit and realistic so that the responsible officials can see first what are the prerequisites for success, and also how any one action affects the others in the developmental process.

ADDED FOR THE SECOND EDITION

Much constructive work has been published over the last dozen years on all but a couple of these problems. As a result the priorities are shifting somewhat. It would be possible now to formulate an equal number of applied research objectives at least as significant as this list. Some would take up the exciting new technologies of education, others the fabrication of light, serviceable housing, and still others the problems of water reclamation and air pollution in densely urbanized environments, the settlement of the seas, etc. Apparently the knowledge about important bottlenecks in development has broadened, so that the current studies of a much larger number of investigators would be relevant to the paths of development charted here.

INDEX

257

THE M.I.T. PAPERBACK SERIES